PROGRAMMED PHYSICS

PART II: *Electricity and Magnetism*

PROGRAMMED PHYSICS

Alexander Joseph and Daniel J. Leahy

PART I: Mechanics
PART II: Electricity and Magnetism
PART III: Optics and Waves
PART IV: Topics in Modern Physics
        (*In preparation*)

PROGRAMMED PHYSICS

PART II: *Electricity and Magnetism*

Alexander Joseph

Chairman, Division of Science and Mathematics
  College of Police Science of
  the City University of New York
Lecturer, Physics, City University of New York

Daniel J. Leahy

Chairman, Science Department
  The Collegiate School
Lecturer, Mathematics, School of General Studies
  Hunter College

JOHN WILEY & SONS, INC.   New York London Sydney

QC21
.J77
pt.2

PREFACE TO THE TEACHER

This book is the second in a series of four which together constitute the text for a one-year programmed course in physics. Part I deals with mechanics, Part III with optics and waves, and Part IV with topics in modern physics.

These programmed books are written for use primarily in the senior year of high school or the first year of college. We feel that, on the college level, they are especially suited for liberal arts majors. They should also serve very well for the curricula of junior and community colleges.

Electricity and Magnetism assumes that the student will have a general acquaintance with the principles and concepts of elementary mechanics, especially work, energy, and the second law of motion. He should have a good working knowledge of intermediate algebra and some skill in the manipulation of mathematical symbols and expressions. An understanding of elementary trigonometry is also helpful. A test of these prerequisites is provided following the Instructions to the Student.

Although this programmed series was written to be used without concurrent use of a standard text and with only a minimum of teacher supervision, we strongly advise that it be integrated with suitable classroom demonstrations, discussions, and laboratory exercises wherever possible. We have found that the PSSC laboratory experiments are especially useful supplements to this text, and that classroom demonstrations in electromagnetic induction and the magnetic effects of electric currents are very helpful supplements to Chapters 4 and 5.

ALEXANDER JOSEPH
DANIEL J. LEAHY

New York City
1965

CONTENTS

INSTRUCTIONS TO THE STUDENT

This book is a *programmed* text. This means (1) that the subject matter of an introductory course in physics has been analyzed into a series of short simple steps and (2) that these steps are presented in a manner and sequence found most conducive to effective learning.

Each step is presented in a space called a *frame*. Each frame presents a certain amount of information and then poses a question or problem for the student to answer as a check on his understanding before he goes further in the program. You can write your answers to these questions in the space provided in the frame or on a separate answer sheet as instructed by your teacher.

When you have written your answer(s), you may check against the correct answer(s) which are printed below the row of five stars which indicates the end of each question frame. For example:

1. The meter is a unit of length which contains 39.37 inches. A length of two meters contains _____ inches.

* * * * *

78.74

2. The meter is used to measure (weight/length/time) and is equivalent to _____ inches.

* * * * *

length; 39.37

The *panels* referred to are at the back of the book, and each panel can be folded out for easy reference while the student is working on it.

A masking shield is provided so that you can conceal the correct answer to the frame upon which you are working and all subsequent frames on a page until you have written your answer and are ready to check it by moving the mask down to reveal the correct answer below the stars.

TEST OF PREREQUISITES
FOR *ELECTRICITY AND MAGNETISM*

Write the number of the correct answer in the space provided at the right. If none of the answers is correct, write "0" in the space provided.

1. If $\dfrac{1}{x} = \dfrac{1}{y} + \dfrac{1}{z}$, and $x = 4$ and $y = 8$, $z =$

(1) $\frac{1}{8}$ (2) $\frac{1}{4}$ (3) $\frac{2}{3}$ (4) $\frac{1}{16}$ (5) 8   1. _____

2. A mass of 10 kg is moving in a circular path of radius 2 m at a constant speed of 5 m/sec. The centripetal force applied to it is:

(1) 125 (2) 4 (3) $\frac{1}{50}$ (4) 10 (5) 100 newtons   2. _____

3. The kinetic energy of the 10-kg mass in Problem 2 is:

(1) 125 (2) 150 (3) 4 (4) $\frac{1}{50}$ (5) 100 joules   3. _____

4. A 3-kg mass is lowered at constant speed through a distance of 10 m. If the gravitational field is 9.8 m/sec², the work done by the lowering force is:

(1) 294 (2) −30 (3) −294 (4) 30 (5) −98 joules   4. _____

5. The gravitational force between masses m_1 and m_2 a distance d apart is given by the expression:

(1) $\dfrac{Gm_1m_2}{d}$ (2) $\dfrac{Gm_1m_2}{d^2}$ (3) $Gm_1 + m_2$ (4) $\dfrac{Gm_1m_2}{\sqrt{d}}$ (5) $\dfrac{m_1m_2}{Gd}$ 5. _____

where G is the gravitational constant.

6. The gravitational potential energy of a mass m in the gravitational field of the Earth (mass M) when it is a distance r from the center of the Earth is:

(1) $\dfrac{GmM}{r^2}$ (2) $GMmr$ (3) $-\dfrac{GMm}{r}$ (4) $\dfrac{GMm}{r^3}$ (5) $\dfrac{-GMm}{r^2}$ 6. _____

7. A constant net force of 10 newtons produces a parallel displacement of 15 meters when applied to a mass of 25 kg. The change in the kinetic energy of the mass is:

(1) 250 (2) 375 (3) 150 (4) 2.5 (5) 100 joules   7. _____

8. If $F = Eq$ and $F = Bvq$, an expression for v in terms of E and B is:

(1) EB (2) $\dfrac{B}{E}$ (3) $\dfrac{qB}{E}$ (4) $\dfrac{Eq}{B}$ (5) $E + B$ 8. _____

x

9. Given $F = \dfrac{mv^2}{R}$ and $F = Bvq$, R equals:

(1) $\dfrac{mv^2}{Bq}$ (2) $\dfrac{v^2 B}{qm}$ (3) $\dfrac{m}{Bvq}$ (4) $\dfrac{mv^2}{B}$ (5) $\dfrac{mv}{Bq}$

9. _____

10. Solve for T if $F = m\left(\dfrac{4\pi^2 R}{T^2}\right)$ and $F = Bvq$. T equals:

(1) $\dfrac{4\pi^2 R}{Bqm}$ (2) $\dfrac{2\pi R}{Bvq}$ (3) $2\pi\sqrt{\dfrac{Rm}{Bvq}}$ (4) $\dfrac{\sqrt{Bvqm}}{2\pi R}$ (5) $\dfrac{Bvq}{4\pi mR}$

10. _____

11. The legs of a right triangle are 7 ft and 24 ft. The hypotenuse is:

(1) 15   (2) 31   (3) 25   (4) 30   (5) 27 ft

11. _____

12. $\vec{A}$ and $\vec{B}$ are vector quantities. $\vec{A} = 10$ units East; $\vec{B} = 15$ units West. Their sum is:

(1) 15 units West   (2) 25 units North   (3) 20 units Northwest
(4) 5 units East   (5) 5 units West

12. _____

13. Compute N if $N = \dfrac{(3 \times 10^{-4})(4 \times 10^{-12})}{24 \times 10^{-6}}$.

(1) 5×10^{11} (2) 5×10^{-7} (3) 5×10^{-11} (4) 5×10^{7}
(5) 5×10^{-22}

13. _____

14. Reduced to its simplest possible form, $\dfrac{1 - x/y}{1 + x/y}$ is:

(1) 1   (2) -1 (3) $\dfrac{y - x}{y + x}$ (4) xy (5) $\dfrac{x}{y}$

14. _____

15. Given $x^2 - 5x + 6 = 0$. x is equal to:

(1) 5 or 1   (2) 2 or 3   (3) 6 or 1   (4) -2 or -3 (5) -5 or -1 15. _____

Chapter One

ELECTROSTATICS

OBJECTIVES

Upon successful completion of this chapter, the student should be able to:

1. Give operational definitions of positive and negative charge.
2. Distinguish between conductors and insulators.
3. State the principle of conservation of charge.
4. Describe the electron theory of charge and apply it to explain the process of charging by induction.
5. State and apply Coulomb's law for point charges.

Section 1.   Definition of Charge
          Like Charges Repel
          Unlike Charges Attract

1. Refer to Panel 1. The letter in the upper right-hand corner is _____.
*   *   *   *   *
B (If your answer is not correct, you have the wrong panel.)

2. Panel 1 describes a typical experiment to investigate *static electricity*. Everything described here can be done in the laboratory. Read through Steps 1 to 4 carefully. There (is a/is no) force observed to be acting between the glass rod and the silk cloth *before* they are rubbed together.
*   *   *   *   *
is no

3. Panel 1. After the glass rod and the silk cloth have been rubbed together, there (is a/is no) force observed acting between them.
*   *   *   *   *
is a

4. Panel 1. We describe the situation in Step 4 by saying that the rubbing of the glass with a silk cloth produces an *electric charge* (or, simply, a charge) on the glass where the glass has been rubbed.

Read the remainder of the steps in this experiment. In Step 5 we observe that a force (exists/does not exist) between the charged glass rod and the uncharged rod.

★   ★   ★   ★   ★

exists

5. In illustrations and figures we will indicate by (+) signs that part of the glass rod which has been rubbed with a silk cloth. In this figure, for example,

the (right/left/center) of the rod has an electric_____.

★   ★   ★   ★   ★

right; charge

6. Panel 1. The force observed in this experiment between a glass rod with an electric charge and one without a charge is a force of (attraction/repulsion).

★   ★   ★   ★   ★

attraction

7. Panel 1, Step 6. When an uncharged rubber rod is brought close to the charged glass rod, we observe that there is a force of (attraction/repulsion) between them.

★   ★   ★   ★   ★

attraction

8. Panel 1. In Step 7 of this experiment (both rods are charged/only one of the rods is charged). In this case, the force between the two rods is a force of (attraction/repulsion).

★   ★   ★   ★   ★

both rods are charged ; repulsion

9. Refer to Panel 2. The letter in the upper right-hand corner is_____.

★   ★   ★   ★   ★

K

10. Panel 2 describes another experiment investigating static electricity. Read Steps 1 to 5 carefully. Note that the portion of the rubber rod which has given an electric charge is marked with (+/−) signs.

★   ★   ★   ★   ★

−

11. Panel 2. In Steps 1 to 5 of this experiment we observe that a rubber rod given a charge by rubbing with _____ acts in a manner (similar to/different from) the glass rod rubbed with _____ in the experiment described in Panel 1.

★ ★ ★ ★ ★

animal fur (wool) ; similar to ; silk

12. Panel 2. Two rubber rods, one with a charge and one without, (repel/ attract) each other.

★ ★ ★ ★ ★

attract.

13. Panel 2. Two rubber rods, both of which have been given a charge by rubbing with animal fur, (attract/repel) each other.

★ ★ ★ ★ ★

repel

14. Two glass rods, both charged by rubbing with silk, (attract/repel) each other.

★ ★ ★ ★ ★

repel

15. Panel 2. In Step 6 of this experiment (both rods are charged/one rod is charged). The force between the rods is one of (attraction/repulsion).

★ ★ ★ ★ ★

both rods are charged
attraction

16. We have seen that two charged rubber rods (attract/repel); that two charged glass rods (attract/repel). A rubber rod charged by rubbing with animal fur and a glass rod charged by rubbing with silk (attract/repel) each other

★ ★ ★ ★ ★

repel ; repel ; attract

17. A charged rubber rod or a charged glass rod (attracts/repels/has no observable effect on) an uncharged glass (or rubber) rod.

★ ★ ★ ★ ★

attracts

18. Panel 2. The result observed in Step 5 of this experiment indicates a basic difference between the charge produced on the glass rod in Panel 1 and the charge produced on the rubber rod in Panel 2. The charged *glass* rod (attracts/repels) another charged *glass* rod. The charged *rubber* rod (attracts/ repels) another charged *rubber* rod. A charged *rubber* rod and a charged *glass* rod (attract/repel) each other.

★ ★ ★ ★ ★

repels ; repels ; attract

19. We now define the charge given to a glass rod when we rub it with silk as a *positive* (+) charge. In Step 7 of panel 1, [(*a*) both rods are positively charged/(*b*) only the suspended rod is positively charged]. Answer (*a*) or (*b*).

In Step 6 of Panel 1 [(*a*) both rods are positively charged/(*b*) only the suspended rod is positively charged]. Answer (*a*) or (*b*).

★ ★ ★ ★ ★

(*a*) ; (*b*)

20. Step 7 of Panel 1 and our definition of positive charge provide us with a method of testing for positive charge. Suppose a glass rod is rubbed with silk, and another object is brought near the rubbed part of the glass and is attracted to it. This object (is/is not) positively charged. Explain your answer.

★ ★ ★ ★ ★

is not (Because like charges repel each other. In this case, if the object were positively charged, it would be repelled by the glass rod, *not* attracted.)

21. By definition the electric charge produced on a glass rod when it is rubbed with silk is _____. In an experiment, we find that a certain object brought close to a glass rod charged in this manner is repelled by it. We know, therefore, that this object (has a/has no) charge.

★ ★ ★ ★ ★

positive ; has a

22. Experiment shows that two positively charged objects (attract/repel) each other.

★ ★ ★ ★ ★

repel

23. We define the charge produced on a rubber rod when it is rubbed with animal fur as *negative* (−). In Step 6 of Panel 2 the glass rod has a _____ charge; the rubber rod has a _____ charge.

★ ★ ★ ★ ★

positive ; negative

24. A rubber rod is rubbed with animal fur. An object brought close to it is repelled. This object has a (positive/negative) charge.

★ ★ ★ ★ ★

negative

25. Reread Panels 1 and 2 in the light of definitions we have chosen for positive and negative charge.

Two negatively charged objects (attract/repel) each other.

Two positively charged objects (attract/repel) each other.

A negatively charged object (attracts/repels) an object with no charge.

A positively charged object (attracts/repels) an object with no charge.

★ ★ ★ ★ ★

repel ; repel ; attracts ; attracts

26. An object with a negative charge (attracts/repels) one with a positive charge.

★ ★ ★ ★ ★

attracts

27. We summarize the results of observations made in Panels 1 and 2 as follows:

(1) Like charges, i.e., both positive or both negative, (attract/repel) each other.

(2) Unlike charges, i.e., one positive and one negative, (attract/repel) each other.

(3) Charged objects (attract/repel/do not affect) neutral, i.e., uncharged, objects.

★ ★ ★ ★ ★

repel ; attract ; attract

28. A glass rod rubbed with silk attracts bits of dust from the air. Does this mean that bits of dust are necessarily negatively charged? (Yes/No). Explain your answer. (*If you are doubtful about the correct answer, refer back to Steps 5 and 6 of Panel* 1 *and Step* 3 *of Panel* 2.)

★ ★ ★ ★ ★

No. (Because the charged rod attracts objects which have no charge as well as those which have an unlike charge.)

29. A beam of particles is made to pass through a vacuum tube in (*a*). When a positively charged rod is brought near the tube, the beam swerves away

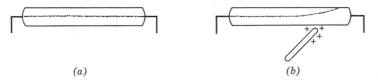

(*a*)   (*b*)

from it. The particles in the beam have (a negative charge/a positive charge/no charge). Explain.

★ ★ ★ ★ ★

A positive charge (Because only positively charged particles are *repelled* by a positive charge.)

30. A cathode ray is a beam of extremely small particles moving at high speeds through a vacuum tube. When a rubber rod which has been rubbed with animal fur is brought near a cathode ray, the ray swerves away from the rod. This observation gives us reason to believe that the particles in a cathode ray are (not charged/negatively charged/positively charged).

* * * * *

negatively charged

31. A small, light ball made of an unknown material is rubbed with cloth and brought near a glass rod which has been rubbed with silk. If the ball is repelled, we know that it has a _____ charge.

* * * * *

positive

32. A small, light ball of unknown material is rubbed with another material and then brought near a rubber rod which has been rubbed with wool. What do you expect to happen (*a*) if the ball has a positive charge, (*b*) if the ball has a negative charge?

* * * * *

(*a*) It will be attracted to the rod.
(*b*) It will be repelled from the rod.

33. A small, light ball is suspended from a support by a thread. When a positively charged object and a negatively charged object are brought close to it (but not allowed to touch it) in turn, it is attracted to both. What conclusion do you draw from this experiment about the charge on the ball?

* * * * *

It has *no* charge. If the ball had a charge, it would have been repelled by one or the other of the objects, which have unlike charges.

34. Which of the following statements are true?
    (1) All glass rods are negatively charged.
    (2) All rubber rods are negatively charged.
    (3) All glass rods are positively charged.
    (4) A glass rod rubbed with silk is negatively charged.
    (5) A rubber rod rubbed with wool has a (+) charge.
    (6) Two positively charged objects repel each other.
    (7) Two negatively charged objects attract each other.
    (8) A negatively charged object repels objects with no charge.
    (9) A positively charged object attracts objects with no charge.
    (10) A glass rod rubbed with silk repels an object which has a positive charge.

* * * * *

(6) ; (9) ; (10)

Section 2.   Conductors and Insulators
The Electroscope
Ground
Charge by Contact

1. Refer to Panel 3. The letter in the upper right-hand corner is _____.
*   *   *   *   *

P

2. Panel 3. Study the experiment described here carefully. In Step 2, the suspended glass rod will be (attracted/repelled).
*   *   *   *   *

repelled

3. Panel 3. In Step 3 of this experiment it is clear that the *unrubbed* end of the suspended rod does *not* have a (positive/negative) charge. Explain your answer.
*   *   *   *   *

positive (Because, if it had a positive charge, it would be repelled by the positively charged rod brought near it.)

4. Panel 3. Step 4 of this experiment proves that the charge on the unrubbed end of the suspended rod cannot be (positive/negative/neutral). Explain.
*   *   *   *   *

negative (Because, if it were negative, it would be repelled by the negatively charged rod.)

5. Panel 3. In effect, then, this experiment shows that the charge given a glass rod when it is rubbed with silk (stays in the place where it is rubbed/spreads to all parts of the glass.)
*   *   *   *   *

stays in the place where it is rubbed

6. Experiments with hard rubber, plastics, a variety of woods, and many other materials give the same result as that observed in Panel 3 with the glass rod. Such substances are called *insulators*. A charge placed at one end of any *metal* rod suspended by a thread from a support spreads all over the surface of metal. Metals (are/are not) insulators.
*   *   *   *   *

are not

7. Certain substances (e.g., all metals and the Earth) allow charges placed on any part of their surfaces to spread out over their entire surfaces. We call these substances *conductors*. Rubber and glass (allow/do not allow) charges to spread over them; we call them (conductors/insulators). Silver and copper objects (allow/do not allow) charges to spread over them. We call materials like copper and silver (conductors/insulators).

★ ★ ★ ★ ★

do not allow ; insulators ; allow ; conductors

8. A metal rod held in the hand and rubbed with fur does not appear to develop a charge. It is possible to charge such a rod if we furnish it with a glass or rubber handle so that the metal is not touched by the hand when it is rubbed. This shows that the human body (the charge enters it through the hand) is a (conductor/insulator) and that glass and rubber are good (conductors/insulators).

★ ★ ★ ★ ★

conductor ; insulators

9. Manufacturers provide plastic handles for screw drivers used in electrical work, because plastic is a good _____. It is dangerous to do electrical work with a screwdriver with a metal handle because metals, the human body, and the Earth are all _____. This means that electric _____ pass easily through them or over their surfaces.

★ ★ ★ ★ ★

insulator ; conductors ; charges

10. A copper rod is held in rubber gloves while it is rubbed with fur. It is then suspended from a metallic frame by a silk thread. Tests show that its charge is

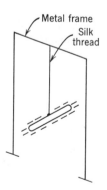

spread uniformly over its surface, but that *no* charge has passed to the frame. What does this indicate about the silk thread?

★ ★ ★ ★ ★

It is an insulator. Otherwise, the charge in the copper rod would have spread through the thread to the metallic frame.

11. Electric charges (are/are not) free to move on the surfaces of insulators. Electric charges (are/are not) free to move on the surfaces of conductors.

★ ★ ★ ★ ★

are not ; are

12. Refer to Panel 4. The letter in the upper right-hand corner is _____.

★ ★ ★ ★ ★

E

13. Panel 4. Read this panel carefully. The tests made with the positively charged rod in Step 2 and the negatively charged rod in Step 3 show that the ball has (a negative/a positive/no) charge.

★ ★ ★ ★ ★

no

14. Panel 4. Steps 4 and 6 of this experiment show that positive and negative charge (can/cannot) be given to an uncharged object by *contact*.

★ ★ ★ ★ ★

can

15. Panel 4. When the ball is touched by the hand (in Step 5), tests show that it (still has/has lost) its charge. Explain why.

★ ★ ★ ★ ★

has lost [Because the body has conducted the charge to the Earth (called "ground").]

16. Panel 4. In Step 7, the balls hang apart (as in Fig. 4) because they have (similar/unlike) charges after coming in _____ with one of the charged rods.

★ ★ ★ ★ ★

similar ; contact

17. An object charged by contact with a negatively charged rod has a (positive/negative) charge. An object charged by contact with a positively charged rod has a (positive/negative) charge.

★ ★ ★ ★ ★

negative ; positive

18. Refer to Panel 5. The letter in the upper right-hand corner is _____.

★ ★ ★ ★ ★

G

19. Panel 5. Read this panel carefully. The device it describes is an _____ and is used to detect _____ _____.

As shown in the simplified diagram (Fig. 2), all the essential parts of this device are (conductors/insulators).

* * * * *

electroscope ; electric charge ; conductors

20. Panel 5. In Fig. 3, a negatively charged rod touches the knob of the electroscope and gives it a (positive/negative) charge by ____________.

The charge (stays on the knob/spreads to all parts) of the electroscope. The leaves (attract/repel) each other because they have (the same charge/different charges).

* * * * *

negative ; contact ;
spreads to all parts ; repel ; the same charge

21. Panel 5. In Fig. 4, the negative rod has been removed. The extended leaves indicate that it has left (a charge/no charge) on the electroscope.

* * * * *

a charge

22. Panel 5. In Fig. 5, the knob of the charged electroscope is touched by a finger. The leaves collapse, indicating that the electroscope is (charged/discharged).

* * * * *

discharged

23. Touching the knob of a charged electroscope with the hand or finger discharges it by *grounding*. This means that its charge passes to the finger, through the body, and into the ____________ or Earth.

* * * * *

ground

24. The symbol for any *sort* of grounding device is ⏚.

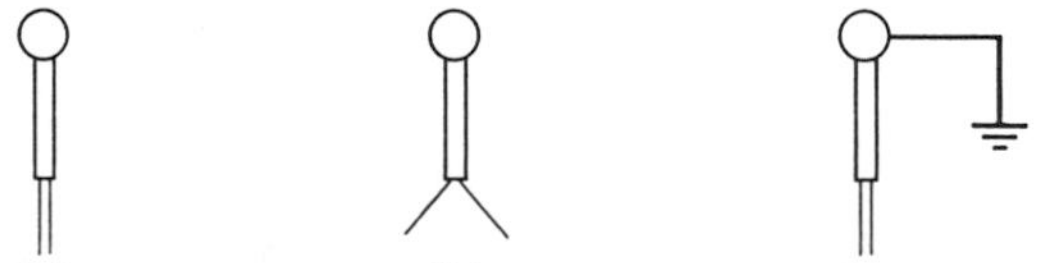

(a) (b) (c)

Which of these electroscopes is grounded—(*a*), (*b*), or (*c*)?

* * * * *

(*c*)

25. Panel 5. In Fig. 6, the electroscope discharged by grounding in Fig. 5 has been touched by a positively charged rod and the rod has been removed. The charge on the electroscope is (positive/negative).

★   ★   ★   ★   ★

positive

26. Panel 5. The symbol ═ in Fig. 7 indicates that the electroscope has been _____ and the collapsed leaves indicate that its charge has passed off to the _____.

★   ★   ★   ★   ★

grounded (or discharged) ; ground (or earth)

27. The leaves of an electroscope diverge when the electroscope has (a charge/no charge). They are collapsed when the electroscope has (a charge/no charge).

★   ★   ★   ★   ★

a charge ; no charge

28. A rod is tested for charge by touching it to an *uncharged* electroscope. The leaves of the electroscope diverge. This tells us that the rod was charged. Does it tell us whether the charge is positive or negative? (Yes/No).

★   ★   ★   ★   ★

No

29. Panel 6 describes a series of tests with a charged electroscope, which show how it can be used to discover whether a test charge is positive or negative. The letter in the upper right-hand corner is _____.

★   ★   ★   ★   ★

R

30. Read Panel 6 carefully. When a negative charge is brought near (but not touching) a positively charged electroscope, the leaves of the electroscope (diverge/collapse) even though the charge (has been/has not been) removed from the electroscope by contact or grounding.

★   ★   ★   ★   ★

collapse ; has not been

31. Panel 6. When a positively charged object is brought near the knob of a negatively charged electroscope, the leaves (diverge/collapse). The electroscope (loses/retains) its negative charge since there is no way for such charge to leave the electroscope.

★   ★   ★   ★   ★

collapse ; retains

32. Panel 6. We know that the charged electroscope retains its charge during these tests because when the rod being tested is withdrawn, the leaves of the electroscope again (diverge/collapse).

★　★　★　★　★

diverge

33. In an experiment a ball which is known to have an electric charge is brought close to the knob of a negatively charged electroscope. The leaves of the electroscope collapse. This means that the ball has a (positive/negative) charge.

★　★　★　★　★

positive

34. In an experiment, a glass rod is rubbed with silk and then *touched* to the knob of an electroscope. A ball known to have an electric charge is then brought close to the knob of the electroscope. The leaves collapse. This means that the ball has a (positive/negative) charge. Explain what has happened.

★　★　★　★　★

negative (After contact with the glass rod, the leaves of the electroscope are positively charged. The unknown charge must repel negative charge into the leaves to make them collapse.)

Section 3. *Electron Theory of Charge*
Conservation of Charge
Charge by Induction

Note: Scientists formulate theories to explain observed facts. This often involves the assumption of the existence of particles or other entities which are not themselves observable. An example is the molecule, assumed in the kinetic theory of gases to explain the observed behavior of gases. In Sections 1 and 2 we have considered some of the observable facts of static electricity. In Section 3 we will formulate a theory to explain these facts, the electron theory of charge, and use it to explain some new and important observations about static electricity. Notice the process by which scientific knowledge develops: a continuing interrelation of observation, theory to explain observation, experiments suggested by theory to provide new observations to test the theory.

1. We account for the results of the experiments described in Panels 1 to 6 by the *electron* theory. One assumption of this theory is that any object which does *not* have an electric charge contains equal numbers of positively charged particles and negatively charged particles. This means that an object which has a negative charge has (equal/unequal) numbers of positive and negative particles.

★   ★   ★   ★   ★

unequal

2. Glass rubbed with silk has an excess of (positive over negative/negative over positive) particles. Rubber rubbed with wool has an excess of (positive over negative/negative over positive) particles.

★   ★   ★   ★   ★

positive over negative ; negative over positive

3. An experiment called the Hall effect (which we will encounter in Chapter 4) leads us to assume further that, in a solid, it is only the *negatively* charged particles called *electrons* which can be moved in the solid if it is a conductor, or removed from its surface if it is an insulator. When a solid is charged by rubbing with another material, (positive/negative) particles are added to it or removed from it.

★   ★   ★   ★   ★

negative

4. Electrons are (positively/negatively) charged particles. Rubbing a glass with silk produces a positive charge on the glass because it (adds electrons to/removes electrons from) the surface of the glass.

★   ★   ★   ★   ★

negatively ; removes electrons from

5. Reread Steps 2 to 4 in Panel 1. After the silk and glass have been rubbed together they (attract/repel) each other. On the assumptions we have made about electric charge, it is reasonable to assume that electrons have been removed from the (glass/silk) and experiment should show that the silk now has a (positive/negative) charge.

★   ★   ★   ★   ★

attract ; glass ; negative (Because it has an excess of electrons.)

6. In an experiment, silk is rubbed on a glass rod. The silk is then brought close to a positively charged electroscope. The leaves collapse. This proves that the silk has a (positive/negative) charge.

★   ★   ★   ★   ★

negative

7. We can use the assumptions of our theory of electric charge to explain the production of negative charge in a rubber rod rubbed with wool. In this case _____ are removed from the wool and deposited on the rubber. Tests with a suitably charged electroscope will show that the charge on the wool is (positive/negative).

★   ★   ★   ★   ★

electrons ; positive

8. The glass-silk and the rubber-wool charge distributions are examples of a general principle called the *conservation of electric charge*. Whenever a positive charge is created, an equal amount of _____ charge is produced at the same time.

★   ★   ★   ★   ★

negative

9. An object *A* is rubbed on an object *B* and produces a negative charge on *B*. This means that a _____ charge has been produced on *A*. This is an example of the law of _____ of electric charge.

★   ★   ★   ★   ★

positive ; conservation

10. In an average time of 1000 sec, a neutron outside an atomic nucleus decays into a variety of other particles. One of these particles is an electron, which is a particle with a _____ electric charge. We know that neutrons have no charge. This means that one of the other decay products must have a _____ charge.

★   ★   ★   ★   ★

negative ; positive

11. According to the theory we have been developing, negative electric charge on a solid insulator or conductor indicates (a deficiency/an excess) of electrons on the insulator or conductor. A positive charge indicates (a deficiency/an excess) of electrons.

★   ★   ★   ★   ★

an excess ; a deficiency

12. Charges move freely on conductors. Electrons are (negatively/positively) charged particles; therefore _____ move freely on conductors

★   ★   ★   ★   ★

negatively ; electrons

13. Electrons on a conductor are (attracted/repelled) by a negative charge; electrons on a conductor are (attracted/repelled) by a positive charge.

★   ★   ★   ★   ★

repelled ; attracted

14. We now apply this theory to Panel 6. When the electroscope is positively charged, there is (an excess/a deficiency) of electrons in its leaves. When a negatively charged rod is brought close to the knob of the electroscope, electrons are (attracted from the leaves to the knob/repelled from the knob to the leaves).

★ ★ ★ ★ ★

a deficiency ; repelled from the knob to the leaves

15. Electrons repelled to the leaves cancel the positive charge in the leaves, and they (diverge/collapse). This is possible because (negatively/positively) charged particles are free to move in (insulators/conductors).

★ ★ ★ ★ ★

collapse ; negatively ; conductors

16. The leaves of a negatively charged electroscope diverge because there is (an excess/a deficiency) of electrons in the leaves. When a positive charge is brought close to the knob of a negatively charged electroscope, electrons are (repelled from the knob to the leaves/attracted from the leaves to the knob).

★ ★ ★ ★ ★

an excess ; attracted from the leaves to the knob

17. Bringing a positive charge close to the knob of a negatively charged electroscope attracts _____ from the leaves. This cancels the _____ charge in the leaves, and they (diverge/collapse).

★ ★ ★ ★ ★

electrons ; negative ; collapse

18. Refer to Panel 7. The letter in the upper right-hand corner is _____.

★ ★ ★ ★ ★

F

19. Read Panel 7 carefully. It describes a method of producing a charge by *induction*. In this experiment, the electroscope (is/is not) given its charge by contact with the charged rod.

★ ★ ★ ★ ★

is not

20. Panel 7. An *induced* charge is one produced in a(n) (conductor/insulator); it is produced in such a way that there is no _____ between the object producing the charge and the object being charged. _____

★ ★ ★ ★ ★

conductor ; contact

21. Panel 7. In Fig. 4, the electroscope has been charged by (contact/induction). It is called an _____ charge.

★ ★ ★ ★ ★

induction ; induced

22. Panel 7. We can explain the induced charge by reference to the assumptions we have made about electrons. When the negatively charged rod is brought close to the knob of an uncharged electroscope, electrons are (attracted from/repelled to) the leaves. This gives the leaves a _____ charge and they diverge.

★   ★   ★   ★   ★

repelled to; negative

23. Panel 7. In Fig. 1, the electrons are repelled to the leaves because there is nowhere else to go. In Fig. 2, electrons can also be repelled to the _____.

★   ★   ★   ★   ★

ground

24. Panel 7. In Fig. 2, some of the electrons repelled from the knob go to the ground. Since the excess of electrons in the leaves become negligible, the leaves (diverge/collapse).

★   ★   ★   ★   ★

collapse

25. Panel 7, Fig. 2. Since electrons have been repelled to the ground, there is (an excess/a deficiency) of electrons in the electroscope. When the ground connection is removed (Fig. 3), the repelled electrons (are/are not) able to return.

★   ★   ★   ★   ★

a deficiency ; are not

26. Panel 7. When the ground and the rod are removed, the electroscope is left with a deficiency of electrons and a _____ charge.

★   ★   ★   ★   ★

positive

27. In Panel 7, the electroscope is given a positive charge by (contact/induction). The charge used to produce this charge is (positive/negative).

★   ★   ★   ★   ★

induction ; negative

28. To give an electroscope a negative charge by contact requires a (negatively/positively) charged rod. To give an electroscope a negative charge by induction requires a (negatively/positively) charged rod.

★   ★   ★   ★   ★

negatively ; positively

29. We now produce a negative charge by induction. When we bring a positively charge rod close to the knob of an uncharged electroscope, electrons are (attracted to/repelled from) the knob. The leaves then have a _____ charge and (diverge/collapse). Draw a diagram of this part of the experiment.

⋆ ⋆ ⋆ ⋆ ⋆

attracted to ; positive ; diverge

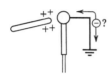

30. Here we ground an uncharged electroscope. When we bring a positively charged rod close to the knob, the rod (attracts electrons from/repels electrons

to) the ground, thus giving the electroscope (an excess/a deficiency) of electrons.

⋆ ⋆ ⋆ ⋆ ⋆

attracts electrons from ; an excess

31. The excess of electrons is held in the knob by the _____

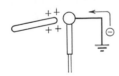

charge held close to the knob. The leaves remain collapsed because the excess of electrons (spreads/cannot spread) into them.

⋆ ⋆ ⋆ ⋆ ⋆

positive ; cannot spread

32. The ground is removed. This leaves the electroscope with a _____ charge. When the positive rod is removed, this charge spreads to the leaves and they (diverge/collapse). Draw a diagram (*a*) after the ground is removed, (*b*) after the (+) rod is removed.

★   ★   ★   ★   ★

negative ; diverge

(*a*)   (*b*)

33.

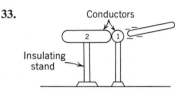

These objects are neutral. When negatively charged the rod is brought near 1, some electrons are (repelled to/attracted from) 2.

★   ★   ★   ★   ★

repelled to

34. If 1 and 2 in the previous frame are separated while the charged rod is held near and then the charge is removed, 1 has (a positive/a negative/no) charge. 2 has (a positive/a negative/no) charge.

★   ★   ★   ★   ★

a positive ; a negative

35. Since the excess of electrons in 2 accounts for the deficiency of electrons in 1, we can say that the magnitudes (disregarding the sign) of the resulting charges in 1 and 2 are (the same/different). This illustrates the law of

_____.

★   ★   ★   ★   ★

the same ; conservation of (electric) charge

Section 4.   Coulomb's Law for "Point" Charges
Units of Charge and Values of k

Note: So far our treatment of static electricity has been qualitative. We have described the forces between charged objects without measuring them. In this section we begin our quantitative treatment of electric forces with one of the fundamental equations of electromagnetism called *Coulomb's law for point charges*. In this particular field of physical science, Coulomb's law has the same central importance as we attribute to Newton's law of universal gravitation in mechanics.

1. Charged objects exert pushes and pulls on one another and on uncharged objects. We call these pushes and pulls which result from electric charges *electric forces*. Masses are attracted toward the center of the Earth by (electric/ gravitational) forces. Bits of paper are attracted to a hairbrush by (electric/ gravitational) forces.

⋆ ⋆ ⋆ ⋆ ⋆

gravitational ; electric

2. We have seen that (gravitational/electric) forces are *both* attracting and repulsing.

⋆ ⋆ ⋆ ⋆ ⋆

electric

3. In order to treat electric forces mathematically, we have to devise a method of producing equal amounts of charge. A simple method of doing this is illustrated in Panel 8. The letter in the upper right-hand corner is _____.

⋆ ⋆ ⋆ ⋆ ⋆

N

4. Panel 8. *A* and *B* are hollow metal spheres with *equal* radii; they are made of the *same conducting* material. *A* is positively charged; *B* is not charged at all. When *A* is touched to *B*, it is reasonable to expect that *A* (shares/does not share) its charge with *B*.

⋆ ⋆ ⋆ ⋆ ⋆

shares

5. Panel 8. Since *A* and *B* have (equal/unequal) radii and are made of the same conducting material, we may expect that they share the original charge on *A* (equally/unequally).

⋆ ⋆ ⋆ ⋆ ⋆

equal ; equally

6. Panel 8. The charge on *B* in Fig. 3 is (twice/one-half/the same as) the charge on *A* in Fig. 1.

⋆ ⋆ ⋆ ⋆ ⋆

one-half

7. Panel 8. In Fig. 4 the charge in *B* has been removed by grounding. In Fig. 5, it is again brought into contact with *A*. When *B* is then separated from *A*, its charge will be (equal/unequal) to the charge left on *A* and (one-half/one-fourth) the charge on *A* in Fig. 1.

★ ★ ★ ★ ★

equal ; one-fourth

8. We now have a procedure for controlling the relative amount of charge on two or more similar metal spheres. We can reduce the charge on a sphere by one-half merely by touching it to a similar (charged/uncharged) sphere.

★ ★ ★ ★ ★

uncharged

9. Refer to Panel 9. The letter in the upper right-hand corner is _____.

★ ★ ★ ★ ★

G

10. Panel 9. Read the descriptive paragraph. Spheres *A* and *B* are similar in radius and material. Suppose there is a charge on *A* and no charge on *B*. When *A* and *B* are brought into contact and then separated by specified distance, they (attract/repel) each other and the pointer moves (up/down). The amount the pointer moves is a measure of the _____ force between the spheres at this distance.

★ ★ ★ ★ ★

repel ; up ; electric

11. Panel 9. Suppose we have a third sphere *C*, identical to *A* and *B*, which we use to reduce the charge on *A* or *B*. When *C* is touched to *A* or *B*, it reduces the charge on *A* or *B* by _____ (amount).

★ ★ ★ ★ ★

one-half

12. Refer to Panel 10. The letter in the upper right-hand corner is _____.

★ ★ ★ ★ ★

P

13. Panel 10. Read Steps 1 to 3 of this experiment. The distance between the centers of the charged spheres is (varied/kept constant) in this part of the experiment; the charge in sphere *A* is (varied/kept constant).

★ ★ ★ ★ ★

kept constant ; varied

14. Panel 10. After sphere *A* is touched to sphere *B*, they have (the same charge/different charges). –

★ ★ ★ ★ ★

the same charge

15. Panel 10. We have not yet defined or determined a standard for measuring charge. For the time being, let us say that each of the spheres A and B has a single unit (1) of charge as they exist in Step 2 of this experiment.

The displacement of the pointer from 10 to 45 is a measure of the _____ _____ between A and B when each has 1 unit of charge and they are _____ cm apart.

★ ★ ★ ★ ★

electric force ; 25

16. Panel 10. Refer to Step 4. When each of the spheres A and B has a charge of 1 unit (as defined in the previous frame), the electric force between them causes the pointer to move _____ units along the scale.

★ ★ ★ ★ ★

35

17. Panel 10, Steps 3 and 4. After A has been touched with C the first time, it has $(1/\frac{1}{2}/\frac{1}{4})$ unit of charge. The electric force between A and B is then (the same/as one-half of/one-fourth of) what it was in Step 2.

$\frac{1}{2}$; one-half

★ ★ ★ ★ ★

18. Panel 10, Steps 3 and 4. When A has been touched to C a second time, it has $(\frac{1}{2}/\frac{1}{4}/\frac{1}{8})$ its initial charge, and the electric force between A and B is _____ (Fraction) of what it was when they carried equal charges.

★ ★ ★ ★ ★

$\frac{1}{4}$; $\frac{1}{4}$

19. Panel 10, Steps 3 and 4. When A has been touched by C a third time, we expect the pointer to be displaced _____ (Fraction) of its displacement when A and B carried unit charges. Is this verified by the table in Step 4 (i.e., $4\frac{3}{8}$ is what fraction of 35)? (Yes/No).

★ ★ ★ ★ ★

$\frac{1}{8}$; Yes ($4\frac{3}{8}$ is $\frac{1}{8}$ of 35)

20. Panel 10. After Step 3(d), sphere A has _____ (Fraction) of its unit charge in Step 2, and sphere B has _____ (*Fraction*) of its unit charge in Step 2.

★ ★ ★ ★ ★

$\frac{1}{8}$; $\frac{1}{2}$

21. Panel 10. After Step 3(d) of this experiment, the electric force is $(\frac{1}{2}/\frac{1}{8}/$ some other fraction) of what is was after Step 2.

★ ★ ★ ★ ★

some other fraction (Because the pointer displacement, $2\frac{3}{16}$, is not $\frac{1}{2}$ of 35 or $\frac{1}{8}$ of 35. It is $\frac{1}{16}$ of 35)

22. Panel 10, Step 4. Compare columns IV and V. The electric force between *A* and *B* is (inversely/directly) proportional to the _____ of the charges in *A* and *B* when the distance between *A* and *B* is _____ .
★   ★   ★   ★   ★
directly ; product ; constant

23. Panel 10. Steps 1 to 4 of this panel show that the _____ force between two charged spheres is directly proportional to the product of the _____ if the _____ between their centers is kept constant.
★   ★   ★   ★   ★
electric ; charges ; distance

24. Panel 10. Read Steps 5 to 7. In this part of the experiment the distance between the charged spheres is (constant/variable) and the product of the charges on the spheres is (constant/variable).
★   ★   ★   ★   ★
variable ; constant

25. Panel 10. Steps 5 to 7 are designed to investigate the relation between the electric force between two charged spheres and [(*a*) the charge on either sphere/(*b*) the product of the charges on the spheres/(*c*) the distance between the centers of the spheres].
★   ★   ★   ★   ★
(*c*)

26. Panel 10, Step 7. The relationship sought here is not as obvious as that between the electric force and the product of the charges. We note first, however, that when the distance between the charged spheres decreases, the electric force (increases/decreases).
★   ★   ★   ★   ★
increases

27. Panel 10, Step 7. The table indicates that electric force *cannot* be (directly/ inversely) proportional to the distance between the centers of the spheres.
★   ★   ★   ★   ★
directly

28. Two variables x and y are inversely proportional if their product is constant, or $xy = k$.

Apply the test to electric force and distance measurements in Step 7 of Panel 10. Are distance and electric force inversely proportional? (Yes/No)
★   ★   ★   ★   ★

No. (Because in the first row, $30 \times 20 = \textbf{600}$. In the second row, $15 \times 80 = \textbf{1200}$. Obviously the product of distance and electric force is *not* a constant.)

29. Panel 10, Step 7. Electric force is not inversely proportional to distance. It may, however, be inversely proportional to the distance *squared*. In that case, (electric force) $\times$ (distance)^2 = a constant. Try it with the data in the table. Is electric force inversely proportional to the square of the distance? (Yes/No)

★   ★   ★   ★   ★

Yes. (Because in the first row, $(30)^2 \times 20 = \textbf{18,000}$

In the second row, $(15)^2 \times 80 = \textbf{18,000}$

And so forth.

In the last row, $(75)^2 \times 3\frac{1}{5} = \textbf{18,000}$.)

30. Panel 10. The experiments described in Panel 10 enable us to make the following statement about the electric force between two charged spheres and the distance between their centers: The electric force is (directly/inversely) proportional to the _____ of the charges and (directly/inversely) proportional to the _____ of the distance between their centers.

★   ★   ★   ★   ★

directly ; product ; inversely ; square

31. Let Q_1 and Q_2 be the charges in two spheres and let d be the distance between their centers. If F_e is the electric force between them, then $F_e = k$ _____ , where k is a constant of proportionality.

★   ★   ★   ★   ★

$$\frac{Q_1 Q_2}{d^2}$$

32. The law we developed in Panel 10 is, strictly speaking, only precise for charged objects whose size is small compared to the distance between them. Physicists say that it is only strictly accurate for *point charges*, i.e., for charges which we can consider to be concentrated at a _____.

★   ★   ★   ★   ★

point

33. We shall refer to the law hereafter as *Coulomb's law for point charges*. This law is precisely applicable only where the sizes of the charged objects are (small/large) compared to the _____ between them.

★   ★   ★   ★   ★

small ; distance

34. .Coulomb's law for point charges is identical in its mathematical form to Newton's law of universal gravitation. The gravitational force, F_g, between masses m_1 and m_2 a distance d apart is $F_g = G$ _____. The electric force between two point charges q_1 and q_2 a distance d apart is $F_e = k$ _____.

G and k are _____ of proportionality.

★ ★ ★ ★ ★

$\dfrac{m_1 m_2}{d^2}$; $\dfrac{q_1 q_2}{d^2}$; constants

35. Coulomb's law for point charges and Newton's law of universal gravitation are both *inverse square* laws. Explain why?

★ ★ ★ ★ ★

The forces they describe are each *inversely proportional* to the *square* of the distance involved.

36. $F_e = k \dfrac{q_1 q_2}{d^2}$

This equation represents _____'s law for electric charges concentrated at _____.

★ ★ ★ ★ ★ ★

Coulomb('s) ; points

37. State Coulomb's law for point charges in words, using the concept of proportionality.

★ ★ ★ ★ ★

The electric force between two point charges is directly proportional to the product of the charges and inversely proportional to the square of the distance between them.

38. $F_e = k \dfrac{q_1 q_2}{d^2}$.

The value of k in this equation depends upon the units used to measure force, distance and _____.

★ ★ ★ ★ ★

charge, or electric charge

39. Electric charge cannot be made indefinitely small. There is a certain *minimum* amount of charge which is in fact the amount of charge on a single electron or proton. We call this minimum amount a unit of *elementary charge* (abbreviated as *elem. chge.*). Is it possible for an object to have one-half a unit of elementary charge? (Yes/No) Explain.

★ ★ ★ ★ ★

No. (Because one unit of elementary charge is the *minimum* amount of charge any object can have.)

40. The minimum amount of *negative* electric charge is that found on a single _____. The miminum amount of *positive* electric charge is

that found on a single _____. This minimum amount of charge (positive or negative) is called a unit of _____ _____.
★　★　★　★　★

electron ; proton ; elementary charge (or elem. chge.).

41. An alpha particle is a helium atom from which two electrons have been removed. An alpha particle, therefore, has (an excess/a deficiency) of two electrons and a (positive/negative) charge of _____ (*Number*) elem. chge.
★　★　★　★　★

a deficiency, positive, 2

42. $F_e = k \dfrac{q_1 q_2}{d^2}$.

When force is measured in newtons, distance in meters, and charge in units of elementary charge, k has the value $2.3 \times 10^{-28} \dfrac{\text{newton-m}^2}{(\text{elem. chge.})^2}$. Compute the electric force between two electrons which are 1 meter apart.
★　★　★　★　★

$$F_e = 2.3 \times 10^{-28} \frac{\text{newton-m}^2}{(\text{elem. chge.})^2} \frac{(-1 \text{ elem. chge.})(-1 \text{ elem. chge.})}{(1 \text{ meter})^2}$$

$$= 2.3 \times 10^{-28} \text{ newton}$$

(*Think!* The product of two charges with the same sign is always positive. This gives us a positive force. What would a negative value for F_e indicate?)

43. The charge on a proton is one positive elementary charge. Compute the electric force of attraction between an electron and a proton at a distance of 1.0×10^{-8} meter.
★　★　★　★　★

$$F_e = (2.3 \times 10^{-28}) \frac{(-1 \text{ elem. chge.})(+1 \text{ elem. chge.})}{(1.0 \times 10^{-8})^2}$$

$$F_e = -\frac{2.3 \times 10^{-28}}{1.0 \times 10^{-16}} = -2.3 \times 10^{-12} \text{ newton}$$

(*Think!* What is the meaning of the minus sign?)

44. The proton and the electrons in the previous problem (attract/repel) each other. The minus sign associated with the force in the previous problem indicates that it is (an attracting/a repulsing) force.
★　★　★　★　★

attract ; attracting

45. $F_e = k \dfrac{q_1 q_2}{d^2}$.

The value of k in Coulomb's law is $2.3 \times 10^{-28} \dfrac{\text{newton-m}^2}{(\text{elem. chge.})^2}$ when q_1

and q_2 are measured in _____ _____ ,
F_e is measured in _____ and d is measured in _____ .
★   ★   ★   ★   ★

units of elem. chge. (or elem. chgs.) ; newtons ; meters

46. An alpha particle is a subatomic particle with two units of positive elementary charge. A deuteron is a subatomic particle with one unit of positive elementary charge. Compute the electric force between these particles at a distance of 2.0×10^{-7} meter.
★   ★   ★   ★   ★

$$F_e = (2.3 \times 10^{-28}) \frac{(+2)(+1)}{(2.0 \times 10^{-7})^2}$$

$$= \frac{4.6 \times 10^{-28}}{4.0 \times 10^{-14}} = 1.2 \times 10^{-14} \text{ newton}$$

47. A unit of elementary charge is extremely small. For instance, the charge placed on a glass rod when it is rubbed with silk involves the removal of many millions of electrons and a charge measured in many millions of units of elementary charge.

The coulomb is a unit of charge used to describe charges like that on the glass rod in smaller numbers. The coulomb is (larger than/smaller than/equal to) a unit of elementary charge.
★   ★   ★   ★   ★

larger than

48. The smallest fraction of a coulomb of charge must be a unit of _____
_____ . This is because charge (can/cannot) be reduced to indefinitely small amounts. There (is a/is no) definite minimum amount of charge.
★   ★   ★   ★   ★

elementary charge ; cannot ; is a

49. $F_e = k \dfrac{q_1 q_2}{d^2}$. When q_1 and q_2 are measured in coulombs, F_e in newtons,

and d in meters, $k = 9.0 \times 10^9 \dfrac{\text{newton-m}^2}{\text{coulomb}^2}$. Compute the electric force

between two positive charges of 1.0×10^{-6} coulomb and 2.0×10^{-5} coulomb when they are 10 meters apart.
★   ★   ★   ★   ★

$$F_e = 9.0 \times 10^9 \frac{\text{newton-m}^2}{\text{coulomb}^2} \cdot \frac{(1.0 \times 10^{-6} \text{ coulomb})(2.0 \times 10^{-5} \text{ coulomb})}{(10 \text{ m})^2}$$

$$= 9.0 \times 10^9 \frac{2.0 \times 10^{-11}}{100}$$

$$= 18 \times 10^{-4} \text{ newton}$$

50. $F_e = k \dfrac{q_1 q_2}{d^2}$. We use $k = $ _____ when F_e is in newtons,

d in meters, and q in elementary charges; we use $k = $ _____ when F_e is in newtons, d in meters, and q in coulombs.

★ ★ ★ ★ ★

2.3×10^{-28} ; 9.0×10^9

51. One coulomb is equivalent to 6.25×10^{18} elementary charges. A positive charge of 2.00×10^{-5} coulomb is equivalent to a deficiency of _____ _____ (*number*) electrons.

★ ★ ★ ★ ★

1 coulomb $= 6.25 \times 10^{18}$ elementary charges.

2.00×10^{-5} coulomb $= (2.00 \times 10^{-5})(6.25 \times 10^{18})$ elem. chge.

$$= 12.5 \times 10^{13} \text{ elem. chge.}$$

52. 1 coulomb $= 6.25 \times 10^{18}$ elem. chge.

1 elem. chge. $= $ _____ coulomb (*Compute to two figures.*)

★ ★ ★ ★ ★

6.25×10^{18} elem. chge. $= 1$ coul

$$1 \text{ elem. chge.} = \frac{1 \text{ coulomb}}{6.25 \times 10^{18}}$$

$$= 0.16 \times 10^{-18} = \mathbf{1.6 \times 10^{-19} \text{ coulomb}}$$

53. A hard rubber rod is rubbed vigorously with wool. How many electrons must be deposited on the rod to give it a negative charge of 3.0×10^{-4} coulomb?

★ ★ ★ ★ ★

Each electron carries an elementary charge. Therefore, $(3.0 \times 10^{-4})(6.25 \times 10^{18}) = 18.75 \times 10^{14}$ electrons must be deposited on the rubber rod.

54. An alpha particle has a charge of two positive elementary charges. What is its charge in coulombs?

★ ★ ★ ★ ★

1 elem. chge. $= 1.6 \times 10^{-19}$ coulomb

2 elem. chge. $= \mathbf{3.2 \times 10^{-19} \text{ coulomb}}$

Section 5.   Review and Problems

Note: If you are doubtful about the answers to the following review frames, reread the experiments described in Panels 1 to 10.

1. We define a negative charge as one which is (attracted/repelled) by the charge placed on a rubber rod when it is rubbed with wool.
★   ★   ★   ★   ★
repelled

2. The charge placed on a glass rod when it is rubbed with silk is a (positive/negative) charge.

The glass rod when charged (attracts/repels/does not affect) uncharged objects; it (attracts/repels/does not affect) objects which have been given a negative charge.
★   ★   ★   ★   ★
positive ; attracts ; attracts

3. One end of a rubber rod is rubbed vigorously with wool. The charge thus placed on the rod [(a) Spreads to all parts of the surface/(b) stays in the place where it has been rubbed] because rubber is (an insulator/a conductor) of electric charge.
★   ★   ★   ★   ★
(b) ; an insulator

4. Charge spreads out on the surface of a conducting metal because a solid conductor contains charged particles called _____ which are free to move under the influence of electric forces.
★   ★   ★   ★   ★
electrons

5. Insulators also contain electrons. Electrons in insulators (are/are not) free to move over the surface of the insulator.
★   ★   ★   ★   ★
are not

6. When a charge is placed on a glass rod from a silk cloth, the rod and the cloth end up with (equal/unequal) charges with (the same sign/opposite signs). This is an illustration of the law of _____ of _____.
★   ★   ★   ★   ★
equal ; opposite ; conservation (of) charge

7. The positive charge placed on a glass rod when it is rubbed with silk is due to the fact that after it is rubbed it has (an excess/a deficiency) of electrons.
★   ★   ★   ★   ★
deficiency

8. State, in words, Coulomb's law for point charges.

★ ★ ★ ★ ★

The electric force between two charged objects is directly proportional to the product of their charges and inversely proportional to the square of the distance between them.

9. A negative charge is used to charge an electroscope by induction. The charge left on the electroscope is (positive/negative/neutral.)

★ ★ ★ ★ ★

positive

10. Write an equation relating electric force F_e between two point charges Q and q with the charges and the distance, r, between their centers. Use k as a constant of proportionality.

★ ★ ★ ★ ★

$$F_e = k\frac{Qq}{r^2}$$

11. $F_e = k\dfrac{Qq}{r^2}$. The numerical value of k is 9.0×10^9 when F_e is measured in

_____, r in _____, and Q and q in _____.

★ ★ ★ ★ ★

newtons ; meters ; coulombs

12. Coulomb's law for electric forces and Newtons' law of universal gravitation have one very important thing in common. They are both _____ square laws.

★ ★ ★ ★ ★

inverse

13. Electric charge (can/cannot) be subdivided indefinitely.

★ ★ ★ ★ ★

cannot

14. The minimum amount of charge available is the amount of charge on a single _____. This is called a unit of _____

_____.

★ ★ ★ ★ ★

electron (or proton) ; elementary~~change~~ (or elem. chge.)

15. Refer to Panel 11. The letter in the upper right-hand corner is _____.

★ ★ ★ ★ ★

H

16. Panel 11. Read Problem 1. In part (a) we use Newton's law of universal gravitation, which in mathematical form is, $F_g = G$ _____ (use m_1, m_2, and d).

★ ★ ★ ★ ★

$$\frac{m_1 m_2}{d^2}$$

17. Panel 11, Problem 1(a). Compute the gravitational force between the electrons described in this problem.

★ ★ ★ ★ ★

$$
\begin{aligned}
F_g &= G \frac{m_1 m_2}{d^2} \\
&= (6.67 \times 10^{-11}) \frac{(9.0 \times 10^{-31})(9.0 \times 10^{-31})}{(1.00)^2} \\
&= (6.67 \times 10^{-11})(81 \times 10^{-62}) \\
&= 5.4 \times 10^{-71} \text{ newton}
\end{aligned}
$$

18. Panel 11, Problem 1. In part (b), q_1 and q_2 are each _____ (sign, number, and unit).

★ ★ ★ ★ ★

-1 elem. chge.

19. Panel 11, Problem 1. Compute the electric force of repulsion required in part (b).

★ ★ ★ ★ ★

$$
\begin{aligned}
F_e &= (2.3 \times 10^{-28}) \frac{(-1)(-1)}{(1)^2} \\
&= 2.3 \times 10^{-28} \text{ newton}
\end{aligned}
$$

20. Panel 11, Problem 1. $F_e = 2.3 \times 10^{-28}$ newton

$$F_g = 5.4 \times 10^{-71} \text{ newton}$$

It is obvious that the electrical force is much (larger/smaller) than the gravitational force.

★ ★ ★ ★ ★

larger

21. Panel 11, Problem 1. Compute the ratio of F_e to F_g as required in (c).

★ ★ ★ ★ ★

$$\frac{F_e}{F_g} = \frac{2.3 \times 10^{-28}}{5.4 \times 10^{-71}} \approx 4.3 \times 10^{42}$$

22. Panel 11, Problem 2. In this problem, the charge is to be found in

_____ (*units*). This means that k must have
the numerical value _____.

★   ★   ★   ★   ★

elementary charges ; 2.3×10^{-28}

23. Panel 11. Read Problem 2. If we assume that these are "point" charges,
we (can/can not) use Coulomb's law to solve this problem.

★   ★   ★   ★   ★

can

24. Panel 11, Problem 2. Let Q = the charge in each object. Compute Q
from the data given.

★   ★   ★   ★   ★

$$F_e = k \frac{QQ}{d^2} = k \frac{Q^2}{d^2}$$

$$9.2 \times 10^{-4} = 2.3 \times 10^{-28} \frac{Q^2}{10^2}$$

$$Q^2 = 4.0 \times 10^{26}$$

$$Q = 2.0 \times 10^{13} \text{ elem. chges.}$$

25. Panel 11, Problem 2. Convert the answer computed in the previous frame
to coulombs.

★   ★   ★   ★   ★

1 elem. chge. $= 1.6 \times 10^{-19}$ coulomb

2.0×10^{13} elem. chge. $= (2.0 \times 10^{13})(1.6 \times 10^{-19})$ coulomb

$$= 3.2 \times 10^{-6} \text{ coulomb}$$

26. Panel 11. Read Problem 3. Since q_1 and q_2 have charges with (the same
sign/opposite signs), the electric force exerted by q_1 on q_2 will be to the (left/
right).

★   ★   ★   ★   ★

opposite signs, left (q_1 will attract q_2 toward itself.)

27. Panel 11, Problem 3(*a*). Compute the magnitude of the electric force of
q_1 on q_2. (*Think:* Which constant of proportionality will you use?) We have
already determined the direction, so you can neglect the signs of the charges
in this computation.

★   ★   ★   ★   ★

$$F_e = (9.0 \times 10^9) \frac{(2.0 \times 10^{-6})(2.0 \times 10^{-6})}{(2 \times 10^{-2})^2}$$

$$= \frac{(9.0 \times 10^9)(4.0 \times 10^{-12})}{4 \times 10^{-4}}$$

$$= 9.0 \times 10^1 = 90 \text{ newtons}$$

28. Panel 11, Problem 3(*a*). The magnitude and direction of the electric force of q_1 on q_2 is _____.

★ ★ ★ ★ ★

90 newtons to the left.

29. Panel 11, Problem 3. The direction of the electric force of q_3 on q_2 is to the _____.

★ ★ ★ ★ ★

right

30. Panel 11, Problem 3(*b*). Compute the magnitude of the electric force of q_3 on q_2.

★ ★ ★ ★ ★

$$F_e = (9.0 \times 10^9) \frac{(2.0 \times 10^{-6})(4.0 \times 10^{-6})}{(6 \times 10^{-2})^2}$$

$$= \frac{(9.0 \times 10^9)(8.0 \times 10^{-12})}{36 \times 10^{-4}}$$

$$= 2 \times 10 = 20 \text{ newtons}$$

31. Panel 11, Problem 3(*c*). The vector sum of these forces [computed in (*a*) and (*b*)] is _____ (*magnitude and direction*).

★ ★ ★ ★ ★

(*a*) 90 newtons to the left, (*b*) 20 newtons to the right, (*c*) vector sum is 70 newtons to the left

32. Panel 11, Problem 3. Consider part (*d*). The direction of the force exerted by q_1 on q_3 is to the _____. The direction of the force exerted by q_2 on q_3 is to the _____.

★ ★ ★ ★ ★

right ; left

33. Panel 11, Problem 3(*d*). Compute the magnitude of the force exerted by q_1 on q_3.

★ ★ ★ ★ ★

$$F_e = 9.0 \times 10^9 \frac{(2.0 \times 10^{-6})(4.0 \times 10^{-6})}{(8 \times 10^{-2})^2}$$

$$= \frac{(9.0 \times 10^9)(8.0 \times 10^{-12})}{64 \times 10^{-4}} = 1.125 \times 10$$

$$= 11.25 \text{ newtons}$$

34. Panel 11, Problem 3(*d*). Compute the magnitude of the electric force of q_2 on q_3.

★ ★ ★ ★ ★

$$F_e = 9.0 \times 10^9 \frac{(2.0 \times 10^{-6})(4.0 \times 10^{-6})}{(6 \times 10^{-2})^2}$$

$$= \frac{(9.0 \times 10^9)(8.0 \times 10^{-12})}{36 \times 10^{-4}} = 20 \text{ newtons}$$

35. Panel 11. What is the answer to Problem 3(d)?

★　★　★　★　★

Force of q_1 on $q_3 = 11.25$ newtons to the right
Force of q_2 on $q_3 = 20$ newtons to the left
Vector sum of these forces is 8.75 newtons to the left.

36. Panel 11. Read Problem 4. The electric force of q_1 on q_2 is directed (to the right/to the left/up/down).

★　★　★　★　★

to the right

37. Panel 11, Problem 4. The electric force of q_3 on q_2 is directed (to the right/to the left/up/down).

★　★　★　★　★

up

38. Panel 11, Problem 4. $\vec{F}_1$ represents the force q_1 on q_2. $\vec{F}_2$ represents the force of q_3 on q_2. $\vec{F}_3$ represents the _____ _____ of $\vec{F}_1$ and $\vec{F}_2$.

★　★　★　★　★

vector sum

39. Panel 11, Problem 4. Compute F_1 and F_2 as defined in the previous frame.

★　★　★　★　★

$$F_1 = k \frac{q_1 q_2}{(AB)^2} = (9.0 \times 10^9) \frac{(1.0 \times 10^{-6})(1.0 \times 10^{-6})}{(3 \times 10^{-2})^2}$$

$$= \frac{(9.0 \times 10^9)(1.0 \times 10^{-12})}{9 \times 10^{-4}} = 10 \text{ newtons}$$

$$F_2 = k \frac{q_3 q_2}{(BC)^2} = \frac{(9.0 \times 10^9)(1.0 \times 10^{-6})(1.0 \times 10^{-6})}{16 \times 10^{-4}}$$

$$= 5.6 \text{ newtons}$$

40. Panel 11, Problem 4. Compute the vector sum of $\vec{F}_1$ and $\vec{F}_2$. (*Think!* These forces act at an angle of 90° to each other.)

★ ★ ★ ★ ★

We use the Pythogorean theorem:

$$(F_3)^2 = (F_1)^2 + (F_2)^2$$

$$(F_3)^2 = 100 + 31.36 = 131.36$$

$$F_3 \approx 11.4 \text{ newtons}$$

41. Panel 11. Read Problem 5. Let Q = the charge on the electron and the charge on the proton (neglect signs). Let r = the radius of the electron orbit. Let m = the mass of the electron. Let v = the orbital speed of the electron. Write equations for the electric force, F_e, of the proton on the electron, and for the centripetal force, F_c, on the electron in terms of its mass, its speed, and the orbital radius.

★ ★ ★ ★ ★

$$F_e = \frac{kQ^2}{r^2} \; ; \; F_c = \frac{mv^2}{r}$$

42. Panel 11. We are told in Problem 5 to assume that F_c and F_e are (equal/ unequal). This means we can write an equation which relates m, v, r, and Q. Write this equation.

★ ★ ★ ★ ★

equal ; Since $F_e = k \dfrac{Q^2}{r^2}$ and $F_c = \dfrac{mv^2}{r}$,

$$k \frac{Q^2}{r^2} = \frac{mv^2}{r} \text{, or, more simply, } k \frac{Q^2}{r} = mv^2$$

43. Panel 11, Problem 5. Substitute the data supplied in Problem 5 and solve for the orbital speed.

★ ★ ★ ★ ★

$$v^2 = \frac{kQ^2}{rm}$$

We use $k = 2.3 \times 10^{-28}$ since Q is in elementary charge.

$$v^2 = \frac{(2.3 \times 10^{-28})(1)^2}{(0.53 \times 10^{-10})(9.0 \times 10^{-31})} = 0.48 \times 10^{13} = 4.8 \times 10^{12}$$

$$v = 2.2 \times 10^6 \text{ m/sec}$$

34 ELECTROSTATICS

PROBLEMS

1. Given the following: a piece of cat fur, a glass rod, a rod made of vulcanite (hard rubber), a silk necktie, Describe how you would produce (*a*) a positive electric charge, and (*b*) a negative electric charge.

2. Given an electroscope and the materials mentioned in Problem 1 above, describe how you would (*a*) give the electroscope a positive charge by contact, (*b*) by induction; (*c*) give the electroscope a negative charge by contact; (*d*) by induction.

3. You are given a charged electroscope, but you do not know whether the charge is positive or negative. You have available the materials mentioned in Problem 1 above. Describe a procedure you would use to determine whether the charge on the electroscope is positive or negative *without* discharging the electroscope.

4. Distinguish between conductors and insulators with respect to their behavior when electric charges are placed on a part of them.

5. Describe the electron theory of charge.

6. Use the electron theory of charge to explain what happens when an electroscope is given a *negative* charge by induction.

7. Use the electron theory of charge to explain what happens when an electroscope is given a *positive* charge by induction.

8. State the law of conservation of electric charge. Explain how the electron theory accounts for the conservation of electric charge.

9. State Coulomb's law for point charges.

10. Compute the number of elementary charges required to provide a charge of 12 coulombs. How many coulombs are there in 1.25×10^{15} elementary charges?

11. Point charges of -15×10^{-6} coulombs and $+300 \times 10^{-6}$ coulombs are 0.2 meter apart. Compute the electric force between them. Is it attracting or repelling?

12. Point charges of -4×10^5 elementary charges and -12×10^6 elementary charges are placed 5 cm apart. Compute the electric force between them. Is it attracting or repelling?

13. The distance between q_1 and q_2 is 5 cm. Between q_2 and q_3 the distance is also 5 cm. The value of q_1 is 5 coulombs, q_2 10 coulombs, and q_3 is -8

coulombs. Compute (a) the total electric force on q_1; (b) the total electric force on q_2 and (c) the total electric force on q_3. The three charges lie along the same straight line as in Problem 3 of Panel 11.

14. Point charges of 2.0×10^5 elementary charges are placed at P, Q, and R. The angle between PQ and QR is $90°$; the distance between P and Q is 5 cm; and between Q and R it is 12 cm. Compute the total electric force on the charge at Q.

15. Compute the total electric force on Q in Problem 14 if the charge at P is negative.

Chapter Two

ELECTRIC FIELD AND

ELECTRIC POTENTIAL

OBJECTIVES

Upon successful completion of this chapter the student should be able to:

1. Define and compute electric fields around point charges.
2. Describe the electric fields around charged spheres, cylinders, inside hollow spheres, and between two oppositely charged plates.
3. Solve problems involving a variety of electric fields.
4. Define electric potential energy.
5. Define electric potential and potential difference.
6. Compute electric potentials and electric potential differences.
7. Define EMF.

INTRODUCTORY NOTE

In mechanics we developed the notion of a *gravitational field* describing quantitatively the influence of a given mass (e.g., the Earth) on other masses in the space around it. Gravitational field is defined as gravitational force per unit mass. An equally important, notion related to electrical forces influencing charges around charged objects is the *electric field*, which we define as electric force per unit charge. Electric fields will be central to our discussion in the next two chapters.

A concept we have not yet encountered is *potential*. Gravitational potential is defined as gravitational potential energy per unit mass and is measured in units like joules per kilogram. A more frequently used, but similar physical quantity, is *electric potential*, which is defined as *electrical potential energy per unit electric charge* and is measured in units like joules per coulomb (called volts). Electric potential occurs more often in the equations of electricity and magnetism than the physical quantity from which it is derived: electric potential energy. A thorough understanding of electric potential is absolutely essential for the study of current electricity which we discuss in Chapter three.

Section 1. Electric Fields

Definition of Electric Field: $\vec{E} = \dfrac{\vec{F}}{q}$

Computation of Electric Field Around a Point Charge:
$$E = \frac{kQ}{R^2}$$
Direction of Field
Field Due to Several Point Charges

1. We define the electric field at any position in space as *the electric* force on a small positive charge q placed at that position divided by q. Let E represent the magnitude of the electric field at a point where the electric force on q is F. Then $E =$ ———.

★ ★ ★ ★ ★

$\dfrac{F}{q}$

2. The electric field at any point in space is the _____ force per unit of _____ at that point.

★ ★ ★ ★ ★

electric ; charge

3. All forces are vector quantities. This means that electric forces have both _____ and _____.

★ ★ ★ ★ ★

In either order: magnitude ; direction

4. $\vec{E} = \dfrac{\vec{F}}{q}$ This equation defines the _____ at a given point in space. It is, like electric force, a _____ quantity. $\vec{E}$ has the same (magnitude/direction) as $\vec{F}$.

★ ★ ★ ★ ★

electric field ; vector ; direction

5. A test charge of 50 elem. chge. is acted upon by an electric force of 4.0 × 10^{-4} newton. $E =$ _____ (*Number and units*).

★ ★ ★ ★ ★

$$E = \frac{4.0 \times 10^{-4} \text{ newton}}{50 \text{ elem. chge.}} = 8 \times 10^{-6} \frac{\text{newton}}{\text{elem. chge.}}$$

6. An electric force of 5×10^{-3} newton acts on a charge of 2.5×10^{-6} coulomb. Compute the electric field in newtons/coulomb.

★ ★ ★ ★ ★

$$E = \frac{5 \times 10^{-3}\,\text{newton}}{2.5 \times 10^{-6}\,\text{coulomb}} = 2 \times 10^3\,\text{newtons/coulomb}$$

7. The units used to measure electric field are units of _____ divided by units of _____. Match the units in column II with the physical quantities in column I.

I	II
(a) charge	· newtons
(b) electric field	joules/coulomb
(c) energy	coulomb
(d) force	newtons/elem. chge.
	elem. chge.
	joules/elem. chge.

★ ★ ★ ★ ★

force ; charge
(a) coulomb and elem. chge.
(b) newtons/elem. chge.
(c) joules
(d) newtons

8. Refer to Panel 12. The letter in the upper right-hand corner is _____.
★ ★ ★ ★ ★

A

9. Panel 12. In Fig. 1, Q is a point charge surrounded by its electric field. We can compute the magnitude of this field at any point by placing a test charge q at that point and finding the ratio of the electric _____ on q to the _____ on q.
★ ★ ★ ★ ★

force ; charge

10. Panel 12, Fig. 1. When q is a distance r_1 from Q, the electric force F_1 on q is given by the equation $F_1 = $ _____.
★ ★ ★ ★ ★

$$\frac{kQq}{r_1^2}$$

11. Panel 12, Fig. 1. By *definition* the electric field E_1, a distance r_1 from q, is given by the equation: $E_1 = $ _____.
★ ★ ★ ★ ★

$$\frac{F_1}{q}$$

12. Panel 12, Fig. 1. (1) $F_1 = \dfrac{kQq}{r_1^2}$. (2) Divide both sides of (1) by q. Then $E_1 = \dfrac{F_1}{q} = $ _____.

★ ★ ★ ★ ★

$k\dfrac{Q}{r_1^2}$

13. Panel 12, Fig. 1. We now have an equation which enables us to compute the _____ _____ at any point in the space around a _____ charge Q if we know Q and the _____ between Q and the point being tested.

★ ★ ★ ★ ★

electric field ; point ; distance

14. Panel 12, Fig. 1. In terms of Q and r_3, $E_3 = $ _____.

★ ★ ★ ★ ★

$k\dfrac{Q}{r_3^2}$

15. Panel 12, Fig. 1. Let $Q = 4 \times 10^6$ elem. chge. and $r_2 = 0.50$ meter. $E_2 = $ _____

(*Number and units*). (*Think!* What value of k should you use here?)

★ ★ ★ ★ ★

$E_2 = k\dfrac{Q}{r_2^2} = \left(2.3 \times 10^{-28}\ \dfrac{\text{newton-m}^2}{(\text{elem. chge.})^2}\right)\left(\dfrac{4 \times 10^6\ \text{elem. chge.}}{(0.50\ \text{m})^2}\right)$

$= 3.68 \times 10^{-21}\ \dfrac{\text{newton}}{\text{elem. chge.}}$

16. $E = k\dfrac{Q}{r^2}$. In general, this is the equation we use to compute the magnitude of the _____ _____ around a point charge (Q/q). Note that the value of E (increases/decreases) as the point at which we are measuring it gets farther from Q. This is because Coulomb's electric force law is an _____ _____ law.

★ ★ ★ ★ ★

electric field ; Q ; decreases ; inverse square

17. By convention we assume that the test charge q in an electric field is always positive. This means that the charge Q in Fig. 1 must be (positive/negative) because the arrows indicate that q is being (attracted/repelled) by Q.

★ ★ ★ ★ ★

positive ; repelled

18. Panel 12. The direction of the electric force between two point charges is always along a line joining their centers. In Fig. 1, the electric force is directed (outward/inward) along this line.

★ ★ ★ ★ ★

outward

19. In the figure in this frame, Q is negatively charged. The electric field at P

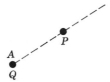

is directed (inward/outward) along line AP.

★ ★ ★ ★ ★

inward

20. $E = k \dfrac{Q}{r^2}$ The direction of $\vec{E}$ is toward Q if Q is (positive/negative). The direction of $\vec{E}$ is away from Q if Q is (positive/negative). This is because, by convention, test charge q is (always/sometimes/never) positive.

★ ★ ★ ★ ★

negative ; positive ; always

21. In the figure in this frame, Q has a charge of -6×10^{-8} coulomb.

Compute the magnitude of the electric field at P and explain the significance of the sign of your result. (*Think!* Which value of k do you use here?)

★ ★ ★ ★ ★

$$E = k\frac{Q}{r^2} = \frac{(9.0 \times 10^9)(-6 \times 10^{-8})}{(0.10)^2}$$
$$= -54 \times 10^3 \text{ newton/coulomb}$$
$$= -5.4 \times 10^4 \text{ newton/coulomb}$$

The $(-)$ sign indicates that the direction of the electric field is *toward* Q.

22. Panel 12. Refer to Fig. 2. Here are two point charges Q_1 and Q_2. We are interested in their combined field at P. $\vec{E}_1$ is the field at P due to Q_1. You can determine from the figure the signs of the charges on Q_1 and Q_2. What are they?

★ ★ ★ ★ ★

Q_1 is negative because the direction of its field is towards it. Q_2 is positive because the direction of its field is away from Q_2.

23. Panel 12, Fig. 2. $\vec{E}$ is the vector sum of $\vec{E}_1$ and $\vec{E}_2$. A test charge placed at P would move (toward Q_1/toward Q_2/along $\vec{E}$).

★ ★ ★ ★ ★

along $\vec{E}$

24. The electric field due to several point charges is the _____ _____ of the fields due to the individual charges.

★ ★ ★ ★ ★

vector sum

25. Write an equation for the combined electric field E of Q_1, Q_2, Q_3 at P.

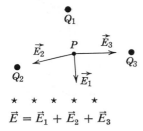

★ ★ ★ ★ ★

$\vec{E} = \vec{E}_1 + \vec{E}_2 + \vec{E}_3$

26. Panel 12. Figure 3 represents a common and interesting field combination called an electric dipole. In the figure $\vec{E}_1$ is the field at P due to charge $(Q/-Q)$, and $\vec{E}_2$ is the field at P due to charge $(Q/-Q)$.

★ ★ ★ ★ ★

Q ; $-Q$

27. Panel 12, Fig. 3. $\vec{E}_3$ is the _____ _____ of $\vec{E}_1$ and $\vec{E}_2$. A test charge placed at P would undergo an electric force in the direction of ($\vec{E}_1$/$\vec{E}_2$/ $\vec{E}_3$).

★ ★ ★ ★ ★

vector sum ; $\vec{E}_3$

28. Panel 12, Fig. 3. By geometry we can show that triangle I and triangle II are similar. This means that $\dfrac{E_1}{r} = \dfrac{E_3}{\underline{\quad}}$

★ ★ ★ ★ ★

L

29. Panel 12, Fig. 3. (1) $\dfrac{E_1}{r} = \dfrac{E_3}{L}$. (2) Solve (1) for E_3, and $E_3 = $ _____.

★ ★ ★ ★ ★

$\dfrac{LE_1}{r}$

30. Panel 12, Fig. 3. (1) $E_3 = \dfrac{LE_1}{r}$. (2) In terms of r and Q, $E_1 = $ _____.

(3) Substitute the right-hand member of (2) for E_1 in (1), and $E_3 = $ ———
(in terms of Q_1, R_1, L).

★　★　★　★　★

$$E_1 = k \frac{Q}{r^2} \; ; E_3 = \frac{LE_1}{r} = \frac{L(kQ/r^2)}{r} = k \frac{LQ}{r^3}$$

31. The electric field due to an electric dipole is (directly/inversely) proportional to the (square/cube/first power) of the distance.

★　★　★　★　★

inversely ; cube

32.

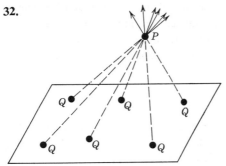

This is a large positively charged plate. We may think of its charge as being distributed over a large number of equal "point" charges (only a few are shown here), each of which has a field at P which can be calculated by the equation $E = $ ———. The field at P due to the total charge in the plate is the ——— ——— of all the fields due to these ——— charges.

★　★　★　★　★

$k \dfrac{Q}{r^2}$; vector sum ; point

Section 2.　Electric Fields (Continued)
　　　　　Electric Field Around Charged Conducting Sphere
　　　　　Electric Field Inside a Charged Conducting Sphere
　　　　　Electric Field Between Two Large Parallel Plates with
　　　　　Equal but Opposite Charges

Note: We now turn our attention to electric fields associated with electric charges *not* actually concentrated at a single point. Examples are the electric fields associated with charges at two or more points in space, charges on the surfaces of spheres, cylinders, large plates, etc.

1. Refer to Panel 13. The letter in the upper right-hand corner is _____.

★   ★   ★   ★   ★

T

2. Panel 13. Refer to Fig. 1. It is a cross section of a sphere made of conducting material. When such a figure is given an electric charge, the charge (*a*) remains at one place on the surface (*b*) spreads out uniformly to all parts of the surface. Explain your answer.

★   ★   ★   ★   ★

(*b*) (Because the sphere is made of *conducting* material.)

3. Panel 13, Fig. 1. Since the charge on the sphere is distributed uniformly, there (is/is no) reason to believe that the field around it is stronger in one direction than another. If points *P* and *T* are equidistant from the center of the sphere, it is reasonable to assume that the magnitudes of the electric field at *P* and *T* (are/are not) equal.

★   ★   ★   ★   ★

is no ; are

4. Panel 13, Fig. 1. If *S* is closer to the center of the sphere than *P* or *T*, it is reasonable to assume that the magnitude of the field at *S* is (less than/greater than/equal to) the magnitude of the field at *P* or *T*.

★   ★   ★   ★   ★

greater than

5. Panel 13, Fig. 1. The last few frames suggest that the field around a charged sphere is (similar/dissimilar) to the field around a "point" charge.

★   ★   ★   ★   ★

similar

6. The suggestions made in the last few frames have been checked by experiment, and we know that the field outside a charged sphere can be treated mathematically in the same way as the field around a point charge. In Fig. 1 of panel 13, the electric field at *P* is $E = k \dfrac{Q}{r^2}$, where *r* represents the (radius of the sphere/distance between *P* and the center of the sphere).

★   ★   ★   ★   ★

distance between *P* and the center of the sphere

7. In our study of mechanics (Part I of *Programmed Physics*), we assumed that the mass of a sphere was concentrated at a geometrical point called its center of mass. In a similar way we consider the _____ on a charged sphere to be concentrated at the _____ of the sphere.

★   ★   ★   ★   ★

charge ; center

8. Panel 13. This is a convenient simplification, but it has an important limitation. Suppose the sphere in Fig. 1 is *hollow*. Theory suggests that at any point *inside* the sphere the vector sum of all the fields due to point charges on the surface of the sphere is zero. This is verified by experiment. In Fig. 1, let $R = 10$ cm. The magnitude of the electric field at a point 8 cm from the center of the sphere is _____.

★　★　★　★　★

zero

9. Panel 13, Fig. 1. Let $R = 10$ cm and $Q = 4 \times 10^{-7}$ coulomb. Compute the magnitude of the electric field at a point 25 cm from the center of the sphere.

★　★　★　★　★

$$E = k\frac{Q}{r^2} = \frac{(9.0 \times 10^9)(4 \times 10^{-7})}{(0.25)^2}$$

$$= 5.8 \times 10^4 \text{ newtons/coulomb}$$

10. Panel 13, Fig. 1. Let $R = 10$ cm and $Q = 4 \times 10^{-7}$ coulomb. Compute the electric field at a point 2 cm from the center of the sphere.

★　★　★　★　★

The point specified is inside the sphere. The field is *zero* anywhere inside a hollow charged sphere of conducting material.

11. A convenient way to represent the electric field around a charged conductor is to draw a number of *electric field lines* (often called lines of force). We construct such lines by moving a point continuously in the direction a test charge would move under the influence of the field under consideration. Refer to Panel 13, Fig. 2. Q is a *positive* point charge, which line ($a/b/c/d$) is an electric field line from Q?

★　★　★　★　★

(*b*)

12. Panel 13, Fig. 2. Suppose Q is a *negative* point charge. Which line ($a/b/c/d$) is an electric field line from Q?

★　★　★　★　★

(*d*)

13. Panel 13. Refer to Fig. 3. The lines radiating outward from the charged sphere are called _____ _____ lines. They represent some of the paths _____ charges would follow under the influence of the electric field around the sphere.

★　★　★　★　★

electric field ; test

14. Panel 13, Fig. 3. Note that there (are/are no) electric field lines inside the sphere. This is because the electric field inside a hollow charged sphere is

_____.

* * * * *

are no ; zero

15. Panel 13, Fig. 3. The direction of the electric field lines here indicates that the charge on this sphere is (positive/negative).

* * * * *

positive

16.

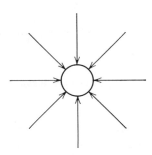

This hollow sphere is *negatively* charged. Sketch electric field lines around it.

* * * * *

The arrows should be pointed toward the center of the sphere, but none should enter the sphere.

17. Panel 13, Fig. 3. An indefinitely large number of electric field lines might be drawn. However, we draw just enough to give a picture of the field. Electric field lines and the electric field (are/are not) identical.

* * * * *

are not

18. Panel 13. We often use electric field lines to represent the relative *density* or strength of the field at different positions in the field. The greater the number of field lines passing through a unit area, the greater the strength of the field at a position included in the area. In Fig. 4, let N = the number of field lines leaving Q. The number of field lines passing through the area of an imaginary spherical surface with radius r is (N/greater than N/less than N).

* * * * *

N (Because every electric field line which leaves Q must pass through the surface of any sphere which has Q at its center.)

19. Panel 13. Fig. 4. The number of field lines passing through the surface area of an imaginary sphere with radius r_2 is (N/greater than N/less than N) The surface area of a sphere is $L = 4\pi r^2$. The field density at any position a distance r_1 from Q is $\dfrac{N}{L_1} =$ _____ (*In terms of N and r_1*).

★ ★ ★ ★ ★

$N\; ; \dfrac{N}{4\pi r_1{}^2}$

20. Panel 13, Fig. 4. The field density at any point a distance r_2 from Q is _____ (*In terms of N and r_2*).

★ ★ ★ ★ ★

$\dfrac{N}{4\pi r_2{}^2}$

21. Panel 13, Fig. 4. Since $r_2\ (=/>/<)\ r_1$, $\dfrac{N}{4\pi r_2{}^2}\ (=/>/<)\ \dfrac{N}{4\pi r_1{}^2}$

★ ★ ★ ★ ★

> ; <

22. Panel 13, Fig. 4. The field density due to Q at P_2 is (equal to/greater than/ less than) the field density at P_1.

★ ★ ★ ★ ★

less than

23. Panel 13, Fig. 4. We might have come to this conclusion visually, by noting that the electric field lines are (more/less) widely separated at a distance r_1 than they are at r_2.

★ ★ ★ ★ ★

less

24. In general, where electric field lines are bunched together the field is (stronger/weaker) than where they are spread farther apart.

★ ★ ★ ★ ★

stronger

25. Refer to Panel 14. The letter in the upper right-hand corner is _____.

★ ★ ★ ★ ★

Y

26. Panel 14. Examine Fig. 1. This is a photograph of the electric field pattern formed when two rods with (equal positive/equal negative/equal and opposite) charges are immersed among grass seeds in an insulating liquid.

★ ★ ★ ★ ★

equal and opposite

27. Panel 14. Figure 2 is a picture of the field lines which represent the electric field described in Fig. 1. Note that the field lines originate at the (positive/negative) charged and terminate at the (positive/negative) charge.
★ ★ ★ ★ ★
positive ; negative

28. Panel 14. Figure 2 shows us that the field strength at *a* is (approximately equal to/greater than/less than) the field strength at *b*. It also shows that the field strength at *c* is (approximately equal to/greater than/less than) the field strength at *a* because the lines at *c* are (more/less) bunched.
★ ★ ★ ★ ★
approximately equal to ; less than ; less

29. Refer to Panel 15. The letter in the upper right-hand corner is _____.
★ ★ ★ ★ ★
K

30. Panel 15. Read the description of Fig. 1(*b*). Figure 1(*a*) is a drawing of field lines which represent the field in Fig. 1(*b*). The field at point *P*, which is exactly between the charges, is _____.
★ ★ ★ ★ ★
zero *or* 0

31. Panel 15, Fig. 2. This is a photograph of the field pattern produced by a charged cylinder. Note that there (is a/is no) electric field *inside* the cylinder.
★ ★ ★ ★ ★
is no

32. Panel 15. Refer to Fig. 3. This is a conductor with an irregular shape (as contrasted to the sphere or cylinder). Note the patterns of grass seed inside and outside its boundary. There (is a/is no) field outside the conductor; there (is a/is no) field inside the conductor.
★ ★ ★ ★ ★
is a ; is no

33. Panel 15. Refer to Fig. 4(*b*). The plates immersed in the seed-in-insulating-liquid mixture are _____ to each other and have _____ and _____ charges.
★ ★ ★ ★ ★
parallel ; *in either order* equal, opposite

34. Panel 15, Fig. 4(*b*). The photograph shows that there (is an/is no) electric field between the plates and that there (is a/is no) field outside the plates.
★ ★ ★ ★ ★
is ; is no

35. Panel 15. Electric field lines are drawn in Fig. 4(*a*) for the kind of field shown in Fig. 4(*b*). A test charge placed between these plates would move from the (positive/negative) plate toward the (positive/negative) plate.

⋆   ⋆   ⋆   ⋆   ⋆

positive ; negative

36. Panel 15, Fig. 4(*a*). Except for the ends of the plates (beyond *A* and *B* in the figure), the field lines between these plates are (always/sometimes/never) perpendicular to the plates and are (equally/unequally) spaced.

⋆   ⋆   ⋆   ⋆   ⋆

always ; equally

37. Panel 15, Fig. 4(*a*). The electric field at any point in the space between the plates and within the boundary marked by *A* and *B* is (constant/variable) in magnitude and direction. We call such a field *uniform*. The field around a point charge (is/is not) uniform.

⋆   ⋆   ⋆   ⋆   ⋆

constant ; is not

38. Panel 15, Fig. 4(*a*). Examine the field lines near the edges of the plates (i.e., beyond points *A* and *B*). They are (straight/curved) which indicates that the direction of the field near the edges is (constant/variable). The electric field near the edges of these plates (is/is not) uniform.

⋆   ⋆   ⋆   ⋆   ⋆

curved ; variable ; is not

39. Panel 15, Fig. 4(*a*). Near the edge of the plates the field lines are (more/less) widely spread than they are within *A* and *B*. This means that the magnitude of the field at the edges is (greater/less) than it is between *A* and *B*.

⋆   ⋆   ⋆   ⋆   ⋆

more ; less

40. The electric field between two parallel plates with equal but opposite charges is said to be _____ except near the edges of the plates. This means that the electric force on a test charge placed between the plates is (constant/variable) in magnitude and direction as long as it is not near the _____ of the plates.

⋆   ⋆   ⋆   ⋆   ⋆

uniform ; constant ; edges

41. Panel 15. The electric field shown in Fig. 4 is an important one in physics. It provides us with a device in which charged particles can be accelerated by a constant net _____. This enables us to apply Newton's laws of motion to particles like electrons which are influenced (strongly/negligibly) by gravitational forces because they have very small masses.

$\star$ $\star$ $\star$ $\star$ $\star$

force ; negligibly

42. At positions which are not too near the edges, the electric field produced when two large parallel plates are given equal but opposite charges is _____ between the plates and _____ beyond the plates.

$\star$ $\star$ $\star$ $\star$ $\star$

uniform ; zero

43. A uniform electric field greater than zero is produced (choose one or more): (*a*) between two large parallel positively charged plates; (*b*) between two large parallel plates with equal but opposite charges; (*c*) around a charged conducting sphere; (*d*) between two equal and opposite point charges.

$\star$ $\star$ $\star$ $\star$ $\star$

(*b*)

Section 3.   Electric Potential Energy

$$Point\ Charge\ Fields:\ V_e = k\,\frac{Qq}{r}$$

$$Parallel\ Charged\ Plate\ Fields:\ V_e = EqD$$

Note: Work and energy are important concepts in all branches of physics. In our study of mechanics, we saw how work could be done by and against the *gravitational* field and how energy could be stored (potential energy) in the gravitational field. In this section, we will apply the concepts of work and energy to the electric field and develop the notion of energy (electric potential energy) stored in an electric field.

1. We have seen that there is a definite similarity in the mathematical equations which describe gravitational forces and electrical forces.

$F_g = $ _____ (*In terms of M, m, and r*).

$F_e = $ _____ (*In terms of Q, q, and r*).

$\star$ $\star$ $\star$ $\star$ $\star$

$G\,\dfrac{Mm}{r^2}$; $k\,\dfrac{Qq}{r^2}$

2. We can carry this identity in mathematical structure further. Let g represent a quantity called the gravitational field and defined as gravitational force divided by the mass affected. Then:

$$g = \frac{F_g}{m} = \underline{\hspace{1cm}}$$ (*In terms of M, G, and r*) in the same way that the electric

field $E = \frac{F_e}{q} = \underline{\hspace{1cm}}$ (*In terms of Q, k, and r*).

★　★　★　★　★

$$G\frac{M}{r^2} \; ; \; k\frac{Q}{r^2}$$

3. We found that the gravitational potential energy of m in the gravitational field of mass M was given by the equation $U_g = -G\dfrac{Mm}{r}$, where the minus sign indicates that gravitational force is (attracting/repelling) and therefore work must be done to move m to infinite separation (i.e., out of the influence of the gravitational field). We chose the reference level for gravitational potential energy at $r = \underline{\hspace{3cm}}$.

★　★　★　★　★

attracting ; ∞ *or* infinity

4. Similarly, the *electric* potential energy of a point charge q in the electric field of charge Q where the electric force is attracting is: $U_e = \underline{\hspace{2cm}}$.

★　★　★　★　★

$$-\frac{kQq}{r}$$

5. $U_e = k\dfrac{Qq}{r}$. This is an equation for $\underline{\hspace{5cm}}$ energy of q due to its presence in the electric field of Q. If Q and q are oppositely charged, their product is (positive/negative) and the value of U_e is (positive/negative).

★　★　★　★　★

electric potential ; negative ; negative

6. $U_e = k\dfrac{Qq}{r}$. If Q and q are both positive (or both negative), the product Qq is (positive/negative) and the value of the electric potential energy is (positive/negative).

★　★　★　★　★

positive ; positive

7. $U_g = -G\dfrac{Mm}{r}$; $\qquad U_e = k\dfrac{Qq}{r}$.

The minus sign is omitted from our equation for electric potential energy, because electric forces, unlike gravitational forces, can _____ as well as _____. The value of U_e is positive *or* negative, depending on the sign of the product _____ .

★ ★ ★ ★ ★

repel ; attract ; Qq (of the charges)

8. An electron in a hydrogen atom is about 0.5×10^{-10} meter from the proton in the atom. Compute its electric potential energy in joules.

★ ★ ★ ★ ★

$$U_e = k\frac{Qq}{r} = 2.3 \times 10^{-28}\,\frac{\text{nt-m}^2}{(\text{elem. chge.})^2}\,\frac{(-1 \text{ elem. chge.})(+1 \text{ elem. chge})}{0.5 \text{ m}}$$

$$= -4.6 \times 10^{-28} \text{ newton-meter}$$

$$= -4.6 \times 10^{-28} \text{ joule}$$

9. The minus sign in the last problem indicates that work is done (by the field/against the field) if the electron is moved to infinite separation.

★ ★ ★ ★ ★

against the field

10. A charge $q_1 = 6 \times 10^{-8}$ coulomb is 10 meters from a charge $q_2 = 5 \times 10^{-5}$ coulomb. Compute the electric potential energy of q_1 in this field.

★ ★ ★ ★ ★

$$U_e = k\frac{q_1 q_2}{r}$$

$$= 9.0 \times 10^9\,\frac{\text{newton-m}^2}{(\text{coulomb})^2}\,\frac{(6 \times 10^{-8} \text{ coulomb})(5 \times 10^{-5} \text{ coulomb})}{10 \text{ m}}$$

$$= 27 \times 10^{-4} \text{ joule}$$

11. The positive value of U_e in the last problem means that work is done by the electric field if q_1 moves to _____ separation.

★ ★ ★ ★ ★

infinite

12. In the nucleus of a helium atom, there are two protons which are 1.5×10^{-15} m apart. The electric potential energy of one proton with respect to the field of the other is a measure of the _____ required to bring these protons together from _____ _____ .

★ ★ ★ ★ ★

work ; infinite separation

13. Compute the work required to bring two protons in to a separation of 1.5×10^{-15} meter from infinite separation.

★　★　★　★　★

$$\text{Work} = U_e = k \frac{q_1 q_1}{r^2}$$

$$= 2.3 \times 10^{-28} \frac{(1)}{(1.5 \times 10^{-15})}$$

$$= 1.53 \times 10^{-13} \text{ joule}$$

14.

— Q and q are point charges. The work required to move q from A to B is equal to the _____ in the electric _____ _____ of q.

★　★　★　★　★

change ; potential energy

15.

Let U_a equal the electric potential energy of q at A, and U_b equal the electric potential energy of q at b. The work done moving q from A to B is $W =$ _____ in terms of U_a and U_b.

★　★　★　★　★

$U_b - U_a$

16. Refer to Frame 15.

In terms of $-Q, q,$ and r_1, $U_a =$ _____

In terms of $-Q, q$ and r_2, $U_b =$ _____

In terms of $-Q, q, r_1,$ and r_2, $W =$ _____

(*Simply by extracting any common factors.*)

★　★　★　★　★

$$U_a = -k\frac{Qq}{r_1}$$

$$U_b = -k\frac{Qq}{r_2}$$

$$W = U_b - U_a = \left(-k\frac{Qq}{r_2}\right) - \left(-k\frac{Qq}{r_1}\right)$$

$$= kQq\left(-\frac{1}{r_2} + \frac{1}{r_1}\right)$$

$$= kQq\left(\frac{1}{r_1} - \frac{1}{r_2}\right)$$

17. If a mass m is free to move in the gravitational field of the Earth, it moves (closer to/farther from) the center of the Earth. A mass free to move in a gravitational field moves to a state of (higher/lower) gravitational potential energy.
★   ★   ★   ★   ★

closer to ; lower

18. Q is a point charge of -5×10^{-6} coulomb. q is a point charge of 2×10^{-6} coulomb. At a separation of 10 meters the electric potential energy $U =$ _____ $\times 10^{-3}$ joule. If q is free to move in this electric field, it moves (farther from/closer to) Q.
★   ★   ★   ★   ★

$$U = k\frac{Qq}{r} = 9.0 \times 10^9 \frac{(-5 \times 10^{-6})(2 \times 10^{-6})}{10}$$

$$= \mathbf{-9.0 \times 10^{-3}} \text{ joule}$$

closer to (Because Q and q have unlike charges.)

19. Suppose q in the previous frame is free to move in the field. Use the data given in the previous frame to compute its electric potential energy when it is 1 meter from Q. $U =$ _____ $\times 10^{-3}$ joule. Now compare this to the value computed for the 10 meter separation. When q is free to move in the electric field, it moves to a state of (lower/higher) electric potential energy.
★   ★   ★   ★   ★

$$U = k\frac{Qq}{r} = (9.0 \times 10^9)\frac{(-5 \times 10^{-6})(2 \times 10^{-6})}{1}$$

$$= \mathbf{-90 \times 10^{-3}} \text{ joule}$$

This is a smaller number than -9×10^{-3}. Therefore, q moves to a state of *lower* potential energy.

20. Q is a point charge of 5×10^{-6} coulomb and q is a point charge of 2×10^{-6} coulomb. At a separation of 1 meter, the electric potential energy of q is $U =$ _____ $\times 10^{-3}$ joule. If q is free to move, it moves (farther from/closer to) Q.

★ ★ ★ ★ ★

$$U = k\frac{Qq}{r} = \frac{(9.0 \times 10^9)(5 \times 10^{-6})(2 \times 10^{-6})}{1}$$

$$= 90 \times 10^{-3}\,\text{joule}$$

farther from (Because Q and q have *like* charges.)

21. Now suppose q in Frame 20 is free to move. Compute its electric potential energy when it has moved to a separation of 10 meters from Q. $U =$ _____ $\times 10^{-3}$ joule. Compare this to the value computed for a 1-meter separation. When q is free to move in the electric field, it moves to a state of (lower/higher) electric potential energy.

★ ★ ★ ★ ★

9×10^{-3} ; lower

22. Suppose Q and q are point charges separated by a distance r and constitute an isolated system since external influence on them is negligible. If Q and q have *like* charges and q is free to move, it moves (closer to/farther from) Q and the electric potential energy of the system (increases/decreases/remains constant). If Q and q have *unlike* charges, q moves (closer to/farther from) Q and the electric potential energy of the system (increases/decreases/remains the same).

★ ★ ★ ★ ★

farther from ; decreases ; closer to ; decreases

23. $U_e = k\dfrac{Qq}{r}$. We have been using this equation to compute the electric potential energy of q in the field of Q where Q and q are both _____ charges.

★ ★ ★ ★ ★

point

24. We found that we were able to treat the field in the space around a charged hollow conducting sphere as if it were produced by a _____ charge located at the _____ of the sphere.

★ ★ ★ ★ ★

point ; center

25. Suppose q is a point charge located at a point outside a hollow conducting sphere with a charge Q. On the basis of our experience with the electric field around such a charge, we can use the equation $U_e =$ _____ for the electric

potential energy of q, where r = the distance between q and the ———————
of the sphere.

★ ★ ★ ★ ★

$k \dfrac{Qq}{r}$; center (of the) sphere.

26. Suppose a point charge q is placed near the center of the positive plate in Panel 15, Fig. 4(*a*). Would you use $U_e = k \dfrac{Qq}{r}$ to measure its electric potential energy in that field? (Yes/No) *Explain.*

★ ★ ★ ★ ★

No, you shouldn't, because Q in Panel 15, Fig. 4(*a*), *cannot* be considered as a single point charge.

27.

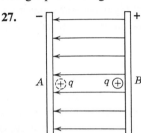

We know the electric potential energy of q at B in this figure if we compute the —————— required to move q from A to B (i.e., across the field).

★ ★ ★ ★ ★

work

28. Refer to figure in previous frame. We have seen that the electric field E across the space between these plates is (uniform/variable) except at the edges of the plate. This means that the force needed to push q at a constant velocity against the field [(*a*) is constant from A to B/(*b*) increases as we move from A to B/(*c*) decreases as we move from A to B].

★ ★ ★ ★ ★

uniform ; (*a*)

29. Refer to figure in Frame 27. Let E be the electric field between the plates and F the electric force on the charge q. By definition, $E =$ ——————. (in terms of F and q).

★ ★ ★ ★ ★

$\dfrac{F}{q}$

30. Refer to figure in Frame 27. $E = \dfrac{F}{q}$. Solving for F: $F =$ ——————.

★ ★ ★ ★ ★

Eq

31. Refer to figure in Frame 27. The work required to push q at a constant velocity from A to B is the product of Eq times the _____ between A and B.

$\star$ $\star$ $\star$ $\star$ $\star$

distance

32. Refer to figure in Frame 27. Let d = the distance between A and B. The work required to move q from A to B at a constant velocity is: $W =$ _____ (in terms of E, q, and d).

$\star$ $\star$ $\star$ $\star$ $\star$

Eqd

33. Refer to figure in Frame 27. The electric potential energy of q at B in the field is given by the equation $U =$ _____.

$\star$ $\star$ $\star$ $\star$ $\star$

Eqd

34. $U = Eqd$. In this text we will usually measure U in *joules*. This requires that d be measured in meters so that if $d = 3$ cm, it must be converted to $d =$ _____ meter. If E is measured in newtons/coulomb, q must be measured in (or converted to) _____. If E is measured in newtons/elem. chge., q must be measured in (or converted to) _____.

$\star$ $\star$ $\star$ $\star$ $\star$

0.03 ; coulombs ; elem. chge.

35.

The electric field between these plates is 3×10^2 newtons/coulomb. q has a charge of 3×10^{-8} coulomb. Compute the electric potential energy of q at B.

$\star$ $\star$ $\star$ $\star$ $\star$

$U = Eqd = (3 \times 10^2 \text{ nt/coul}) (3 \times 10^{-8} \text{ coul}) (0.1 \text{ m})$

$= 9 \times 10^{-7}$ joule

36.

$E = 4 \times 10^3$ nt/coul

$q = 5 \times 10^3$ elem. chge.

$= \underline{\hspace{5cm}}$ coul

$U = \underline{\hspace{5cm}}$ joule

$\star \quad \star \quad \star \quad \star \quad \star$

$q = (5 \times 10^3)(1.6 \times 10^{-19})$

$\quad = 8.0 \times 10^{-16}$ coul

$U = (4 \times 10^3)(8.0 \times 10^{-16})(0.25)$

$\quad = 8.0 \times 10^{-13}$ joule

37. We assume, unless otherwise specified, that the potential energy of q between the plates is measured relative to the plate of charge *unlike* the charge on q. If q is positive, we will be measuring its potential energy relative to the (positive/negative) plate.

$\star \quad \star \quad \star \quad \star \quad \star$

negative

38.

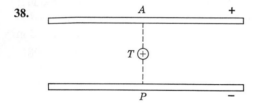

The electric potential energy of q at T is the work required to push it from (T to A/P to T/P to A). $U = Eqd$. In this figure, $d = (TA/TP/AP)$

$\star \quad \star \quad \star \quad \star \quad \star$

P to T ; TP

39.

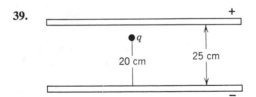

$E = 2 \times 10^{-10}$ nt/elem. chge.

$q = 3 \times 10^5$ elem. chge.

$d = \underline{\hspace{1.5cm}}$ meter

$U = \underline{\hspace{5cm}}$ joule

$\star \quad \star \quad \star \quad \star \quad \star$

$d = 0.20$ meter

$U = (2 \times 10^{-10}$ nt/elem. chge.$)(3 \times 10^5$ elem. chge.$)(0.20$ m$)$

$\quad = 1.2 \times 10^{-5}$ joule

40.

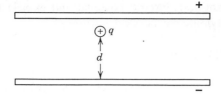

Suppose q is free to move in this field. The value of d (increases/decreases) and q moves to a (lower/higher) state of electric potential energy.

★ ★ ★ ★ ★

decreases ; lower

Section 4.   *Electric Potential*

Definition: $V = \dfrac{U_e}{q}$

Units: Joules/Elem. Chge.; Volts; Conversion Factors
The Electron Volt
Calculation of Electric Potential due to Point Charges:

$V = k\dfrac{Q}{r}$

Calculation of Electric Potential in Field Between Parallel Plates: $V = Ed$
Electric Potential at a Point Due to a Group of Point Charges

1. Let a test charge q be acted upon by a net electric force $\vec{F}$ and have an electric potential energy U_e. We used the ratio $\vec{F}/q$ to define a physical quantity called the _____ _____. We now use the ratio of the electric potential energy of q to the charge q to define another physical quantity, called *electric potential, V.* $V = $ _____ (*Symbols*).

★ ★ ★ ★ ★

electric field ; $\dfrac{U_e}{q}$

2. $V = \dfrac{U_e}{q}$. This equation defines (electric field/electric potential energy/ electric force/electric potential).

★ ★ ★ ★ ★

electric potential

3. Electric potential and electric potential energy are (the same physical quantity/different physical quantities). Electric potential and electric field are (the same physical quantity/different physical quantities).

⋆   ⋆   ⋆   ⋆   ⋆

different physical quantities ; different physical quantities

4. By definition, $\vec{E} = \dfrac{\vec{F_e}}{q}$ and $V = \dfrac{U_e}{q}$. Electric field is a (scalar/vector) quantity; electric potential is a (scalar/vector) quantity.

⋆   ⋆   ⋆   ⋆   ⋆

vector ; scalar

5. Electric potential energy, as we have seen (is always positive/may be positive or negative). Electric potential (is always positive/may be positive or negative).

⋆   ⋆   ⋆   ⋆   ⋆

may be positive or negative ; may be positive or negative (Because its computation involves U_e, which may be positive or negative.)

6. When we combine signed quantities (i.e., involving plus or minus signs) we are adding *algebraically*. When we combine vector quantities, we are adding vectorally. How do we combine electric potentials?

⋆   ⋆   ⋆   ⋆   ⋆

algebraically

7. A test charge $q = 5 \times 10^2$ elem. chges. Its electric potential energy is 1.5×10^{-5} joule. Its electric potential $V =$ _____ (*Number and units*).

⋆   ⋆   ⋆   ⋆   ⋆

$$V = \frac{U_e}{q} = \frac{1.5 \times 10^{-5} \text{ joule}}{5 \times 10^2 \text{ elem. chge.}}$$

$$= 0.3 \times 10^{-7} \text{ joule/elem. chge.}$$

8. When U_e is measured in joules and in elem. chge., electric potential is measured in _____.

⋆   ⋆   ⋆   ⋆   ⋆

joule/elem. chge.

9. A test charge of $q = 5 \times 10^{-6}$ coulomb has an electric potential energy of 4.0×10^{-4} joule. Compute its electric potential. $V =$ _____ (*Number and units*)

⋆   ⋆   ⋆   ⋆   ⋆

$$V = \frac{4.0 \times 10^{-4} \text{ joule}}{5 \times 10^{-6} \text{ coul}}$$

$$= 0.8 \times 10^2 \text{ joules/coulomb}$$

$$= 80 \text{ joules/coulomb}$$

10. The unit joule/coulomb occurs very frequently in physics and is called a *volt*. The volt is a unit used to measure (electric field/electric potential/electric charge/electric force).

★ ★ ★ ★ ★

electric potential

11. The sum of 10 volts and -15 volts is _____ volts.

★ ★ ★ ★ ★

-5 volts

12. 1 volt = 1 joule/1 coulomb
We know that 1 coulomb = 6.25×10^{18} elem. chge.

$$1 \text{ volt} = \frac{1 \text{ joule}}{6.25 \times 10^{18} \text{ elem. chge.}}$$

$$= \text{_____} (\textit{Two figures}) \text{ joule/elem. chge.}$$

★ ★ ★ ★ ★

1.6×10^{-19}

13. A test charge of 6×10^{-8} coulomb has an electric potential energy of 3×10^{-5} joules.

$V =$ _____ volts

$V =$ _____ joule/elem. chge.

★ ★ ★ ★ ★

$$V = \frac{U_e}{q} = \frac{3 \times 10^{-5} \text{ joule}}{6 \times 10^{-8} \text{ coulomb}} = 0.5 \times 10^3 \text{ volts} = 500 \text{ volts}$$

$$V = (500)(1.6 \times 10^{-19}) = 8.0 \times 10^{-17} \text{ joule/elem. chge.}$$

14. (1) $1 \text{ volt} = \dfrac{1 \text{ joule}}{1 \text{ coulomb}}$

(2) $1 \text{ volt} = \dfrac{1 \text{ joule}}{6.25 \times 10^{18} \text{ elem. chge.}}$

(3) We multiply both sides of (2) by (6.25×10^{18} elem. chge.), and we get:

$1 \text{ joule} =$ _____ (*Number and units*).

★ ★ ★ ★ ★

6.25×10^{18} (elem. chge.) · (volts).

15. We call the product (elem. chge.)(volt) an *electron volt*. 1 joule = _____ electron volts. The electron volt is a measure of (electric field/electric potential/energy).

★ ★ ★ ★ ★

6.25×10^{18} ; energy

16. Refer to Panel 16. The letter in the upper right-hand corner is _____.

★ ★ ★ ★ ★

G

17. Panel 16. Refer to Fig. 1. Q is a point charge which may be positive or negative. q is a test charge and by convention is always (positive/negative). The electric potential energy of q at point A is given by the equation $U =$ _____.

★ ★ ★ ★ ★

positive ; $k \dfrac{Qq}{r_1}$

18. Panel 16, Fig. 1.

(1) At A, $U = k \dfrac{Qq}{r_1}$.

(2) By definition, $V = \dfrac{U}{q}$.

(3) At A, then, $V =$ _____ in terms of Q, r_1, etc.).

★ ★ ★ ★ ★

$$V = \frac{U}{q} = k \frac{Q}{r_1}$$

19. Panel 16, Fig. 1. The electric potential at B is given by the equation:
$V =$ _____.

★ ★ ★ ★ ★

$k \dfrac{Q}{r_2}$

20. In general, the electric potential at any position around an isolated point charge Q is given by the equation $V = k \dfrac{Q}{r}$. Note that the electric potential at a point (depends/does not depend) on the charge placed *at that point*. Note also that V is positive or negative depending on whether _____ is positive or negative.

★ ★ ★ ★ ★

does not depend ; Q

21. Panel 16, Fig. 1. Let $Q = -5 \times 10^{-8}$ coulomb. Let $r_1 = 50$ cm and $r_2 = 30$ cm. Compute the electric potential at A.

★ ★ ★ ★ ★

$$V_a = k \frac{Q}{r_1} = \frac{(9.0 \times 10^9)(-5 \times 10^{-8})}{0.5} = -900 \text{ volts}$$

22. Panel 16, Fig. 1. Use the data in Frame 21 to compute the electric potential at B.

$\star$ $\star$ $\star$ $\star$ $\star$

$$V_b = k\frac{Q}{r_2} = \frac{(9.0 \times 10^9)(-5 \times 10^{-8})}{0.3} = -1500 \text{ volts}$$

23. Panel 16, Fig. 1. Compare the potentials computed for points A and B in Frames 21 and 22. Remember that Q is negative. As we consider points closer to Q, the electric potential (increases/decreases/remains the same). A positive charge placed in this field and free to move will move toward positions of (higher/lower/the same) electric potential.

$\star$ $\star$ $\star$ $\star$ $\star$

decreases (Because -1500 volts is less than -900 volts.) ; lower

24. Panel 16, Fig. 1. Let Q remain negative. Now if a negative charge is placed in the field of Q and it is free to move, it will move (closer to/farther from) Q; that is, in the direction of (higher/lower) electric potential.

$\star$ $\star$ $\star$ $\star$ $\star$

farther from ; higher

25. Panel 16, Fig. 1. Now let $Q = 5 \times 10^{-8}$ coulomb, and let $r_1 = 50$ cm and $r_2 = 30$ cm. Compute the electric potentials at points A and B. Compare them. As we move to points closer to Q, the electric potential (increases/decreases).

$\star$ $\star$ $\star$ $\star$ $\star$

$$V_a = k\frac{Q}{r^1} = \frac{(9.0 \times 10^9)(5 \times 10^{-8})}{0.5} = 900 \text{ volts}$$

$$V_b = k\frac{Q}{r^2} = \frac{(9.0 \times 10^9)(5 \times 10^{-8})}{0.3} = 1500 \text{ volts}$$

increases

26. Panel 16, Fig. 1. If Q is positive, a *positive* charge placed in its field and free to move will move (away from/closer to) Q; that is, toward positions of (lower/higher) potential.

$\star$ $\star$ $\star$ $\star$ $\star$

away from ; lower

27. Panel 16, Fig. 1. Let Q remain positive. A *negative* charge placed in its field and free to move will move (away from/closer to) Q; that is, toward positions of (lower/higher) potential.

$\star$ $\star$ $\star$ $\star$ $\star$

closer to ; higher

Electric Potential Definition: $V = (U_e/q)$ 63

28. We have uncovered an important characteristic of charges and the fields in which they exist. A positive charge placed in an electric field and free to move (always/sometimes/never) moves to a position of lower electric potential. An electron placed in an electric field and free to move (always/sometimes/never) moves to a position of lower electric potential.

★   ★   ★   ★   ★

always ; never (Because an electron is negatively charged and therefore moves to position of higher potential.)

29. A negative charge placed in an electric field and free to move will move toward positions of (higher/lower/equal) electric potential.

★   ★   ★   ★   ★

higher

30. It is characteristic of a conductor that charges placed on it (are/are not) free to move.

★   ★   ★   ★   ★

are

31. All parts of a conductor are at the same electric potential because all *positive* charges will move until they are at the (lowest/highest) possible potential or all *negative* charges will move until they are at the (lowest/highest) possible potential.

★   ★   ★   ★   ★

lowest ; highest

32. When a charge is placed on a conductor, it moves until all parts of the conductor are at (the same electric potential/different electric potentials).

★   ★   ★   ★   ★

the same electric potential

33. The time needed for this redistribution of charge to take place is extremely small, so that for all practical purposes we can say that (all/no) points on the surface of a conductor have the same electric potential.

★   ★   ★   ★   ★

all

34. Panel 16. Refer to Fig. 2. The electric field between these plates is _____ at all points which are *not* near the _____. Call this field E. The electric potential energy of a test charge q at point A is given by the equation: $U =$ _____

★   ★   ★   ★   ★

uniform (constant) ; edges ; Eqd_1

35. Panel 16, Fig. 2.

(1) $U = Eqd_1$.

(2) By definition, $V_a =$ _____.

(3) $V_a =$ _____ (*in terms of E, d_1, etc.*).

★ ★ ★ ★ ★

$$\frac{U}{q} \; ; V_a = \frac{Eqd_1}{q} = Ed_1$$

36. Panel 16, Fig. 2. The electric potential at B is: $V_b =$ _____. d_2 is (greater/less) than d_1. V_b is (greater/less) than V_a.

★ ★ ★ ★ ★

Ed_2 ; less ; less

37. Panel 16, Fig. 2. A positive charge placed at A or anywhere between the plates and free to move will move to positions of (lower/higher/equal) electric potential.

★ ★ ★ ★ ★

lower

38. Panel 16, Fig. 2. A negative charge on the negative plate, or anywhere between the plates, and free to move in the field will move to position of (lower/equal) electric potential.

★ ★ ★ ★ ★

higher

39. Panel 16, Fig. 2. If E is the field between the plates and d is the distance between them, we now have an equation for the electric potential of every point on the positive plate. It is $V =$ _____.

★ ★ ★ ★ ★

Ed

40. Panel 16. Fig. 2. It is easier to measure the electric potential of points on the positive plate relative to the negative plate than it is to measure the field between them. Suppose the voltmeter reads 90 volts and the distance between the plates is 0.02 m. Then $E =$ _____ (number and units).

★ ★ ★ ★ ★

$V = Ed$

$$E = \frac{V}{d} = \frac{90 \text{ volts}}{0.02 \text{ meter}} = 4500 \text{ volts/meter}$$

The units *volts/meter* are equivalent to:

joules/(coulomb meter) = *newton meter/coulomb meter* = *newton/coulomb*
which are the units we used earlier for the field.

Electric Potential Definition: $V = (U_e/q)$ **65**

41. Panel 16. Refer to Fig. 3*a*. We want to compute the electric field and the electric potential at *P*. The electric field at *P* is the _____ _____ of the fields produced at that point by Q_1 and Q_2.

★ ★ ★ ★ ★

vector sum

42. Panel 16, Fig. 3*a*. Let $\vec{E}_1$ and $\vec{E}_2$ represent the electric fields produced at *P* by Q_1 and Q_2, respectively.

$$\vec{E}_1 = \underline{\qquad\qquad} \frac{\text{newtons}}{\text{coulomb}} \text{ (up/down/to the right/to the left)}$$

$$\vec{E}_2 = \underline{\qquad\qquad} \frac{\text{newtons}}{\text{coloumb}} \text{ (up/down/to the right/to the left)}$$

★ ★ ★ ★ ★

$$\vec{E}_1 = \frac{kQ_1}{r_1^2} = \frac{(9.0 \times 10^9)(-1.6 \times 10^{-7})}{(0.40)^2} = \frac{(9.0 \times 10^9)(-1.6 \times 10^{-7})}{0.16}$$

$= -9.0 \times 10^3$ newtons/coulomb. The minus sign indicates that the field is directed *toward* Q_1, i.e., to the left.

$\vec{E}_1 = 9.0 \times 10^3$ newtons/coulomb to the left.

$$\vec{E}_2 = \frac{kQ_2}{r_2^2} = \frac{(9.0 \times 10^9)(1.6 \times 10^{-7})}{(.30)^2} = 1.6 \times 10^4 \text{ newtons/coulomb away}$$
from Q_2, i.e., *down*

43. Panel 16, Fig. 3*b*. The electric field at *P*, $\vec{E} = $ _____ + _____.

★ ★ ★ ★ ★

$\vec{E}_1 + \vec{E}_2$

44. Panel 16, Fig. 3*b*. The angle between $\vec{E}_1$ and $\vec{E}_2$ is _____ degrees. Construct the vector sum of $\vec{E}_1$ and $\vec{E}_2$ drawn here. Label it $\vec{E}$. We can find the

magnitude of $\vec{E}$ by using the _____ theorem.

★ ★ ★ ★ ★

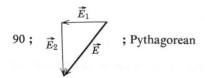

90 ; ; Pythagorean

45. Panel 16, Fig. 3b.

$E_1 = 9.0 \times 10^3$ newtons/coulomb

$E_2 = 16 \times 10^3$ newtons/coulomb

$E = $ _____ newtons/coulomb

★ ★ ★ ★ ★

$E^2 = E_1^2 + E_2^2$

$E^2 = (9 \times 10^3)^2 + (16 \times 10^3)^2$

$\quad = (81 \times 10^6) + (256 \times 10^6)$

$\quad = 337 \times 10^6$

$E \approx 18 \times 10^3$ newtons/coulomb

46. Panel 16, Fig. 3. Let V_1 and V_2 represent the electric potentials at P due to Q_1 and Q_2, respectively. The total electric potential at P due to Q_1 and Q_2 is the (vector/algebraic) sum of V_1 and V_2.

★ ★ ★ ★ ★

algebraic. (Because electric potential is a scalar, *not* a vector quantity.)

47. Panel 16, Fig. 3.

$V_1 = $ _____ volts.

$V_2 = $ _____ volts.

$V = $ _____ volts.

★ ★ ★ ★ ★

$V_1 = \dfrac{kQ_1}{r_1} = \dfrac{(9.0 \times 10^9)(-1.6 \times 10^{-7})}{0.4} = -3.6 \times 10^3$ volts

$V_2 = k\dfrac{Q_2}{r_2} = \dfrac{(9.0 \times 10^9)(1.6 \times 10^{-7})}{0.30} = 4.8 \times 10^3$ volts

$V = V_2 + V_1 = (4.8 \times 10^3) + (-3.6 \times 10^3) = 1.2 \times 10^3$ volts

48. Electric potential is measured in units called (joules/coulombs/volts/

$\dfrac{\text{joules}}{\text{elem. chge.}}$ /ergs/electron volts). (*Choose as many as apply.*)

★ ★ ★ ★ ★

volts ; joules/elem. chge.

49. The electron volt is a unit of (energy/charge/electric potential/electric field).

★ ★ ★ ★ ★

energy

50. We define electric potential generally as the ratio of _____
_____ _____ to _____.

★ ★ ★ ★ ★

electric potential energy ; charge

51. A negatively charged particle free to move in an electric field moves toward positions of (higher/lower/equal) electric potential.

★ ★ ★ ★ ★

higher

52. The electric potential across two parallel plates with equal but opposite charges is given by the equation $V =$ _____, where E is the _____
_____ between the plates and d is the _____ between the plates. V is measured in volts when E is in _____ and d is in _____.

★ ★ ★ ★ ★

Ed ; electric field ; distance ; newton/coulomb ; meters

73. A voltmeter placed across two parallel plates with equal but opposite charges reads 250 volts. The distance between the plates is 5.0×10^{-2} meter. Compute the magnitude of the electric field at a point 4.0×10^{-2} meter from the negative plate.

★ ★ ★ ★ ★

$V = Ed$

$$E = \frac{V}{d} = \frac{250}{5.0 \times 10^{-2}} = 5000 \text{ newtons/coulomb}$$

d is the distance between the plates. Remember that the field is the same at all points between the plates.

54. Use the data in Frame 53 to compute the electric potential at a point 4.0×10^{-2} meter from the negative plate.

★ ★ ★ ★ ★

$V = Ed$, where d is distance from negative plate.

$V = (5000 \text{ newtons/coulomb})(4.0 \times 10^{-2} \text{ meter})$

$\quad = 200 \text{ newtons-m/coulomb} = 200 \text{ joule/coulomb}$

$\quad = 200 \text{ volts}$

Section 5. Electric Potential Difference

Definition: $\dfrac{W_{ab}}{q} = V_b - V_a$

1. Refer to Panel 17. The letter in the upper right-hand corner is _____.

⋆   ⋆   ⋆   ⋆   ⋆

P

2. Panel 17. Refer to Fig. 1. Let Q be a positive charge and q a test charge placed in the field of Q. To move q from A to B in the field at a constant speed requires that _____ be done by an external agent against the electric field.

⋆   ⋆   ⋆   ⋆   ⋆

work

3. Panel 17, Fig. 1. When an external agent applies a force to q to move it from A to B, the electric potential energy of q (increases/decreases/remains the same).

⋆   ⋆   ⋆   ⋆   ⋆

increases

4. Panel 17, Fig. 1. The change in the _____ _____ _____ of q as it is moved from A to B is a measure of the work required to move q from A to B

⋆   ⋆   ⋆   ⋆   ⋆

electric potential energy

5. Panel 17, Fig. 1. Let U_a and U_b be the electric potential energies of q at A and B, respectively. Let W_{ab} be the work required to move q from A to B. $W_{ab} =$ _____ (*in terms of U_a and U_b*).

⋆   ⋆   ⋆   ⋆   ⋆

$U_b - U_a$

6. Panel 17, Fig. 1.

(1) $W_{ab} = U_b - U_a$.

(2) Divide both sides by q, and

$$\frac{W_{ab}}{q} = \frac{U_b - U_a}{q} = \underline{\quad\quad} \ (\textit{In terms of } U_b, U_a, \textit{ and } q.)$$

⋆   ⋆   ⋆   ⋆   ⋆

$\dfrac{U_b}{q} - \dfrac{U_a}{q}$

7. Panel 17, Fig. 1.

(1) $W_{ab} = U_b - U_a$.

(2) $\dfrac{W_{ab}}{q} = \dfrac{U_b}{q} - \dfrac{U_a}{q}$.

(3) But $\dfrac{U_b}{q}$ and $\dfrac{U_a}{q}$ are the _____ _____ of q at A and B, respectively.

★   ★   ★   ★   ★

electric potentials

8. Panel 17, Fig. 1.

(1) $W_{ab} = U_b - U_a$.

(2) $\dfrac{W_{ab}}{q} =$ _____ (*in terms of V_a and V_b*).

(3) We define the quantity $\dfrac{W_{ab}}{q}$ or the *electric potential difference* (or difference in potential) from A to B. It is the _____ per unit of _____ required to move a charge from A to B.

★   ★   ★   ★   ★

$V_b - V_a$; work ; charge

9.

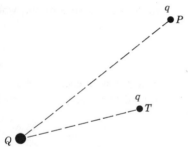

The work (W_{pt}) required to move q from P to T is measured by the change in the electric (potential/potential energy) of q as it is moved from P to T. The ratio $\dfrac{W_{pt}}{q}$ is called electric _____ _____ from P to T, or $\dfrac{W_{pt}}{q} =$ _____ .

★   ★   ★   ★   ★

potential energy ; potential difference ; $V_t - V_p$

10. $\dfrac{W_{ab}}{q} = V_b - V_a$. If V_b and V_a are measured in volts, the electric potential difference between A and B is measured in _____ . If V_a and V_b are measured in joules/elem. chge., the electric potential difference between A and B is measured in _____.

★ ★ ★ ★ ★

volts ; joules/elem. chge.

11. Panel 17, Fig. 1. $V_a = k\dfrac{Q}{r_1}$ and $V_b = k\dfrac{Q}{r_2}$.

When Q is positive, V_a is (greater/less) than V_b, and $\dfrac{W_{ab}}{q}$ is (positive/negative).

★ ★ ★ ★ ★

less ; positive (Because $\dfrac{W_{ab}}{q} = V_b - V_a$ and V_a is less than V_b).

12. Panel 17, Fig. 1. If Q is positive, the electric potential difference from A to B is (positive/negative). Now consider the electric potential difference from B to A. $\dfrac{W_{ba}}{q} = V_a - V_b$. Since V_a is (less/greater) than V_b, the electric potential difference from B to A is (positive/negative).

★ ★ ★ ★ ★

positive ; less ; negative

13. Panel 17, Fig. 1. Suppose q is moved from A to a point C which is the same distance from Q as A is. Then $\dfrac{W_{ac}}{q} = V_c - V_a$. Since V_c ($>$/$=$/$<$) V_a, the electric potential difference from A to C is (positive/negative/zero).

★ ★ ★ ★ ★

$=$; zero

14. The electric potential difference between two points in an electric field (*choose one*): (*a*) must be positive; (*b*) must be negative; (*c*) must be positive or negative; (*d*) may be positive, negative, or zero.

★ ★ ★ ★ ★

(*d*)

15. $\dfrac{W_{ab}}{q} = V_b - V_a$. If the electric potential difference from A to B is positive, the electric potential at A is (higher than/lower than/the same as) the electric potential at B. If the electric potential difference from A to B is zero, the electric potential at A is (higher than/lower than/the same as) the electric potential at B. If $V_b - V_a$ is negative, the electric potential at A is (higher than/lower than/the same as) the electric potential at B.

★ ★ ★ ★ ★

lower than ; the same as ; higher than

16. If the electric potential difference between two points in an electric field is zero, (work/no work) is required to move a charge from one point to the other.

★ ★ ★ ★ ★

no work

17.

Charge q is moved from point A to point P along the curved path shown. A and P are equidistant from the negative plate. $V_p(>/=/<)V_a$. The difference in electric potential from A to P is (positive/negative/zero). (Work/no work) is done in moving q from A to P.

★ ★ ★ ★ ★

= ; zero ; no work

18. When the work done against electric forces in moving a charge from one point to another in the electric field is zero, the electric potential difference between those points is (positive/negative/zero).

★ ★ ★ ★ ★

zero

19.

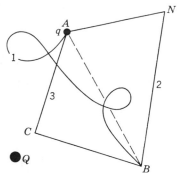

$\dfrac{W_{ab}}{q} = V_b - V_b$ This definition of electric potential difference makes no reference to the path followed when q is moved from A to B. This means that the electric potential difference from A to B is (*choose one*): [(a) the same for 2 and 3, but different for 1/(b) different for 1, 2, and 3/(c) the same for 1, 2, 3].

★ ★ ★ ★ ★

(c)

20.

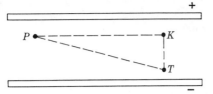

The potential difference from P to T measured by moving a unit of charge from P to K to T is (greater than/less than/equal to) that measured by moving a unit of charge directly from P to T.

★ ★ ★ ★ ★

equal to

21.

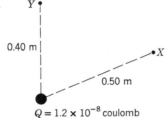

Compute the electric potential difference from X to Y.

$X_{xy} = $ _____ (*number and unit*).

★ ★ ★ ★ ★

$$V_{xy} = \frac{W_{xy}}{q} = V_y - V_x$$

$$V_x = \frac{kQ}{r_1} = \frac{(9.0 \times 10^9)(1.2 \times 10^{-8})}{0.50} = 2.16 \times 10^2 \text{ volts} = 216 \text{ volts}$$

$$V_y = k\frac{Q}{r_2} = \frac{(9.0 \times 10^9)(1.2 \times 10^{-8})}{0.40} = 270 \text{ volts}$$

$V_{xy} = 54$ volts

22. Refer to figure and data in Frame 21. Suppose a charge $q = 3.0 \times 10^{-6}$ coulomb is placed at x.

(1) $\dfrac{W_{xy}}{q} = V_y - V_x.$

(2) Multiply both sides by q, and $W_{xy} = $ _____.

(3) The work, in joules, required to move q from X to Y is _____.

★ ★ ★ ★ ★

$$q(V_y - V_x)$$

$W_{xy} = (3.0 \times 10^{-6} \text{ coulomb}) \, (54 \text{ volts})$

$\quad\;\; = (3.0 \times 10^{-6} \text{ coulomb}) \, (54 \text{ joules/coulomb})$

$\quad\;\; = 1.62 \times 10^{-4} \text{ joule}$

23. Let V_{ab} be the electric potential difference from A to B in the electric field around Q. The work, W_{ab}, required to move a charge q from A to B is given by the equation: $W_{ab} = $ _____ (*use* V_{ab} *and* q).

★　★　★　★　★

qV_{ab}

24.

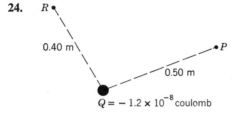

$Q = -1.2 \times 10^{-8} \text{ coulomb}$

Compute the electric potential difference from P to R.

★　★　★　★　★

$$V_{pr} = \frac{W_{pr}}{q} = V_r - V_p$$

$$V_r = k\frac{Q}{r} = \frac{(9.0 \times 10^9)(-1.2 \times 10^{-8})}{0.4} = -270 \text{ volts}$$

$$V_p = k\frac{Q}{r} = \frac{(9.0 \times 10^9)(-1.2 \times 10^{-8})}{0.5} = -216 \text{ volts}$$

$$V_{pr} = (-270 \text{ volts}) - (-216 \text{ volts}) = -54 \text{ volts}$$

25. The negative electric potential difference found in the answer to the problem in the last frame indicates that the electric potential at R is (higher than/ lower than/ the same as) the electric potential at P.

★　★　★　★　★

lower than

Section 6. *Electric Potential Difference (Continued)*
Electric Potential Inside a Charged Conductor.
Motion of Charges in an Electric Field: $\Delta E_k = -q\Delta V$

1. Panel 17. Refer to Fig. 2. This is a hollow conducting sphere with a charge Q. There is a small hole in the surface of the sphere. We have seen that the electric field *outside* the sphere is the same as if Q were concentrated at the _____ of the sphere, and that the magnitude of the electric field at P,

$E =$ _____.
★ ★ ★ ★ ★

center ; $k\dfrac{Q}{r^2}$

2. Panel 17, Fig. 2. The magnitude of the electric field on the surface of the sphere is given by the equation: $E =$ _____.
★ ★ ★ ★ ★

$k\dfrac{Q}{R^2}$

3. Panel 17, Fig. 2. The electric field at P is $E = k\dfrac{Q}{r^2}$. The electric potential at P is: $V =$ _____
★ ★ ★ ★ ★

$\dfrac{kQ}{r}$

4. Panel 17, Fig. 2. The electric potential at the surface of the sphere is:
$V =$ _____.
★ ★ ★ ★ ★

$\dfrac{kQ}{R}$

5. Panel 17, Fig. 2. The magnitude of the electric field inside this sphere is

_____.
★ ★ ★ ★ ★

zero *or* 0

6. Panel 17, Fig. 2. By definition, $E = \dfrac{F_e}{q}$. *Inside* the sphere $F_e =$ _____.
★ ★ ★ ★ ★

zero *or* 0

7. Panel 17, Fig. 2. Inside a charged conducting sphere (or any other hollow conductor like a cylinder, etc.), there (is an/is no) electric force applied to a charge. This means that (work/no work) must be done against electric forces to move a charge from the surface of a sphere to point inside the sphere.

★　★　★　★　★

is no ; no work

8. Panel 17, Refer to Fig. 3. A is a point *outside* a hollow conducting sphere with charge Q. S is a point *on* the surface, and X is a point *inside* the sphere. The electric potential difference from S to X is given by the equation:

$$\frac{W_{sx}}{q} = \underline{\hspace{2cm}}. \text{ (use } V_s \text{ and } V_x)$$

★　★　★　★　★

$V_x - V_s$

9. Panel 17, Fig. 3.

(1) $\dfrac{W_{sx}}{q} = V_x - V_s.$

(2) But since the field between S and X, i.e., the field inside the sphere, is $\underline{\hspace{2cm}}$, $W_{sx} = \underline{\hspace{2cm}}.$

★　★　★　★　★

zero ; zero *or* 0.

10. Panel 17, Fig. 3.

(1) $\dfrac{W_{sx}}{q} = V_x - V_s.$

(2) $W_{sx} = 0.$ Therefore,

(3) $V_x - V_s = \underline{\hspace{1.5cm}}$　　or　　$V_x = \underline{\hspace{1.5cm}}.$

★　★　★　★　★

$0 ; V_s$

11. Panel 17, Fig. 3. X is any point inside the sphere. S is any point on the surface of the sphere. We have just shown that the electric potential at any point inside a charged conductor is (greater than/less than/equal to) the electric potential at the surface of the conductor.

★　★　★　★　★

equal to

12. Panel 17, Fig. 2. The electric potential at the center of this sphere is (equal/unequal) to the electric potential at P. The electric potential at the surface of this sphere is (equal/unequal) to the electric potential at P. The electric potential at the center of the sphere is (equal/unequal) to the electric potential at the surface.

★　★　★　★　★

unequal ; unequal ; equal (Because the center of the sphere is a point *inside* the sphere.)

76　ELECTRIC FIELD AND ELECTRIC POTENTIAL

13. Panel 17, Fig. 3. The electric *field* at the center of this charged conducting sphere is (equal/unequal) to the electric *field* on the surface. The electric field at the center of the sphere is (equal/unequal) to the electric field at *A*.

★ ★ ★ ★ ★

unequal (We are talking about *fields*, *not* potential.) ; unequal

14. A mass *m* in the gravitational field of the Earth is said to have a certain amount of gravitational _____ energy. When *m* is allowed to fall freely, this energy is transformed into _____ energy.

★ ★ ★ ★ ★

potential ; kinetic

15. When a mass *m* falls in the gravitational field, there is (an increase/a decrease) in its gravitational potential energy and (an increase/a decrease) in its kinetic energy.

★ ★ ★ ★ ★

decrease ; increase

16. For a mass in a state of free fall: $\Delta E_k = -\Delta U_g$. The minus sign indicates that kinetic energy (increases/decreases) as the gravitational potential energy decreases.

★ ★ ★ ★ ★

increases

17. When a mass is thrown upward in the Earth's gravitational field, its gravitational potential energy (increases/decreases) while its kinetic energy (increases/decreases).

$\Delta E_k = -\Delta U_g$. The minus sign indicates that kinetic energy (increases/decreases) while gravitational potential energy increases.

★ ★ ★ ★ ★

increases ; decreases ; decreases

18. Whenever there is a mass which is under the influence of the gravitational field of the Earth only, we can relate changes in its kinetic and gravitational potential energy by the equation: $\Delta E_k =$ _____.

★ ★ ★ ★ ★

$-\Delta U_e$

19. A *positively charged* mass allowed to move freely in an electric field moves to positions of (lower/higher/the same) electric potential. In doing so there is (an increase/a decrease/no change) in its electric potential energy and (an increase/a decrease/no change) in its kinetic energy.

★ ★ ★ ★ ★

lower ; a decrease ; an increase

20. Refer to Panel 17, Fig. 1.

(1) $V_B - V_A = \dfrac{U_B}{q} - \dfrac{U_A}{q}$.

(2) Combining the terms on the right-hand side of this equation over the same denominator, $V_B - V_A = \dfrac{U_B - U_A}{q}$.

(3) Multiplying both sides by q: $U_B - U_A = $ _____.

* * * * *

$q(V_B - V_A)$

21. Panel 17, Fig. 1. The change (ΔU_e) in the electric potential energy of q as it moves from A to B is given by the equation $\Delta U_e = $ _____ (*In terms of q, V_A, and V_B.*)

* * * * *

$q(V_B - V_A)$

22. Panel 17, Fig. 1. Let ΔV equal the electric potential difference from A to B, and ΔU_e and ΔE_k represent the corresponding changes in the electric potential energy and the kinetic energy of q.

(1) $\Delta E_k = -\Delta U_e$.

(2) $\Delta U_e = $ _____ (*In terms of q and ΔV.*)

(3) $\Delta E_k = $ _____ (*In terms of q and ΔU.*)

* * * * *

$q\Delta V$

$-q\Delta V$ (*Don't forget the minus sign.*)

23. Panel 17, Fig. 1. Suppose $V_A = 190$ volts and $V_B = 210$ volts, and $q = 3 \times 10^{-6}$ coulomb. Compute the change in the kinetic energy of q as it moves from A to B.

* * * * *

$\Delta E_k = -q\Delta V = -q(V_B - V_A)$

$\Delta E_k = -(3 \times 10^{-6}\,\text{coulomb})\,(210\,\text{volts} - 190\,\text{volts})$

$\quad\;\; = -(3 \times 10^{-6}\,\text{coulomb})\,(20\,\text{joules/coulomb})$

$\quad\;\; = -6.0 \times 10^{-5}\,\text{joule}$

24. The minus sign in the answer to the last frame means that there is (an increase/a decrease/no change) in the kinetic energy of q and that there is (an increase/a decrease/no change) in the electric potential energy of q.

* * * * *

a decrease ; an increase

PHYSICAL FORMULAS

Point charges: $F = k \dfrac{Qq}{r^2}$

$$E = \frac{F}{q} = k \frac{Q}{r^2}$$

$$U = k \frac{Qq}{r}$$

$$V = \frac{U}{q} = \frac{kQ}{r}$$

Parallel plates: $F = Eq$

$$V = Ed$$

$$\tfrac{1}{2}mv^2 = Eqd = Vq$$

Electric current: $i = \dfrac{Q}{t}$

Electric resistance: $R = \rho \dfrac{l}{A}$

$$R = \frac{V}{i}$$

Series circuits: $R = R_1 + R_2 + R_3 + \cdots$

$$V = iR_1 + iR_2 + iR_3 + \cdots$$

Parallel circuits: $\dfrac{1}{R} = \dfrac{1}{R_1} + \dfrac{1}{R_2} + \dfrac{1}{R_3} + \cdots$

$$i = \frac{V}{R_1} + \frac{V}{R_2} + \frac{V}{R_3} + \cdots$$

Power: $P = iV = i^2R = \dfrac{V^2}{R}$

Magnetic fields and forces:

$$B_{\text{st. wire}} = k \frac{i}{d}$$

$$F_B = Bil = Bvq$$

$$F = k \frac{i_1 i_2 l}{d}$$

Electromagnetic induction: $\mathscr{E} = Bvl = \dfrac{\Delta \phi}{\Delta t}$

Impedance: $Z = \sqrt{(X_L - X_c)^2 + R^2}$

Ohm's law for a-c circuits: $i = \dfrac{V}{Z}$

Masking Shield

SYMBOLS USED IN THIS TEXT

= equals
≠ is not equal to
≈ is approximately equal to
> is greater than
< is less than
∝ is proportional to
→ approaches (e.g., as $x \to 0$, $y \to 3$)
∞ infinity, indefinitely large, increasing without limit
∠ angle
△ triangle

PHYSICAL CONSTANTS

1 meter = 39.37 inches
1 Angstrom Unit (Å) = 10^{-10} meter
Speed of light in a vacuum:

$c = 3 \times 10^8$ meters/sec

Coulomb's law constant:

$$k = 9 \times 10^9 \frac{\text{nt} \cdot \text{m}^2}{(\text{coul})^2}$$

$$= 2.3 \times 10^{-28} \frac{\text{nt} \cdot \text{m}^2}{(\text{elem. chge.})^2}$$

Magnetic field constant:

$$k = 2 \times 10^{-7} \frac{\text{nt}}{(\text{amp})^2}$$

(for long straight wire)
1 coulomb = 6.25×10^{18} elem. chge.;
1 elem. chge. = 1.6×10^{-19} coulomb

MATHEMATICAL FORMULAS

Quadratic formula:
If $ax^2 + bx + c = 0$,

$$\text{then } x = \frac{-b \pm \sqrt{b^2 - 4ac}}{2a}$$

Simple direct variation:
$y = kx$
Simple inverse variation:
$xy = k$
Pythagorean theorem:
$c^2 = a^2 + b^2$

USEFUL NUMERICAL CONSTANTS

$\pi = 3.14$
$\sqrt{2} = 1.414$
$\sqrt{3} = 1.732$
$\sqrt{5} = 2.236$

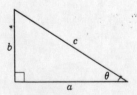

$$\sin \theta = \frac{b}{c}$$

$$\cos \theta = \frac{a}{c}$$

$$\tan \theta = \frac{b}{a}$$

25.

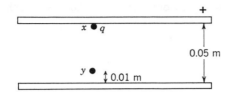

The electric potential difference from x to y is -200 volts. q has a charge of 6×10^3 elem. chge. Compute the kinetic energy of q at y if it starts from rest at x. (Use electron volts as your units.)

★   ★   ★   ★   ★

$$\Delta E_k = -q \,\Delta V = -(6 \times 10^3 \text{ elem. chge.})(-200 \text{ volts})$$
$$= +1.2 \times 10^6 \text{ electron volts.}$$

26. The plus sign in the answer to this problem indicates that there is (an increase/a decrease/no change) in the kinetic energy of q as it moves from x to y.

★   ★   ★   ★   ★

an increase

27. Refer to Panel 18. The letter in the upper right-hand corner is _____.

★   ★   ★   ★   ★

D.

28. Panel 18, Fig. 1. Read the descriptive paragraph. Protons have a (positive/negative) charge of 1 (coulomb/elem. chge.). The kinetic energy with which the protons hit the target is determined by the change in their electric _____ _____ as they move from P to A because the electric _____ at any point inside a charged conductor is the same as it is on the surface.

★   ★   ★   ★   ★

positive ; elem. chge. ; potential energy ; potential

29. Panel 18, Fig. 1. Compute the electric potential difference from P to A.

★   ★   ★   ★   ★

$$V_{PA} = V_A - V_P$$
$$V_A = k\frac{Q}{r} = \frac{(2.3 \times 10^{-28})(-6.25 \times 10^{12})}{0.50}$$
$$= -028.8 \times 10^{-16} \frac{\text{joule}}{\text{elem. chge.}}$$
$$V_P = k\frac{Q}{r} = \frac{(2.3 \times 10^{-28})(-6.25 \times 10^{12})}{5.0}$$
$$= -2.88 \times 10^{-16} \text{ joule/elem. chge.}$$
$$V_{PA} = (-2.88 \times 10^{-15}) - (-0.288 \times 10^{-15})$$
$$= -2.59 \times 10^{-15} \text{ joule/elem. chge.}$$

30. Panel 18, Fig. 1. The kinetic energy of the protons when they reach A is _____ joule.

★ ★ ★ ★ ★

$\Delta E_k = -q\,\Delta V = -$ (1 elem. chge.)$(-2.59 \times 10^{-15}$ joule/elem. chge.)

$\qquad = 2.59 \times 10^{-15}$ joule

31. Panel 18, Fig. 1. The kinetic energy of the protons when they strike the target is _____ joule. Convert this to electron volts. (*Check your answer mask if you have forgotten the conversion factor.*)

★ ★ ★ ★ ★

1 joule $= 6.25 \times 10^{18}$ electron volts

2.59×10^{-15} joule $= (2.59 \times 10^{-15})(6.25 \times 10^{18})$

$\qquad\qquad = 1.62 \times 10^4$ electron volts

32. Panel 18, Fig. 1. If the target is placed between 0 and the hole in the sphere, there is (an increase/decrease/no change) in the kinetic energy with which the protons strike it. Explain your answer.

★ ★ ★ ★ ★

no change (Because the electric potential of *all* points inside the sphere are the same as the electric potential at the surface.)

33. Panel 18, Fig. 1. $E_k = \frac{1}{2}mv^2$. The mass of a proton is 1.67×10^{-27} kg. Compute the speed of a proton as it strikes the target.

★ ★ ★ ★ ★

$E_k = \frac{1}{2}mv^2$

$\frac{1}{2}mv^2 = 2.59 \times 10^{-15}$ joule

$\frac{1}{2}(1.67 \times 10^{-27})v^2 = 2.59 \times 10^{-15}$

$v^2 = \dfrac{5.18 \times 10^{-15}}{1.67 \times 10^{-27}} = 3.1 \times 10^{12}$

$v \approx 1.76 \times 10^6$ m/sec

34. Panel 18. Refer to Fig. 2. The electric field E between the plates is (constant/variable) except at the _____ of the plates.

★ ★ ★ ★ ★

constant ; edges

35. Panel 18, Fig. 2. The electric force on a positive charge q anywhere in or between these plates is given by the equation: $\vec{F} = $ _____ (*In terms of E and q*) the direction being (from positive to negative plate/from negative to positive plate/parallel to the plates.)

★ ★ ★ ★ ★

$\vec{E}q$; from positive to negative plate

36. Panel 18, Fig. 2. The work done on (+) charge q as it moves a distance d from any point between the plates to the negative plate is:

(1) Work = Fd.

(2) Since $F = Eq$.

(3) Work = _____ (*In terms of charge, field, and distance moved.*)

★   ★   ★   ★   ★

Eqd

37. Panel 18, Fig. 2. But Ed is the electric _____ at any point a distance d from the negative plate.

★   ★   ★   ★   ★

potential

38. Panel 18, Fig. 2.

(1) Work = $Fd = Eqd$.

(2) $Ed = V$.

(3) ∴ Work done on a charge (+) q as it moves a distance d between the plates toward the negative plate is: $W =$ _____ in terms of electric potential and charge.

★   ★   ★   ★   ★

Vq

39. Panel 18, Fig. 2. The work done on charge q by electric forces between the plates is equal to the _____ in the kinetic energy of q. If q starts from rest, then after it has moved a distance d in this field, its kinetic energy $E_k =$ _____ in term of electric potential and charge.

★   ★   ★   ★   ★

change ; *Vq*

40. Panel 18, Fig. 2. A negative charge placed at the negative plate or anywhere in the space between the plates will undergo an electric force in a direction from the (positive/negative) plate to the (positive/negative) plate.

★   ★   ★   ★   ★

negative ; positive

41. Panel 18, Fig. 2. Except for direction of motion, the change in the kinetic energy of a negative charge is the same as that for an equal positive charge q in the same field. If V is the potential between the plates, the change in the kinetic energy of a negatively charged particle as it goes from one plate to the other is $E_k =$ _____.

★   ★   ★   ★   ★

Vq

42.

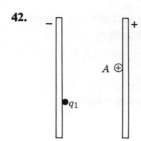

A voltmeter placed across these plates reads 100 volts. A proton starts from rest at A. Compute its kinetic energy in joules when it reaches the negative plate. (*Remember* 1 volt $= 1.6 \times 10^{-19}$ joule/elem. chge.)

★　★　★　★　★

$E_k = Vq = 100(1.6 \times 10^{-19}$ joule/elem. chge.)(1 elem. chge.)

　　$= 1.6 \times 10^{-17}$ joule

43. Use data and figure of previous frame to compute the kinetic energy of $q_1 = 1$ coulomb when it strikes the positive plate.

★　★　★　★　★

$E_k = Vq = (100$ volts)(1 coulomb)

　　$= (100$ joule/coulomb)(1 coulomb)

　　$= 100$ joules

44.

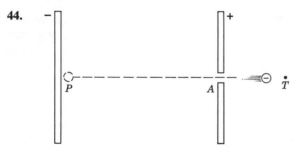

The electric potential across these plates is 1000 volts. An electron leaves the negative plate at P, crosses the field, and passes through the hole in the positive plate. Compute its kinetic energy at point A in electron volts.

★　★　★　★　★

$E_k = Vq = (1000$ volts)(1 elem. chge.)

　　$= 1000$ electron volts

45. Refer to data and figure of Frame 44. What is the kinetic energy of the electron at point T? Explain your answer.

★　★　★　★　★

1000 electron volts (Because there is no electric field outside the plates; therefore, there are no electric forces to change the kinetic energy of the electron
after it leaves A.)

46.

$m_1 = m_2$. The potential energies of m_1 and m_2 at A relative to B are (equal/
unequal). When they are allowed to fall from level A to level B, the decreases
in their potential energies are (equal/unequal). Their kinetic energies as they
reach B are (equal/unequal).

⋆   ⋆   ⋆   ⋆   ⋆

equal ; equal ; unequal

47. Refer to figure in Frame 46. The mass falling through water uses some
of the _____ energy it possesses at A to do work against the
resistance of the water. Very likely the temperature of the water rises slightly
as m_2 passes through it, and this means that some of the energy available at A
has been transformed into _____.

⋆   ⋆   ⋆   ⋆   ⋆

potential ; heat

48. When we say that a decrease in gravitational potential energy involves an
equal increase in kinetic energy, we are making the assumption that (work/
no work) is done against friction, air resistance, etc.

⋆   ⋆   ⋆   ⋆   ⋆

no work

49. In Figs. 1 and 2 of Panel 18, we have made the assumption that all of the
electric potential energy lost has been changed to kinetic energy. This is true if
work against "electric resistance" (is/is not) negligible.

⋆   ⋆   ⋆   ⋆   ⋆

is

50. Panel 18. Refer to Fig. 3. Here the parallel plates of Fig. 2 have been
immersed in a solution which can conduct charges. Since the charges moving

from one plate to another are *not* moving in a vacuum, it is likely they will encounter some sort of resistance. This means that ΔE_k is probably (greater than/less than/equal to) Vq.

⋆ ⋆ ⋆ ⋆ ⋆

less than

51. Panel 18, Fig. 3. The electric potential from A to B is V. The electric potential energy of a positive charge at A is given by the equation $U =$ ____. As q moves across through the solution, it reaches a uniform velocity v quickly. The quantity $\frac{1}{2}mv^2$ is (greater than/less than/equal to) U. The remainder probably changes to a form of energy we call _____.

⋆ ⋆ ⋆ ⋆ ⋆

Vq ; less than ; heat

Section 7.   Electromotive Force (EMF)

1.

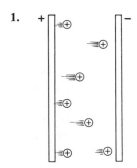

As positive charges leave the (+) plate and move to the (−) plate, the (+) plate becomes (more/less) positive and the (−) plate becomes (more/less) negative.

⋆ ⋆ ⋆ ⋆ ⋆

less (Because there is a loss of + charge.)
less (Because + charges cancel − charges.)

2. Refer to figure in Frame 1. Suppose negative charge were moving from the negative to the positive plate. In this case, the positive plate would become (more/less) positive and the negative plate would become (more/less) negative.

⋆ ⋆ ⋆ ⋆ ⋆

less ; less

3. In either case, the charges on the plates would (increase/decrease/remain the same), and as a consequence the magnitude of the electric field (increases/decreases/remains the same).

★   ★   ★   ★   ★

decrease ; decreases

4. Refer to figure in Frame 1. As the electric field across the plates decreases, the electric potential across the plates (increases/decreases).

★   ★   ★   ★   ★

decreases

5. Refer to figure in Frame 1. When there is no electric potential across the plates, there (is an/is no) electric force acting to move charges from one plate to the other. Thus charges will [(a) continue to move indefinitely from one plate to the other/(b) cease to move from one plate to the other when the electric potential becomes zero].

★   ★   ★   ★   ★

is no ; (b)

6.

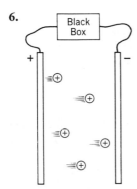

Suppose this Black Box was a device which took (+) charges from the negative plate as fast as they arrived and returned them to the positive plate; then (+) charges (would/would not) be able to move between the plates as long as the Black Box was operating.

★   ★   ★   ★   ★

would

7. The Black Box described in Frame 6 would enable us to maintain an electric _____ across the plates indefinitely.

★   ★   ★   ★   ★

potential *or* field

8. A device which is able to maintain an electric potential difference greater than zero between two points to which it is attached is called a seat of EMF (*electromotive force*). The Black Box described in Frame 6 which removes (+) charge from the [(+)/(−)] plate and returns it to the [(+)/(−)] plate (is/is not) a seat of EMF.

⋆   ⋆   ⋆   ⋆   ⋆

(−) ; (+) ; is

9.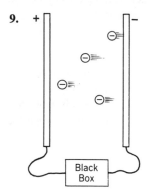

This Black Box removes (−) charge from the (+) plate as it arrives and returns it to the (−) plate. In so doing, it (maintains/does not maintain) a potential difference across the plates. It (is/is not) a seat of EMF.

⋆   ⋆   ⋆   ⋆   ⋆

maintains ; is

10. The name "electromotive force" is misleading because a potential difference is *not* a force. As a result, physicists use just the initials EMF. A seat of EMF is any device which maintains an electric _____
_____ across the points to which it is attached.

⋆   ⋆   ⋆   ⋆   ⋆

potential difference

11. Refer to Panel 19. The letter in the upper right-hand corner is _____.

⋆   ⋆   ⋆   ⋆   ⋆

F

12. Panel 19. In Fig. 1(*a*), two oppositely charged plates are immersed in a liquid which has an indefinitely large number of positively charged particles. These particles will move toward the negative plate until the electric potential between the plates is _____ (*Number*).

⋆   ⋆   ⋆   ⋆   ⋆

0 *or* zero

13. Panel 19. The potential difference across the plates in Fig. 1(*a*) vanishes

in a very few seconds and (+) charges cease to move to the right. In Fig. 1(*b*), a device called a *battery* is attached to the plates, and a potential difference is maintained across the plates indefinitely. A battery is, therefore, one example of a device we call a _____ of _____.

⋆   ⋆   ⋆   ⋆   ⋆

seat (of) EMF

14. Panel 19, Fig. 1(*b*). In order to maintain potential difference across the plates, the battery must continually remove (+) charge from the [(+)/(−)] plate and place it in the [(+)/(−)] plate. We find that a generator will do the same thing. A generator (is/is not) a seat of EMF.

⋆   ⋆   ⋆   ⋆   ⋆

(−) ; (+) ; is

15. Panel 19, Fig. 1(*b*). The removal of (+) charges from the (−) plate and their return to the (+) plate requires that _____ be done against the electric field. In a battery, this work comes from the *chemical* potential energy of the materials in the battery. We will not go into the internal chemistry of a battery in this course; for our purposes, it is sufficient to know that a battery is a seat of _____ in which _____ energy is changed to _____ potential energy.

⋆   ⋆   ⋆   ⋆   ⋆

work ; EMF ; chemical ; electric

16. Not all seats of EMF are chemical in structure. In a generator, for example, *mechanical* energy (e.g., the turning of a shaft) is used to move charges from one point to another of different potential against the electric field. In this case, _____ energy is changed into _____ _____ _____.

⋆   ⋆   ⋆   ⋆   ⋆

mechanical ; electric potential energy

17. In general, a seat of EMF is a device which is able to maintain an electric _____ between two points to which it is attached. It is any device in which chemical, mechanical, or some other form of _____ is changed into _____ _____ _____.

⋆   ⋆   ⋆   ⋆   ⋆

potential *or* field ; energy ; electric potential energy

18. The EMF of a battery (or any other seat of EMF) is the *work per unit of charge* (coulomb or elem. chge.) required to move a charge against an electric field and thus maintain an electric potential difference greater than zero between two points. We will use the letter $\mathscr{E}$ to represent this physical quantity, and $\mathscr{E}$ is measured in units of (force/charge/electric potential/electric field/electric potential energy).

★   ★   ★   ★   ★

electric potential

19. $\mathscr{E}$ is the letter we use to represent the _____ of a battery, generator, etc. It is a measure of the _____ per unit _____ required to move a charge from one point to another in an electric field (with/against) the field. $\mathscr{E}$ may be measured in (newtons/newtons per coulomb/joules/joules per elem. chge./electron volts/volts/coulombs). (*Choose any which apply.*)

★   ★   ★   ★   ★

EMF ; work (per unit) charge ; against ; joules per elem. chge. *and* volts

20. Panel 19, Fig. 1(*b*). The battery removes 3×10^{-6} coulomb of charge from the ($-$) plate and returns it to the positive plate. In the process, it does 1.2×10^{-4} joule of work. $\mathscr{E} = $ _____ volts.

★   ★   ★   ★   ★

$$\mathscr{E} = \frac{\text{work}}{\text{charge}} = \frac{1.2 \times 10^{-4} \text{ joule}}{3 \times 10^{-6} \text{ coulomb}} = 40 \text{ joules/coulomb} = 40 \text{ volts}$$

21. Panel 19, Fig. 1(*b*). Let $\mathscr{E} = 6$ volts. What work is done by the battery as it moves 5 coulombs of charge back to the ($+$) plate?

★   ★   ★   ★   ★

$$\mathscr{E} = \frac{\text{work}}{\text{charge}}$$

$$6 \text{ volts} = \frac{\text{work}}{5 \text{ coulomb}}$$

Work $= (6 \text{ joules/coulomb})(5 \text{ coulombs}) = 30 \text{ joules}$

22. Panel 19, Fig. 1(*b*). Compute $\mathscr{E}$ if the battery moves 6×10^{23} elem. chge. back to the positive plate while it does 12 joules of work.

★   ★   ★   ★   ★

$$\mathscr{E} = \frac{\text{work}}{\text{chge}} = \frac{12 \text{ joules}}{6 \times 10^{23} \text{ elem. chge.}} = 2 \times 10^{-23} \text{ joule/elem. chge.}$$

Section 8.   Review and Problems

1. Electric potential and EMF (can/cannot) be measured in the same units. Electric potential and electric potential energy (can/cannot) be measured in the same units.

★   ★   ★   ★   ★

can ; cannot

2.

Q and q are point charges. Write equations in terms of $Q, q,$ and r for:

(1) E, the electric field at P.

(2) V, the electric potential at P.

(3) U, the electric potential energy of q.

(4) F, the electric force of Q acting on q.

★   ★   ★   ★   ★

(1) $E = k \dfrac{Q}{r^2}$ (2) $V = k \dfrac{Q}{r}$

(3) $U = k \dfrac{Qq}{r}$ (4) $F = k \dfrac{Qq}{r^2}$

3. Refer to figure in Frame 2.
By definition, $E =$ _____. By definition, $V =$ _____
★   ★   ★   ★   ★

$\dfrac{F}{q}$; $\dfrac{U}{q}$

4. Refer to figure in Frame 2. If Q is negative, the direction of $\vec{E}$ at P is (toward/away from) Q. If Q and q are both negative, the electric potential energy of q at P is (positive/negative) and the electric potential at P is (positive/negative).
★   ★   ★   ★   ★

toward ; positive ; negative

5. A positive charge free to move in an electric field moves to positions of (higher/lower/equal) electric potential. A negative charge free to move in an electric field moves to positions of (higher/lower/equal) electric potential.
★   ★   ★   ★   ★

lower ; higher

6.

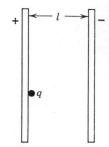

These plates are parallel. The field between them is E. Write equations in terms of E, q, and l for the following:

(1) V, the potential difference across the plates.

(2) F, the electric force on q when it is halfway between the plates.

(3) U, the electric potential energy of q when it is at the (+) plate.

★   ★   ★   ★   ★

$V = El$; $F = Eq$; $U = Eql$

7. Refer to figure in Frame 6. If q is positive and starts from rest at the positive plate and the space between the plates is a vacuum, the kinetic energy of q when it reaches the negative plate is: $E_k =$ _____ (*In terms of E, q, and l*) and $E_k =$ _____ (*In terms of V and q*).

★   ★   ★   ★   ★

Eql ; Vq

8. Refer to figure in Frame 6. Let $q = 3$ elem. chge. and the potential difference across the plates be 150 volts. Compute the kinetic energy of q when it reaches the negative plate (1) in electric volts, (2) in joules.

★   ★   ★   ★   ★

$E_k = Vq = $ (150 volts)(3 elem. chge.) $= 750$ electron volts

1 electron volt $= 1.6 \times 10^{-19}$ joule

$E_k = (750)(1.6 \times 10^{-19})$ joule $= 1.2 \times 10^{-16}$ joule

9. The volt is a unit of electric_____.

The newton/coulomb is a unit of electric _____.

The joule/elem. chge. is a unit of electric _____.

The electron volt is a unit of _____.

★   ★   ★   ★   ★

potential ; field ; potential ; energy

10. Panel 19. Refer to Fig. 2. Examine these graphs carefully. They are plots of (*a*) electric _____ and (*b*) electric _____ against distance (r) measured from the (center/surface) of a hollow conducting sphere with charge Q.

★　★　★　★　★

potential ; field ; center

11. Panel 19, Fig. 2. The fact that V and E are never (positive/negative) indicates that the charge on Q is (positive/negative).

★　★　★　★　★

negative ; positive

12. Panel 19, Fig. 2. As r approaches R, the electric *potential* (increases/ decreases/remains constant) and the electric *field* (increases/decreases/ remains constant). As r goes from $r = R$ to $r = 0$, the electric potential (increases/decreases/remains constant) and the electric field (increases/ decreases/remains constant).

★　★　★　★　★

increases ; increases ; remains constant ; decreases

13. Panel 19, Fig. 2. These graphs verify the fact that the electric field inside a charged conductor is (the same as it is on the surface/zero/greater than it is on the surface), and that the electric potential inside a charged conductor is (the same as it is on the surface/zero/greater than it is on the surface).

★　★　★　★　★

zero ; the same as it is on the surface.

14. Refer to panel 20. The letter in the upper hight-hand corner is _____.

★　★　★　★　★

H

15. Panel 20. Read Problem 1. Let Q = the positive charge on the surface of an atom of gold. Q = _____ (*Number and unit*).

★　★　★　★　★

79 elem. chge.

16. Panel 20, Problem 1. For a sphere with charge Q and radius R, the field at the surface is given by the equation: $E =$ _____.

★　★　★　★　★

$$k\frac{Q}{R^2}$$

17. Panel 20, Problem 1. Calculate the answer to part (a) in newtons/elem. chge.

★　★　★　★　★

$$E = k\frac{Q}{R^2} = \frac{(2.3 \times 10^{-28})(79)}{(10^{-10})^2} = 1.8 \times 10^{-6} \text{ newton/elem. chge.}$$

18. Panel 20, Problem 1. The electric potential at the surface of a charged sphere with radius R and charge Q is: $V = $ _____.

★ ★ ★ ★ ★

$$V = k\frac{Q}{R}$$

19. Panel 20, Problem 1. Calculate the answer to part (b) in joules/elem. chge.

★ ★ ★ ★ ★

$$V = k\frac{Q}{R} = \frac{(2.3 \times 10^{-28})(79)}{10^{-10}} = 1.8 \times 10^{-16} \text{ joule/elem. chge.}$$

20. Panel 20. Read Problem 2. In Problem 1 the positive charge is (spread on the surface/concentrated at the center) of the atom.

★ ★ ★ ★ ★

spread on the surface

21. Panel 20, Problem 2. The positive charge in a Rutherford atom is concentrated in a region (at the center/on the surface) of the atom called the

_____.

★ ★ ★ ★ ★

at the center ; nucleus

22. Panel 20, Problem 2. Compare the radius of the atom (R_a) from Problem 1 with the radius of the nucleus (R_n). $\dfrac{R_a}{R_n} = $ _____ (*Number*).

★ ★ ★ ★ ★

$$\frac{10^{-10}}{10^{-14}} = 10^4$$

23. Panel 20, Problem 2. Compute the answer to part (a) in newtons/elem. chge. Compute the answer to part (b) in joules/elem. chge.

★ ★ ★ ★ ★

$$E = k\frac{Q}{r^2} = \frac{(2.3 \times 10^{-28})(79)}{(10^{-14})^2} = 180 \text{ newton/elem. chge.}$$

$$V = \frac{kQ}{r} = \frac{(2.3 \times 10^{-28})(79)}{10^{-14}} = 1.8 \times 10^{-12} \text{ joule/elem. chge.}$$

24. Panel 20. Read Problem 3. For part (a) let l be the separation of the plates and V the potential difference across them. (1) Write an equation for E in terms of V and l: $E = $ _____. (2) Calculate E in newtons/coulomb.

★ ★ ★ ★ ★

(1) $E = \dfrac{V}{l}$

(2) $E = \dfrac{90 \text{ volts}}{3 \times 10^{-3} \text{ m}} = 3.0 \times 10^4 \text{ newtons/coulomb}$

25. Panel 20, Problem 3. For part (b), let E be the magnitude of the electric field and q the charge between the plates. Write an equation for the force on q produced by the electric field: $F = $ _____.

★ ★ ★ ★ ★

Eq

26. Panel 20, Problem 3(b). The electric force acting on a charge between the plates (depends/does not depend) on the distance of q from the negative plate.

★ ★ ★ ★ ★

does not depend

27. Panel 20, Problem 3. Calculate the answer to part (b): $F = $ _____ newtons.

★ ★ ★ ★ ★

$E = 3.0 \times 10^4 \text{ newtons/coulomb}$

$F = Eq = (3.0 \times 10^4 \text{ newton/coulomb})(5 \times 10^{-5} \text{ coulomb})$

$= 15 \times 10^{-1} = 1.5 \text{ newtons}$

28. Panel 20, Problem 3. For part (c), the electric potential at any distance d from the negative plate is given by the equation: $V = $ _____.

★ ★ ★ ★ ★

Ed

29. Panel 20. Calculate the answer to Problem 3(c) in volts.

★ ★ ★ ★ ★

$V = Ed = (3.0 \times 10^4 \text{ newton/coulomb})(1.5 \times 10^{-3} \text{ m})$

$= 45 \text{ joules/coulomb} = 45 \text{ volts}$

30. Panel 20, Problem 3. For part (d), $V = $ ____ volts and $l = $ _____ m. Calculate the electric field between the plates under these conditions.

★ ★ ★ ★ ★

$180 \; ; 6 \times 10^{-3} \; ;$

$E = \dfrac{V}{l} = \dfrac{180 \text{ volts}}{6 \times 10^{-3}} = 3 \times 10^4 \text{ newtons/coulomb}$

31. Panel 20, Problem 3. When we change the electric potential and the plate separation by the same factor, the magnitude of the electric field (increases/decreases/remains constant).

★ ★ ★ ★ ★

remains constant

32. Panel 20, Problem 3. Read part (*e*). Here we are using (coulomb/elem. chge.) to measure charge. This requires us to change the potential difference to _____ (*Units*) if we want to get kinetic energy in joules.

★ ★ ★ ★ ★

elem. chge. ; joules/elem. chge.

33. Panel 20, Problem 3(*e*). $V = 2 \times 10^3$ volts = _____ joules/elem. chge.

★ ★ ★ ★ ★

1 volt $= 1.6 \times 10^{-19}$ joule/elem. chge.

2×10^3 volt $= (2 \times 10^3)(1.6 \times 10^{-19})$ joule/elem. chge.

$\qquad = 3.2 \times 10^{-16}$ joule/elem. chge.

34. Panel 20, Problem 3(*e*). Let V be the electric potential across the plates and q be the charge on the alpha particle. An equation for the kinetic energy of the alpha particle as it passes through the hole is: $E_k =$ _____.

★ ★ ★ ★ ★

Vq

35. Panel 20. Compute the answer to Problem 3(*e*) in joules.

★ ★ ★ ★ ★

$E_k = Vq = (2$ elem. chge.$)(3.2 \times 10^{-16}$ joule/elem. chge.$)$

$\qquad = 6.4 \times 10^{-16}$ joule

36. Panel 20, Problem 3(*f*). We assume that the alpha particle emerges into a vacuum. We know that the charges on the plates exert (a force/no force) on it after it emerges from the hole. After it emerges from the hole, the speed of the alpha particle (increases/decreases/remains constant).

★ ★ ★ ★ ★

no force ; remains constant

37. Panel 20, Problem 3(*f*). The equation for E_k in terms of mass m and speed v is: $E_k =$ _____. After the alpha particle leaves the whole, $E_k =$ _____ joules.

★ ★ ★ ★ ★

$\frac{1}{2}mv^2$; 6.4×10^{-16} joule

38. Panel 20, Problem 3(*f*). Calculate the speed of the alpha particle in m/sec.

★ ★ ★ ★ ★

$$\tfrac{1}{2}mv^2 = 6.4 \times 10^{-16}$$
$$\tfrac{1}{2}(6.7 \times 10^{-27})v^2 = 6.4 \times 10^{-16}$$
$$v^2 = \frac{12.8 \times 10^{-16}}{6.7 \times 10^{-27}} = 1.91 \times 10^{11}$$
$$v \approx 4.4 \times 10^5 \text{ m/sec}$$

PROBLEMS

1. A test charge of 2.00×10^{12} elementary charge units is placed in the vicinity of an object with a charge Q. If Q exerts a force of 8.00×10^{-5} newton on the test charge, compute the electric field of Q at the position of the test charge.

2. A charge of 5.0×10^{16} elementary charge units is placed on a hollow metallic sphere which has a radius of 10 cm. Compute the electric field at a distance of (*a*) 15 cm; (*b*) 100 cm; (*c*) 5 cm from the center of the sphere. Compute the electric potential energy of a point charge of 2.0×10^5 elementary charges at position (*a*), (*b*), and (*c*) above. Compute the electric potentials at these points.

3. Compute the electric field and electric potential 2 meters from the point charge of 10 coulombs.

4. Compute the magnitude of the total electric field at B is q_1 is 5 coulombs, and q_2 is -15 coulombs. Compute the electric potential at B.

5. Compute the magnitude of the electric field at B if q_1 is 5 coulombs, q_2 is -15 coulombs, and AB and BC are perpendicular. Compute the electric potential at B.

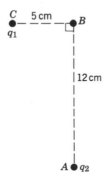

6. Compute the electric potential difference from A to B if Q is -25 coulombs, $r_1 = 1$ m, and $r_2 = 10$ m. Compute the electric potential difference from B to A. Interpret any differences in signs in your answers.

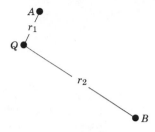

7. Physicists sometimes distinguish between vector and scalar fields. How would you classify electric fields and electric potentials in these terms?

8. A proton is accelerated from rest toward the center of a charged sphere. The sphere has a charge of $-10,000$ coulombs and a radius of 1 meter. The charge on a proton is 1 elementary charge unit. Compute the change in the potential energy of the proton by the time it is just about to hit a target placed at the center of the sphere (a) in electron volts; (b) in joules, and (c) compute the velocity of the proton when it hits the target if the mass of a proton is 1.67×10^{-27} kg.

9. Compute the electric field between two large parallel plates which are 5 cm apart when a potential difference of 2,000 volts is placed across them. Compute the field when the plates are separated by 25 cm. Compute the field when they are 5 cm apart and a potential difference of 20,000 volts is placed across them. Compute the field when the plates are 25 cm apart and a potential difference of 20,000 volts is placed across them.

10. Compute the electric force on a -3-coulomb charge when it is midway between two large parallel plates which are 10 cm apart, if a potential difference of 90 volts is placed across the plates. Compute the electric force on this charge when it is 2 cm from the negatively charged plate.

11. Compute the kinetic energy of the particle in Problem 10 as it crashes into the positive plate if it starts from rest at the negative plate. Compute the work done in moving the particle from the negative plate to a position 2 cm from the positive plate.

Chapter Three

CURRENT ELECTRICITY

OBJECTIVES

Upon successful completion of this chapter, the student should be able to:

1. Describe the motion of charge in a variety of different types of conductors: solids, liquids, gases, and vacuum.
2. Give a quantitative definition of electric current.
3. Define and compute electric resistance.
4. State Ohm's law.
5. Distinguish between ohmic and nonohmic devices.
6. Describe energy changes in an electric circuit.
7. Solve problems involving resistors in series and in parallel circuits.

INTRODUCTORY NOTE

Thus far we have considered primarily charges which stand and do not necessarily move in an electric field. However, an important characteristic of charges in certain fields is that they are free to move under the influence of the field and thereby constitute a flow or current of charges from one place to another. We call this branch of physics *current electricity*, and this is the subject of this chapter.

Section 1. *Movement of Charges in Electric Fields*
Positive and Negative Ions
Conduction Electrons
Direction of Electric Current

1. Atoms consist of smaller particles called electrons, protons, and neutrons. A neutron has *no* electric charge.
An electron has a (positive/negative) charge of 1 (coulomb/elem. chge)
A proton has a (positive/negative) charge of one (coulomb/elem. chge.)
★ ★ ★ ★ ★

negative ; elem. chge. ; positive ; elem. chge.

2. From the outside, atoms appear to have *no* charge. This is because they have equal numbers of (protons and neutrons/protons and electrons/electrons and neutrons) and neutrons have (a positive charge/a negative charge/no charge at all).

★　★　★　★　★

protons and electrons ; no charge at all

3. An atom which has gained or lost one or more electrons is called an *ion*. An alpha particle is a helium atom which has lost two electrons. An alpha particle (is/is not) an ion.

★　★　★　★　★

is

4. An atom which has lost one or more electrons is left with (a positive charge/a negative charge/no charge at all). Such an atom is called an_____.

★　★　★　★　★

a positive charge ; ion

5. An alpha particle is a *positive* ion of the helium atom; i.e., a helium atom which has (lost/gained) electrons.

★　★　★　★　★

lost

6. Sodium is an element whose atoms lose electrons easily. A sodium atom which has lost one electron is a (positive/negative) _____.

★　★　★　★　★

positive ; ion

7. Atoms of chlorine gain extra electrons easily. A chlorine atom which has gained one extra electron is a (positive/negative) _____.

★　★　★　★　★

negative ; ion

8. Refer to Panel 21. The letter in the upper right-hand corner is _____.

★　★　★　★　★

R

9. Panel 21. Refer to Fig. 1. When the X rays knock electrons off the atoms of the gas (positive/negative) ions are formed, and these continue to move toward the (positive/negative) plate as long as the seat of EMF maintains an electric _____ across the plates.

★　★　★　★　★

positive ; negative ; potential *or* field

10. Panel 21. *The motion of charges in an electric field constitutes an electric* *current.* In Fig. 1, it is the motion of the (atoms/ions) of the gas which constitutes an electric current.

★ ★ ★ ★ ★

ions

11. Panel 21, Fig. 1. The movement of ions which constitutes an electric current here is toward the (positive/negative) plate. Whenever an atom of this gas is ionized by an X ray, one or more _____ is freed from the atom. Under the influence of the electric field, these move toward the (positive/negative) plate.

★ ★ ★ ★ ★

negative (Because these are positive ions, they move toward the *positive* plate.)
electrons
positive (Because electrons are *negatively* charged and are therefore attracted to the positive plate.)

12. Panel 21, Fig. 1. The electrons freed from atoms of this gas when they are ionized constitute an electric current; (True/False). Explain your answer.

★ ★ ★ ★ ★

True (Because they are moving charges, and moving charges constitute an electric current.)

13. Panel 21. Refer to Fig. 2. The battery is a _____ of _____ which maintains an electric potential between the plates to which it is attached. The plates are immersed in a solution in which ions (are/are not) free to move.

★ ★ ★ ★ ★

seat (of) EMF ; are

14. Panel 21, Fig. 2. Under the influence of the electric field, the ions of hydrogen move toward the (positive/negative) plate and the ions of chlorine move toward the (positive/negative) plate.

★ ★ ★ ★ ★

negative ; positive

15. In a solution containing positive and negative ions, the ions move under the influence of an _____ _____. This movement constitutes what we call an electric _____.

★ ★ ★ ★ ★

electric field *or* potential ; current

16. Panel 21. Electrons on the surface of a metal sometimes act like the molecules on the surface of a pan of water. As the water is heated, (more/less) of it is likely to evaporate, and eventually the temperature of the water will be high enough for large numbers of molecules to b_____l off in the form of steam. In Fig. 3, as the *A*-battery heats the filament, electrons are (more/ less) likely to leave its surface.

★   ★   ★   ★   ★

more ; boil ; more

17. Panel 21, Fig. 3. The filament eventually gets hot enough to "boil" off _____, which then move under the influence of the electric potential provided by the (*A/B*)-battery toward what is called in this figure the _____.

★   ★   ★   ★   ★

electrons ; *B* ; plate

18. Panel 21, Fig. 3. The production of free electrons by heating a metal filament to high temperature is called *thermionic* emission. The electrons produced in Fig. 1 (are/are not) the result of thermionic emission.

★   ★   ★   ★   ★

are not

19. The prefix "therm-" (compare *thermostat, thermometer*, etc.) refers to the fact that in _____ emission of electrons, the f_____ must be heated to a high temperature.

★   ★   ★   ★   ★

thermionic ; filament

20. Panel 21. In Fig. 3, the electrons which move from the heated filament to the plate constitute an _____ _____.

★   ★   ★   ★   ★

electric current

21. It is a characteristic of substances called metals that their atoms have certain electrons (called *conduction* electrons) which are only weakly attached to the rest of the atom and are therefore (free/not free) to move under the influence of an electric field.

★   ★   ★   ★   ★

free

22. The atoms (strictly speaking, ions) which otherwise constitute a metal are held together in an array called a *lattice*. When an electric potential is placed across the ends of a metallic conductor, the (ions in the lattice/ conduction electrons) move under the influence of the field and constitute an electric current.

★   ★   ★   ★   ★

conduction electrons

23. Panel 21. In a piece of copper wire whose ends are attached to the terminals of a battery, _____ electrons move in the direction of the (positive/negative) terminal.

* * * * *

conduction ; positive (Because electrons are negatively charged and therefore move in the direction of the positive terminal.)

24. Panel 21. In Fig. 1, free _____ move towards the positive plate and positive _____ move towards the _____ plate. In Fig. 2, the charged particles which are free to move are (ions only/electrons only/both ions and electrons). In Fig. 3, the charged particles which move towards the plate are (ions/electrons/both ions and electrons).

* * * * *

electrons ; ions ; ions only ; electrons

25. In a solid metallic conductor across which an electric potential is maintained, the electric current is provided by the motion of _____
_____ toward the (positive/negative) end of the conductor. The *ions* in the array called a _____ (are/are not) free to move under the influence of the electric field.

* * * * *

conduction electrons ; positive ; lattice ; are not

26. Panel 21 shows that in *fact* an electric current may result from positive charges moving in one direction or negative charges moving in the other, or both kinds moving in opposite directions. However, it is convenient to assign to *all* electric currents a unique *sense* or *direction*. By convention, we assume that *all* electric currents flow from (+) to (−). In Fig. 3 of Panel 21, the electrons *actually* move from left to right, i.e., from (−) to (+). By *convention*, we consider that the electric current their motion produces is going from (left to right/right to left).

* * * * *

right to left

27. A positive charge moving in one direction is equivalent in almost all of its external effects to a negative charge moving in the opposite direction. For this reason we are able to make the assumption that *all* electric current goes from [(+) to (−)/(−) to (+)]. When electrons are the charge carriers in an electric field, they actually move from [(+) to (−)/(−) to (+)]; our convention requires that we consider the electric current they produce as going from [(+) to (−)/(−) to (+)].

* * * * *

(+) to (−) ; (−) to (+) ; (+) to (−)

28. Panel 21. In Fig. 3, the beam of electrons moving from the filament to the plate constitutes an electric current which, by convention, we assume flows from the (filament/plate) to the (filament/plate).

★ ★ ★ ★ ★

plate ; filament

29. Panel 21, Fig. 2. The movement of Cl⁻ ions from the right to the left in this figure constitutes an electric current from the (right/left) to the (right/left). The movement of H⁺ ions from the left to the right constitute an electric current from the (right/left) to the (right/left).

★ ★ ★ ★ ★

left ; right ; left ; right

30. Panel 21. Refer to Fig. 4. This is a section of metallic conductor through which an electric field $\vec{E}$ is maintained in the direction indicated. Under the influence of the field the _____ _____ move at a drift velocity $\vec{v}_d$ whose direction is (parallel/antiparallel) to $\vec{E}$.

★ ★ ★ ★ ★

conduction electrons ; antiparallel

31. Panel 21. In Fig. 4 the electric current flows with a sense (direction) which is (the same as/opposite to) the actual direction of $\vec{v}_d$.

★ ★ ★ ★ ★

opposite to

Section 2.   Quantitative Definition of Electric Current: $i = \dfrac{Q}{t}$

Units: The Ampere; Current Density: $j = \dfrac{i}{A}$

1. The movement of positive and negative ions and electrons described in Panel 21 all constitute electric currents inasmuch as they all represent movement of _____ under the influence of an electric _____ maintained by a seat of _____.

★ ★ ★ ★ ★

charges *or* charged particles ; potential ; EMF

2. Panel 21. Imagine a plane placed across (i.e., extending in and out of the page) the electric field in Fig. 1. Electrons moving from left to right through this plane are considered by convention to be equivalent to (positive/negative) charges moving from right to left.

★ ★ ★ ★ ★

positive

3. Panel 21, Fig. 1. We define the current i passing through this imaginary plane as the *total positive charge* Q passing through the plane in time t divided by the time t. In symbols, $i =$ _____.
★ ★ ★ ★ ★

$$\frac{Q}{t}$$

4. Panel 21, Fig. 1. Suppose the ions formed here are H^+ ions and that 3×10^4 of them pass through our imaginary plane in 5 sec. Suppose, further, that during the same time, 3×10^4 electrons pass through the plane from right to left. By convention we consider the electric current produced by the electrons as if it were produced by the same number of positive charges moving from (right to left/left to right). Thus the total positive charge assumed to move through the plane in 5 sec is _____ elem. chge.
★ ★ ★ ★ ★

left to right ; $(3 \times 10^4) + (3 \times 10^4) = 6 \times 10^4$

5. The current passing the plane in the previous frame is_____ (*number and unit*).
★ ★ ★ ★ ★

$$\frac{6 \times 10^4 \text{ elem. chge.}}{5 \text{ sec}} = 1.2 \times 10^4 \text{ elem. chge./sec}$$

6. Panel 21, Fig. 3. Suppose an imaginary plane is placed across this field, and 6×10^8 electrons cross from left to right in 3 sec. This means that the total positive charge assumed to move from right to left in 3 sec is_____ elem. chge. and the electric current passing through the plane is _____ (*Number and units*).
★ ★ ★ ★ ★

6×10^8

$$i = \frac{Q}{t} = \frac{6 \times 10^8 \text{ elem. chge.}}{3 \text{ sec}} = 2 \times 10^8 \text{ elem. chge./sec}$$

7. Panel 21. Our imaginary plane is placed across the field in Fig. 2. A total positive charge of 2.5 coulombs passes through it in 10 sec. The current passing through the plane is: $i =$ _____ (*Number and unit*).
★ ★ ★ ★ ★

$$i = \frac{Q}{t} = \frac{2.5 \text{ coulombs}}{10 \text{ sec}} = 0.25 \text{ coulomb/sec}$$

8. The elem. chge. per second and the coulomb per second are units used to measure electric (charge/current/potential).

★   ★   ★   ★   ★

current

9. The coulomb per second is a frequently used unit in physics and electrical engineering, and has been given the name *ampere* (abbreviated amp). The ampere is a unit used to measure electric (charge/potential/current/force).

★   ★   ★   ★   ★

current

10. Panel 21, Fig. 4. Assume an imaginary plane across this conductor. Suppose 1,000 coulombs of charge passes through this plane in 4.5 minutes. Compute the current passing through this plane in *amperes*.

★   ★   ★   ★   ★

$$i = \frac{Q}{t} = \frac{1000 \text{ coulombs}}{(4.5)(60) \text{ sec}} = \frac{1000 \text{ coulomb}}{270 \text{ sec}} = 3.7 \text{ amperes}$$

11. 1 ampere $= \dfrac{1 \text{ coulomb}}{1 \text{ sec}}$

    1 coulomb = _____ elem. chge.

    1 ampere = _____ elem. chge./sec

★   ★   ★   ★   ★

6.25×10^{18} ; 6.25×10^{18}

12. Panel 21, Fig. 4. A charge Q passes through the cross-sectional area A in Fig. 4 in a time t. The current through A is given by the equation: $i = $ _____.
If Q is measured in coulombs, t must be measured in (or converted to) _____ if i is to be measured in amperes.

★   ★   ★   ★   ★

$\dfrac{Q}{t}$; seconds

13. Panel 21, Fig. 4. A charge of 2000 coulombs passes through A in 1.5 hours. Compute the current through A in amperes.

★   ★   ★   ★   ★

$t = 1.5$ hours $= (1.5)(3600)$ sec

$$i = \frac{Q}{t} = \frac{2000 \text{ coul}}{5400 \text{ sec}} = 0.37 \text{ amp}$$

14. Panel 21, Fig. 4. If a current of 10 amp passes through A, what time (in seconds) is required for 1500 coulombs of charge to pass through A?

★   ★   ★   ★   ★

$$i = \frac{Q}{t}$$

$$t = \frac{Q}{i} = \frac{1500 \text{ coul}}{10 \text{ coul/sec}} = \textbf{150 sec}$$

15. Panel 21, Fig. 4. If the current passing through A is 2.5 amp, what charge in coulombs passes through A in 7 min?

★   ★   ★   ★   ★

$$i = \frac{Q}{t} \; ; Q = it$$

$t = 7 \text{ min} = (7)(60) \text{ sec} = 420 \text{ sec}$

$Q = (2.5 \text{ coul/sec})(420 \text{ sec}) = 1050 \text{ coulombs}$

16. Another important physical quantity is *current density j* which is the ratio of current to the cross-sectional area through which it is passing. In Panel 21, Fig. 4, a current i passes through A. In this conductor, $j = $ _____ (*Use symbols*).

★   ★   ★   ★   ★

$$\frac{i}{A}$$

17. A piece of wire carries a current of 1.8 amp. Its cross-sectional area is 0.02 cm². Its current density is: $j = $ _____
(*Number and units*).

★   ★   ★   ★   ★

$$j = \frac{i}{A} = \frac{1.8 \text{ amp}}{0.02 \text{ cm}^2} = 90 \text{ amp/cm}^2$$

18. The current density in a conducting wire is defined as the ratio _____.

★   ★   ★   ★   ★

i/A

19. The current density in a piece of wire is 650 amp/cm². The cross sectional area of the wire is 0.3 cm². The current in the wire is _____ amp.

★   ★   ★   ★   ★

$$j = \frac{i}{A}$$

$i = jA = (650 \text{ amp/cm}^2)(0.3 \text{ cm}^2) = 195 \text{ amp}$

Electric Resistance
Average Drift Speed in Metallic Conductor
Electric Potential across Length of Wire
Definition of Electric Resistance: $R = \dfrac{V}{i}$
Resistivity: $P = \dfrac{E}{j}$
$R = \rho\,\dfrac{l}{A}$
Temperature and Electric Resistance

1.

A stone allowed to fall through a distance in a vacuum encounters (resistance/ no resistance) and therefore (accelerates/does not accelerate) all the way down.
★ ★ ★ ★ ★ ★
no resistance ; accelerates

2. Refer to figure in Frame 1. The stone allowed to fall through water encounters a resistance which very quickly equals its weight and the stone thereafter moves with (an accelerated/a constant) speed.
★ ★ ★ ★ ★ ★
a constant

3. Refer to figure in Frame 1. When the stone has fallen through the entire distance in a vacuum, all of its potential energy at the top has become _____ energy at the bottom.
★ ★ ★ ★ ★ ★
kinetic

4. This kinetic energy is then dissipated in the form of _____ which raises the _____ of the stone and the surface it collides with.
★ ★ ★ ★ ★ ★
heat ; temperature

5. Refer to figure in Frame 1. The stone falling through water never attains the _____ energy it attains falling in the vacuum. Most of its potential energy is used to overcome the _____ of the water and is continually dissipated in the form of heat which raises the temperature of the _____ and the _____.

$\star$ $\star$ $\star$ $\star$ $\star$

kinetic ; resistance *or* friction, or similar ; *in either order:* stone, water

6. Refer to Panel 21, Fig. 3. These electrons are moving in a vacuum. As they cross the electric field, they [(*a*) accelerate continually/(*b*) first accelerate and then move at a constant speed].

$\star$ $\star$ $\star$ $\star$ $\star$

(*a*)

7. Panel 21, Fig. 3. When the electrons collide with the plate, their _____ energy is used to _____ the plate and raise its _____.

$\star$ $\star$ $\star$ $\star$ $\star$

kinetic ; heat ; temperature

8. Conduction electrons in a metal wire move under the influence of an electric field. However, they continually collide with the ions which make up the lattice of the metal. These lattice collisions have the same external effect on the motion of the conduction electrons as the water has on the stone falling through it. The conduction electrons [(*a*) continue to accelerate until they reach the end of the wire/(*b*) move in such a way as to give the effect of a constant current throughout the wire].

$\star$ $\star$ $\star$ $\star$ $\star$

(*b*)

9. The conduction electrons in a metallic conductor are not continously accelerated by electric field forces because they encounter a "resistance" due to collisions with _____ in the _____.

$\star$ $\star$ $\star$ $\star$ $\star$

ions ; lattice

10. The over-all effect of the collisions of conduction electrons with the lattice of a metal conductor is to increase the _____ of the conductor. Most of the kinetic energy of the conduction electrons is dissipated in the form of _____.

$\star$ $\star$ $\star$ $\star$ $\star$

temperature ; heat

11. Panel 21. In Fig. 4, the electric current through different cross sections along the length *l* is (constant/variable).

$\star$ $\star$ $\star$ $\star$ $\star$

constant

12. When *no* electric field is present, the conduction electrons in a length of wire move in a random fashion like the molecules in a gas; this means that there (is a/is no) tendency for more electrons to move in one direction than any other.

★   ★   ★   ★   ★

is no

13. When an electric potential is applied across the ends of a wire conductor, the conduction electrons acquire a component of velocity called *electron drift velocity* ($\vec{v}_d$ in Fig. 4 of Panel 21), which is (parallel/antiparallel/ perpendicular) to the electric field in the wire. It is the (random motion/drift velocity) which accounts for the external effect we call an electric _____.

★   ★   ★   ★   ★

antiparallel ; drift velocity ; current

14. Refer to Panel 22. The letter in the upper right-hand corner is _____.

★   ★   ★   ★   ★

M

15. Read Panel 22 carefully. It describes a procedure for calculating the (random/drift) speed of (all/conduction) electrons in a metal wire conductor.

★   ★   ★   ★   ★

drift ; conduction

16. Panel 22. The variable n which occurs in equation (3) represents the number of _____ _____ per unit _____ in the material out of which the wire is made. It is [(a) the same for all metals/(b) different for each metal].

★   ★   ★   ★   ★

conduction electrons ; volume ; (b)

17. Panel 22. Equation (3) shows that the average drift speed of conduction electrons depends upon which of the following factors (*choose as many as apply*):

(a) the length of the wire
(b) the current in the conductor
(c) the kind of material from which the conductor is made
(d) the cross-sectional area of the conductor

★   ★   ★   ★   ★

(b) ; (c) ; (d)

18. Panel 22. Compared with the random speed of the conduction electrons the average drift speed is (very small/very large/about equal).

★   ★   ★   ★   ★

very small (10^{-2} cm/sec compared to 10^8 cm/sec)

19. Panel 22. We know that "electricity," i.e., the transfer of energy through a wire, travels much faster than 10^{-2} cm/sec. This means that for electric energy to be transferred it (is/is not) necessary for particular electrons to move from one end of a wire to another.

★ ★ ★ ★ ★

is not

20. In this respect, the transfer of energy through a conductor is similar to the transfer of energy by wave motion. In a wave motion (e.g., sound) the particles of the medium through which a wave travels move very (short/long) distances in the same time the wave itself travels relatively (short/long) distances.

★ ★ ★ ★ ★

short ; long

21. We have seen that conduction electrons in a wire encounter a _____ which is similar in its external effects to that encountered by the stone falling through water.

★ ★ ★ ★ ★

resistance

22. We define the electric resistance R between two points in a conductor by applying a potential difference V across those points, measuring the current i, and finding the quotient of the potential difference divided by the current:

$R = $ _____.

★ ★ ★ ★ ★

$$\frac{V}{i}$$

23.

The —$\bigwedge\!\bigwedge$— represents a specific resistance we are concerned with. When there is a potential difference of 10 volts across points a and b, a current of 5 amp flows through the resistor. The resistance is $R = $ _____.

(Number and units)

★ ★ ★ ★ ★

$$R = \frac{V}{i} = \frac{10 \text{ volts}}{5 \text{ amp}} = 2 \text{ volts/amp}$$

24. The volt per ampere is frequently encountered in physics, practical electricity, and electrical engineering and is commonly called an *ohm*. We often use the Greek capital omega (Ω) to represent it. An ohm is a unit used to measure electrical (charge/field/current/resistance/potential).

★ ★ ★ ★ ★

resistance

25. A resistance of 4 Ω is an abbreviation of 4 _____.

★ ★ ★ ★ ★

ohms

26. A charge of 1000 coulombs passes a point on a wire conductor in 25 minutes when a potential difference of 30 volts is placed across the ends of the wire. Compute the current i in the wire and the electric resistance R of the wire.

★ ★ ★ ★ ★

$$i = \frac{Q}{t} = \frac{1000 \text{ coul}}{(25)(60) \text{ sec}} = \frac{1000 \text{ coul}}{1500 \text{ sec}} = \frac{2}{3} \text{ or } 0.67 \text{ amp}$$

$$R = \frac{V}{i} = \frac{30 \text{ volts}}{\frac{2}{3} \text{ amp}} = 45 \text{ } \Omega$$

27. There is a resistance of 500 Ω between points a and b on a wire. Compute the current in the wire, if the potential difference across a and b is 100 volts.

★ ★ ★ ★ ★

$$i = \frac{V}{R} = \frac{100 \text{ volts}}{500 \text{ ohms}} = 0.2 \text{ amp}$$

28. Refer to Panel 23. The latter in the upper right-hand corner is _____.

★ ★ ★ ★ ★

Q

29. Panel 23. Read the descriptive paragraph to Table 1 and examine Table 1. The only ways in which these samples of wire differed from one another were in their electric _____ and the _____ out of which they were made.

★ ★ ★ ★ ★

resistance ; materials

30. Panel 23, Table 1. Of the three metals tested here, the electric resistance of _____ was highest and the electric resistance of _____ was lowest. It appears from this table that different metals of the same length and cross section offer (the same resistance/different resistance) to the flow of electric current.

★ ★ ★ ★ ★

steel ; copper ; different resistance

31. We call this specific property of a metal its *resistivity*. We represent it with the Greek letter rho (ρ) and define it as the ratio of the electric field E

between two points in a conductor to the current density j in the wire.
$\rho = $ _____ (*Symbols*).
★   ★   ★   ★   ★

$$\frac{E}{j}$$

32. Let the electric field in a wire conductor be E and let j be the current density in the wire. The ratio E/j is a measure of the _____ of the material out of which the wire is made. We use the letter _____ to represent it.
★   ★   ★   ★   ★

resistivity ; ρ (rho)

33. We can treat the relationship of the electric potential between two points on a wire to its field in the same way we have treated the electric potential across two parallel plates with equal and opposite charges. In Panel 21, Fig. 4, the electric potential V across the length l of the conductor is $V = $ _____ (*In terms of l and E*).
★   ★   ★   ★   ★

$V = El$

34. (1) $\rho = \dfrac{E}{j}$.   (2) The electric field between two points on a conductor a length l apart with a potential difference V between them is $E = $ _____ (*In terms of V and l*).   (3) $j = $ __ (*In terms of i and cross-sectional area A*).
★   ★   ★   ★   ★

$$\frac{V}{l} ; \frac{i}{A}$$

35. (1) $\rho - \dfrac{E}{j}$.   (2) $E - \dfrac{V}{l}$.   (3) $j - \dfrac{i}{A}$.
(4) Substitute the right-hand members of (2) and (3) for E and j in (1), and $\rho = $ _____. (*Simplify to a simple fraction.*)
★   ★   ★   ★   ★

$$\frac{E}{j} = \frac{V/l}{i/A} = \frac{VA}{il}$$

36. (1) $\rho = \dfrac{E}{j}$.   (2) $\rho = \dfrac{VA}{il} = \left(\dfrac{V}{i}\right)\left(\dfrac{A}{l}\right)$.   (3) Since $\dfrac{V}{i} = R$,

(4) $\rho = R\dfrac{A}{l}$.   (5) Solving (4) for R, we get $R = $ _____.
★   ★   ★   ★   ★

$$\rho\frac{l}{A}$$

37. $R = \rho \dfrac{l}{A}$. This is a useful equation which indicates that the resistance of a sample of wire is (directly/inversely) proportional to its cross-sectional area and (directly/inversely) proportional to its length. ρ represents a physical quantity called the _____ of the metal out of which the wire is made.

⋆　⋆　⋆　⋆　⋆

inversely ; directly ; resistivity

38. From the definition of electric resistance $R = \dfrac{V}{i}$ we can show that $i = \dfrac{V}{R}$. Since $R = \rho \dfrac{l}{A}$, we can predict that, given constant length and potential difference, the current in a sample of wire is (directly/inversely) proportional to its cross-sectional area.

⋆　⋆　⋆　⋆　⋆

directly

39. The "thicker" a sample of wire, the (greater/less) the current it carries with a given potential difference.

⋆　⋆　⋆　⋆　⋆

greater

40. Panel 23. Refer to Table 2. Note the units used in the table. We can derive them as follows: (1) $R = \rho \dfrac{l}{A}$. (2) $\rho = \dfrac{RA}{l}$. (3) If R is in ohms, A in m² and l in m, then $\rho = \dfrac{(\text{ohm})(\text{m}^2)}{\text{m}} =$ _____.

⋆　⋆　⋆　⋆　⋆

ohm-meter

41. Panel 23, Table 2. In order to use ρ as given in *this* table to find R in the equation $R = \rho \dfrac{l}{A}$, l must be measured in _____ (*Units*) and A in _____ (*Units*). R will be measured in _____ (*Units*).

⋆　⋆　⋆　⋆　⋆

meters ; m² *or* square meter ; ohms

42. Panel 23, Table 2. Note also that these values of resistivity are given for (all temperatures/one specific temperature). This suggests that resistivity (changes/remains constant) with change in temperature.

⋆　⋆　⋆　⋆　⋆

one specific temperature ; changes

43. Panel 23. Experiment shows, in fact, that the resistivity of *most* metals increases and decreases with corresponding increases and decreases in temperature. At 50°C most of the values of ρ in Table 2 would be (greater than/less than/the same as) they are at 20°C. At 0°C most of the value of ρ in Table 2 would be (greater than/less than/the same as) they are at 20°C.

★　★　★　★　★

greater than ; less than ; (In this table carbon is the exception. As its temperature increases, the resistivity of a sample of carbon *decreases*.)

44. The change in resistivity due to temperature changes of a few degrees is very small. For instance, the resistivity of copper changes by a factor of about 4×10^{-3} per degree for temperatures near 20°C. Compute the *change* in ρ for copper when temperature rises to 21°C.

★　★　★　★　★

$(4 \times 10^{-3})(1.7 \times 10^{-8}) = 6.8 \times 10^{-11}$ ohm-m

45. Refer to Panel 24. The letter in the upper right-hand corner is _____.

★　★　★　★　★

K

46. Panel 24. Read Problem 1. We have an equation which relates R to l, A and the resistivity of any specific material. It is: $R = $ _____. If we use ρ from Table 2 of Panel 23, l must be measured in _____ (*Units*) and A in _____ (*Units*).

★　★　★　★　★

$\rho \dfrac{l}{A}$; meters ; m²

47. Panel 24. Calculate the answer to Problem 1 in ohms.

★　★　★　★　★

$R = \rho \dfrac{l}{A} = (1.7 \times 10^{-8}) \dfrac{(30)}{5 \times 10^{-6}} = 10.2 \times 10^{-2} = 0.102$ ohm

48. Panel 24. Read Problem 2. $R = \rho \dfrac{l}{A}$.

Solve this equation for l: $l = $ _____. Substitute data from problem and table, and calculate l in meters.

★　★　★　★　★

$l = \dfrac{RA}{\rho}$; $l = \dfrac{(50)(2 \times 10^{-6})}{1.8 \times 10^{-7}} = 560$ m

49. Panel 24. Read Problem 3. Calculate the resistance from the potential difference and the current. $R = $ _____ ohms.

★　★　★　★　★

$R = \dfrac{V}{i} = \dfrac{1500 \text{ volts}}{2 \times 10^{-3} \text{ amp}} = 7.5 \times 10^5$ ohms

50. Panel 24, Problem 3. Now compute the cross-sectional area of this wire if it is to provide an electric resistance of 7.5×10^5 ohms.

★ ★ ★ ★ ★

$$R = \rho \frac{l}{A}$$

$$A = \frac{\rho l}{R} = \frac{(2.8 \times 10^{-8})(100)}{7.5 \times 10^5} = 3.74 \times 10^{-12} \, \text{m}^2$$

51. Panel 24. Read Problem 4.

$A = $ _____ m². $\ l = $ _____ m $\ R = $ _____ ohms.

★ ★ ★ ★ ★

$1 \, \text{mm}^2 = 10^{-6} \, \text{m}^2$

$A = 0.5 \, \text{mm}^2 = \mathbf{0.5 \times 10^{-6} \, \text{m}^2}$

$l = 10 \, \text{cm} = 0.1 \, \text{m}$

$$R = \frac{(1.6 \times 10^{-8})(0.1)}{0.5 \times 10^{-6}} = 3.2 \times 10^{-3} \, \text{ohm}$$

52. Panel 24. Read Problem 5. We have shown that electric resistance of a wire is (directly/inversely) proportional to its length. The second wire is _____ (*Number*) times the length of the first, all other factors affecting resistance remain constant. The resistance of the second wire is _____ ohms.

★ ★ ★ ★ ★

directly ; 3 *or* three ; 1500

53. Panel 24. Read Problem 6. We have seen that the resistance of a wire conductor is (directly proportional to/inversely proportional to/independent of) its cross-sectional area. The cross-sectional area of the second wire is _____ (*Number*) times the cross-sectional area of the first. The resistance of the second under the condition described in this problem is _____ ohms.

★ ★ ★ ★ ★

inversely proportional to ; $\frac{1}{2}$ *or* one-half ; 100 ohms

54. Panel 24. Read Problem 7. Let R_1, l_1, A_1 be the resistance, length, and cross-sectional area respectively of the first wire, and R_2, l_2, A_2 the corresponding quantities in the second wire. If ρ is the resistivity of the material at the temperature of the experiment, write separate formulas for $R_1 = $ _____, and $R_2 = $ _____.

★ ★ ★ ★ ★

$$R_1 = \rho \frac{l_1}{A_1} \; ; R_2 = \rho \frac{l_2}{A_2}$$

55. Panel 24, Problem 7.

(1) $R_1 = \rho \dfrac{l_1}{A_1}$. (2) $R_2 = \rho \dfrac{l_2}{A_2}$.

(3) Divide equation (1) into equation (2). The result after cancelling like

factors and simplification is: $\dfrac{R_1}{R_2} = $ _____.

★ ★ ★ ★ ★

$$\frac{R_2}{R_1} = \frac{\rho(l_2/A_2)}{\rho(l_1/A_1)} = \frac{l_2 A_1}{l_1 A_2}$$

56. Panel 24, Problem 7. Use the equation derived in the last frame to compute the resistance of the second wire.

★ ★ ★ ★ ★

$$\frac{R_2}{R_1} = \frac{l_2 A_1}{l_1 A_2}$$

$$\frac{R_2}{5} = \frac{(100)(2 \times 10^{-6})}{(2)(5 \times 10^{-6})}$$

$$R_2 = (5)\frac{(100)(2 \times 10^{-6})}{2(5 \times 10^{-6})} = \textbf{100 ohms}$$

Section 4. Ohm's Law

1. Refer to Panel 25. The letter in the upper right-hand corner is _____.

★ ★ ★ ★ ★

F

2. Read the description of Fig. 1. This is a graph of the electric current through a (solid conductor/liquid/gas) plotted against potential difference. Examine the $i-V$ relationships from left to right. At first the current increases (slowly/rapidly) with a small change in potential; then it increases (slowly/rapidly) between 1000 and 10,000 volts. After 11,000 to 12,000 volts, the current (increases/decreases) (slowly/rapidly) with a small change in potential.

★ ★ ★ ★ ★

gas ; rapidly ; slowly ; increases ; rapidly

3. Panel 25, Fig. 2 shows the *i–V* relationship in what is called a *diode*. This is a heated *f* _____ and a *p* _____ separated by a potential difference in a (gas/vacuum). Note that the current in the diode (depends on/ is independent of) the temperature of the filament.

* * * * *

filament ; plate ; vacuum ; depends on

4. Panel 25, Fig. 2. When the filament temperature is around 1600°C, the increase is (slow/rapid) and (uniform/nonuniform). At higher filament temperature, the current at first increases (rapidly/slowly), then (increases slowly/decreases/remains constant).

* * * * *

slow ; uniform ; rapidly ; increases slowly

5. Panel 25, Fig. 3 is a graph of the current to potential difference relationships at (the same temperature/different temperatures) in a (gas/diode/solid conductor).

* * * * *

different temperatures ; solid conductor

6. Panel 25, Fig. 3. Note that the *i–V* curve for each temperature is a (straight/ broken/curved) line. This means that the slope $\dfrac{i}{V}$ at a specific temperature is (constant/variable).

* * * * *

straight ; constant

7. Recall that the resistance of a conductor is $\dfrac{V}{i}$. Figure 3 of Panel 25 shows us that at a constant temperature the resistance of this solid conductor (varies/does not vary) with potential difference.

* * * * *

does not vary (Because Fig. 3 shows that $\dfrac{i}{V}$ is a constant; therefore $\dfrac{V}{i} = R$ must also be constant.)

8. Panel 25. This result, shown graphically in Fig. 3, is an important property of most metallic conductors, and is often called *Ohm's law*. Ohm's law states that the _____ of most metallic conductors is constant (at a specified temperature) no matter what the potential difference applied to measure it.

* * * * *

resistance

9. Panel 25. The resistance of the devices whose i to V graphs are shown in Figs. 1 and 2 (vary/remain constant) as the potential difference used to measure resistance varies. The devices (obey/do not obey) Ohm's law.

★ ★ ★ ★ ★

vary ; do not obey

10. The resistance of the metallic conductor is the same no matter what potential difference is used to measure it. This is a statement of _____ law. This law (applies/does not apply) to diodes.

★ ★ ★ ★ ★

Ohm's ; does not apply

11. Ohm's law is important where it applies. It applies to most but not all metallic conductors. Figure (a) is the i to V graph for a metal called thermistor.

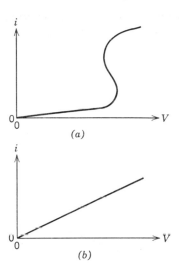

(a)

(b)

Figure (b) is the i to V graph for a metal called mercury. Mercury (obeys/does not obey) Ohm's law. Thermistor (obeys/does not obey) Ohm's law.

★ ★ ★ ★ ★

obeys ; does not obey

12. A metallic conductor to which Ohm's law applies will have an i to V graph which is a (curved/broken/straight) line.

★ ★ ★ ★ ★

straight

13. Unless otherwise stated, we will assume that metallic resistors are "*ohmic*" devices, i.e., that they obey Ohm's law. Sketch an *i* to *V* curve for the metal German nickel.

★   ★   ★   ★   ★

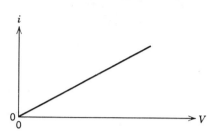

Any *straight* line passing through the origin will do.

14. Ohm's law applies to conductors in which the ratio of potential difference to current is (variable/constant). Such conductors are called _____ devices.

★   ★   ★   ★   ★

constant ; ohmic

15.

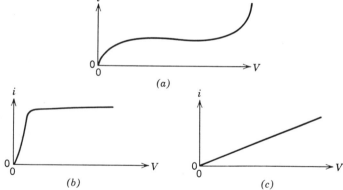

(*a*)

(*b*)   (*c*)

(*a*) is a graph of (an ohmic/a nonohmic) conductor. (*b*) is a graph of (an ohmic/ a nonohmic) conductor. (*c*) is a graph of (an ohmic/a nonohmic) conductor.

★   ★   ★   ★   ★

nonohmic ; nonohmic ; ohmic

Section 5. Energy Changes in an Electric Circuit

$$\Delta U_{ab} = qV_{ab} = itV_{ab}$$

$$Power: P = \frac{\Delta U_{ab}}{t} = iV_{ab}$$

$$Heat\ Energy\ in\ Resistor:\ H = \Delta U_c = Pt = itV =$$

$$i^2Rt = \frac{V^2}{R}t$$

1. We will use the symbol —|⊢ to represent a battery. The short thick bar is the negative terminal; the long thin bar is the positive terminal. *Inside* the battery, positive charges are moved from the terminal represented by the (short/long) bar to the terminal represented by the (short/long) bar.

* * * * *

short ; long (Remember that the function of the battery is to move charges *against* the field *internally* and thereby increase electric potential energy.)

2.

This is an electric circuit; it is a device through which electric current can flow. The (—/\/\/—) represents a (battery/resistor) in the circuit; the (—|⊢) represents a (battery/resistor) in the circuit. Electric current moves in the *external* circuit from the (positive/negative) terminal to the (positive/negative) terminal of the battery.

* * * * *

resistor ; battery ; positive ; negative

3. Refer to figure in Frame 2. The current *inside* the battery is the direction in which (positive/negative) charge is moved in the battery. This is from (positive/negative) to (positive/negative) terminal. In this circuit, the electric current flows always in a (clockwise/counter clockwise) direction.

* * * * *

positive ; negative ; positive ; clockwise

4. In (*a*) the current flows (clockwise/counterclockwise). In (*b*) the current flows (clockwise/counterclockwise).

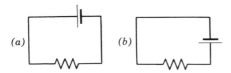

(*a*)   (*b*)

★   ★   ★   ★   ★

counterclockwise ; clockwise

5. The symbol —/\/\/— represents a circuit element called a *resistor*. A resistor is any device in which electric potential energy is transformed into _____. An electric iron (is/is not) a resistor.

★   ★   ★   ★   ★

heat ; is

6. In a resistor electric potential energy from a seat of EMF is transformed into _____ energy.

★   ★   ★   ★   ★

heat

7. The electric potential at b is (higher than/lower than/equal to) the electric

potential at a. This means that a positive charge q moving through the resistor from a to b (loses/gains/neither loses nor gains) electric potential energy.

★   ★   ★   ★   ★

higher ; loses

8. Let V_{ba} = the electric potential difference from b to a. The change in

electric potential energy as a charge q moves from b to a is: $\Delta U =$ _____ (*In terms of charge and potential difference*).

★   ★   ★   ★   ★

qV_{ba}

9. (1) $\Delta U = qV_{ba}$. (2) We divide both sides of (1) by the time t it takes for charge q to move from b to a, and we get: $\dfrac{\Delta U}{t} =$ _____.

(3) By definition, the current in the resistor is $i =$ _____. (*Use symbols.*)
$\star \quad \star \quad \star \quad \star \quad \star$

$$\frac{qV_{ba}}{t} ; \frac{q}{t}$$

10. Refer to figure in Frame 9.

(1) $\Delta U = qV_{ba}$.

(2) $\dfrac{\Delta U}{t} = \dfrac{q}{t} V_{ba}$.

(3) $\dfrac{q}{t} = i$.

(4) $\dfrac{\Delta U}{t} =$ _____ (*In terms of the potential difference across ba and the current in the resistor*).
$\star \quad \star \quad \star \quad \star \quad \star$

iV_{ba}

11. Refer to figure in Frame 9. We define *power* as the work done (or the corresponding changes in potential or kinetic energy) *per* unit time. The power used in the resistor between *b* and *a* is: $P =$ _____ (*In terms of t and ΔU*).
$\star \quad \star \quad \star \quad \star \quad \star$

$$\frac{\Delta U}{t}$$

12. Refer to figure in Frame 9. Power $= \dfrac{\Delta U}{t} =$ _____ (*In terms of current and potential difference*).
$\star \quad \star \quad \star \quad \star \quad \star$

iV_{ba}

13. The power used in a circuit element in which a current *i* flows and across which there is an electric potential difference V is given by the equation: $P =$ _____. If the circuit element is a resistor, this power is a measure of the amount of _____ _____ _____ transformed into _____ energy in a unit of _____.
$\star \quad \star \quad \star \quad \star \quad \star$

iV ; electric potential energy ; heat ; time

14. A variety of other circuit elements might be put in the place of the resistor: an electrolytic plating bath, an electric motor, etc. In each case, _____ _____ _____ is changed into some other form of

_____. The time rate at which this transformation takes place is a physical quantity we call _____.

★ ★ ★ ★ ★

electric potential energy ; energy ; power

15. Ten joules of electric potential energy are used up in operating an electric motor for 50 sec. The power used is: $P = $ _____ (*Number and units*).

★ ★ ★ ★ ★

$$P = \frac{\Delta U}{t} = \frac{10 \text{ joules}}{50 \text{ sec}} = 0.2 \text{ joule/sec}$$

16. The joule per second is a frequently used unit in physics and is called a *watt*. A larger unit equivalent to 1000 joules/sec is the kilowatt (kw). The watt and kilowatt are units used to measure (potential energy/kinetic energy/ work/power/heat energy).

★ ★ ★ ★ ★

power

17. A machine does 1200 joules of work in 0.01 sec. Compute its power in watts. In kilowatts.

★ ★ ★ ★ ★

$$P = \frac{W}{t} = \frac{1200 \text{ joules}}{0.01 \text{ sec}} = \textbf{120,000 watts} \text{ ; 1 kilowatt} = 1000 \text{ watts ;}$$

120,000 watts = **120 kilowatts**

18. The circuit element from *b* to *a* is an electrolytic plating bath. The

electric potential difference across the bath is 6.0 volts; the current is 0.5 amp. What power is used? Show that the units you get are equivalent to watts.

★ ★ ★ ★ ★

$$P = iV = (0.5 \text{ amp})(6.0 \text{ volts}) \text{ ; } = 3.0 \text{ volt-amp ; volt} = \frac{\text{joule}}{\text{coulomb}} \text{ and amp} =$$

$$\frac{\text{coulomb}}{\text{sec}} \text{ ; volt-amp} = \frac{\text{joule}}{\text{coulomb}} \cdot \frac{\text{coulomb}}{\text{sec}} = \frac{\text{joule}}{\text{sec}} = \text{watt}$$

19. (1) $P = iV_{ab}$.   (2) $i =$ _____ (*In terms of V_{ab} and R*).

(3) $\therefore P =$ _____ (*In terms of V_{ab} and R*).
★   ★   ★   ★   ★

$\dfrac{V_{ab}}{R}$ $\left(\text{Because, by definition, } R = \dfrac{V_{ab}}{i}\right)$; $P = \left(\dfrac{V_{ab}}{R}\right) V_{ab} = \dfrac{V_{ab}^2}{R}$

20. Refer to figure in Frame 19. Let $V_{ab} = 10$ volts and $R = 25$ ohms.
$P =$ _____ watts.
★   ★   ★   ★   ★

$P = \dfrac{V^2}{R} = \dfrac{100}{25} = 4$ watts

21. (1) $P = iV_{ab}$.   (2) $V_{ab} =$ _____ (*In terms of i and R*).

(3) $P -$ _____ (*In terms of i and R*).
★   ★   ★   ★   ★

$V_{ab} = iR$ $\left(\text{Because, by definition, } R = \dfrac{V_{ab}}{i}\right)$; $P = i(iR) = i^2R$

22. Refer to figure in Frame 21. Let $i = 5$ amp and $R = 12$ ohms. $P =$ _____ watts.
★   ★   ★   ★   ★
$P = i^2R = (25)(12) = 300$ watts

23. Refer to Panel 24. Read Problem 8. To compute the power we must find first the _____ of the wire.
★   ★   ★   ★   ★
resistance

24. Panel 24, Problem 8. Use table in Panel 23 for ρ. The resistance of the wire is _____ ohms.

$P =$ _____ (in terms of potential difference and resistance).

$P =$ _____ watts.

★ ★ ★ ★ ★

$$R = \rho \frac{l}{A} = \frac{(1.7 \times 10^{-8})(10)}{2 \times 10^{-6}} = 8.5 \times 10^{-2} \text{ ohm}$$

$$P = \frac{V^2}{R}$$

$$P = \frac{36}{8.5 \times 10^{-2}} = 4.2 \times 10^2 \text{ watts}$$

25. (1) $\dfrac{\Delta U}{t} = P = iV = i^2 R = \dfrac{V^2}{R}$.

(2) Multiply each equation in (1) by t, simply where possible, and:

$\Delta U =$ _____ = _____ = _____ = _____.

★ ★ ★ ★ ★

$$Pt = iVt = i^2 Rt = \frac{V^2}{R} t$$

26. Current i flows through resistor R across which an electric potential V_{ab} is maintained for a time t. Write algebraic expressions for the heat developed

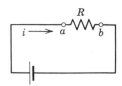

in R in time t in terms of the following:

(1) Potential difference and resistance;

(2) Current and resistance;

(3) Change in electric potential energy;

(4) Power P;

(5) Potential difference and current.

★ ★ ★ ★ ★

(1) $\dfrac{V_{ab}^2 \, t}{R}$; (2) $i^2 Rt$; (3) ΔU ; (4) Pt ; (5) $it V_{ab}$

27. Refer to figure Frame 26. Compute the heat energy (in joules) developed in 7 sec when the power used in R is 10 watts: $H =$ _____.

★ ★ ★ ★ ★

$H = Pt = (10 \text{ watts})(7 \text{ sec}) = (10 \text{ joules/sec})(7 \text{ sec}) = 70 \text{ joules}$

28. Refer to figure in Frame 26. Compute the heat energy developed in 5 minutes in R if the potential difference across it is 6 volts and the current is 2 amp: $H =$ _____ joules.

⋆ ⋆ ⋆ ⋆ ⋆

$H = itV = $ (2 amp)(6 volts)(5 min)

   $= $ (2 coulombs/sec)(6 joules/coul)(5 × 60) sec $= $ 3600 joules

29. Refer to figure in Frame 26. Compute the heat developed in 12 minutes if $R = 5$ ohms and $i = 1.2$ amp.

⋆ ⋆ ⋆ ⋆ ⋆

$H = i^2Rt = $ (1.2 amp)^2(5 ohms)(12 min)

   $= $ (1.44 amp)^2(5 volts/amp)(12 × 60) sec

   $= $ (1.44 amp)^2(5 volts)(720 sec) $= 5.2 \times 10^3$ joules

30. The energy to which electric potential energy is transformed in a resistor is often called *joule* heat. If a current i passes through a resistor R for time t, the joule heat developed in the resistor is given by the equation $H = $ _____. Joule heat is measured in (watts/kilowatts/amps/joules).

⋆ ⋆ ⋆ ⋆ ⋆

i^2Rt

joules

31. When the ends of a piece of wire are attached to a seat of EMF, the temperature of the wire (increases/decreases/remains constant). The energy developed in the wire is called _____ heat.

⋆ ⋆ ⋆ ⋆ ⋆

increases ; joule

Section 6.   *Series Resistors*

$$R = R_1 + R_2 + R_3 + \cdots$$
$$V = V_1 + V_2 + V_3 + \cdots$$
$$i = \frac{V}{R}$$
$$i = \frac{\mathscr{E}}{r + R}$$

Terminal Voltage of a Battery

1. Refer to Panel 26. The letter in the upper right-hand corner is _____.

⋆ ⋆ ⋆ ⋆ ⋆

P

2. Panel 26. Refer to Fig. 1. $\mathscr{E}_A$ and $\mathscr{E}_B$ are the potential differences maintained by the _____ represented by the $\left(\;\;\dashv\!\vdash\;\; \right)$ symbols. The $(\circ\!\!\longrightarrow)$ symbol indicates the direction in which $\mathscr{E}$ tends to push (+) charges around the circuit. In this figure ($\mathscr{E}_A$ only/$\mathscr{E}_B$ only/both $\mathscr{E}_A$ and $\mathscr{E}_B$/ neither $\mathscr{E}_A$ nor $\mathscr{E}_B$) tend(s) to push (+) charges in a counterclockwise direction.

★ ★ ★ ★ ★

batteries ; both $\mathscr{E}_A$ and $\mathscr{E}_B$

3. Panel 26. In Fig. 2, $\mathscr{E}_A$ tends to push (+) charges in a _____- wise direction; $\mathscr{E}_B$ tends to push (+) charges in a _____-wise direction. If $\mathscr{E}_B = 40$ volts and $\mathscr{E}_A = 25$ volts, the current will flow around the circuit in a _____-wise direction.

★ ★ ★ ★ ★

counterclock(wise) ; clock(wise) ; clock(wise)

4. Panel 26. In Fig. 2, if $\mathscr{E}_A = 50$ volts and $\mathscr{E}_B = 30$ volts, then the current will flow _____-wise around the circuit, and the total EMF, $\mathscr{E}$, of the circuit is _____ volts.

★ ★ ★ ★ ★

counterclock(wise)
20 volts[$\mathscr{E} = \mathscr{E}_A + \mathscr{E}_B = 50$ volts $+ (-30$ volts$) = 20$ volts]. (Remember that EMF's and potential differences are added algebraically.)

5. Panel 26. In Fig. 1, if $\mathscr{E}_A = 50$ volts and $\mathscr{E}_B = 30$ volts, the total EMF, $\mathscr{E} = $ _____ volts.

★ ★ ★ ★ ★

$50 + 30 = 80$ volts (Because they have the same sense or direction.)

6. Panel 26. In Fig. 3, the $(\longrightarrow)$ under the i indicates the direction in which the current is flowing in the circuit. (Note that it has no o on the tail, this distinguishes it from $(\circ\!\!\longrightarrow)$, which identifies $\mathscr{E}$). The electric current is flowing in a _____-wise direction.

★ ★ ★ ★ ★

counterclock(wise)

7. Panel 26, Fig. 3. The direction of the current indicates that the magnitude of $\mathscr{E}_A$ is (equal to/less than/greater than) the magnitude of $\mathscr{E}_B$. If $\mathscr{E}_A = \mathscr{E}_B$ in this figure, [(a) the current would be clockwise/(b) there would be no current/ (c) the current would remain counterclockwise].

★ ★ ★ ★ ★

greater than ; (b)

8. Unless otherwise noted we will assume that the resistance of the wires connecting circuit elements like resistors and batteries is negligible. This (means/does not mean) that R is negligible in Fig. 2. It (means/does not mean) that the resistance of wires connecting R to the circuit is negligible.

★　★　★　★　★

does not mean ; means

9. Refer to Panel 27. The letter in the upper right-hand corner is _____.

★　★　★　★　★

L

10. Panel 27. Refer to Fig. 1. Resistances R_1, R_2, R_3 are connected in *series*; this means that there is (only one/more than one) conducting path through them.

★　★　★　★　★

only one

11. In this case there are three conducting paths around the circuit. R_1, R_2,

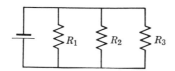

and R_3 (are/are not) connected in series.

★　★　★　★　★

are not

12. Panel 27, Fig. 1. It is a property of series circuit that *all* the current that passes through one resistor in the series must also pass through the other resistors. If the current in R_1 is 5 amp, the current in R_2 is _____ amp.

★　★　★　★　★

5

13. Panel 27. In Fig. 1, let the potential difference from a to d be V_{ad}, the potential difference from a to b be V_{ab}, the potential difference from b to c be V_{bc} and the potential difference from c to d be V_{cd}. Write an equation which relates these potential differences to each other.

★　★　★　★　★

$V_{ad} = V_{ab} + V_{bc} + V_{cd}$

14. Panel 27, Fig. 1.

(1) $V_{ad} = V_{ab} + V_{bc} + V_{cd}.$

(2) By definition, $R_1 =$ _____ (*In terms of current and potential difference*).

(3) From (2), $V_{ab} =$ _____.

★ ★ ★ ★ ★

$\dfrac{V_{ab}}{i}$; iR_1

15. Panel 27, Fig. 1.

(1) $V_{ad} = V_{ab} + V_{bc} + V_{cd}.$

(2) $V_{ab} = iR_1.$

(3) $V_{bc} =$ _____, and $V_{cd} =$ _____.

★ ★ ★ ★ ★

$V_{bc} = iR_2$; $V_{cd} = iR_3$

16. Panel 27, Fig. 1.

(1) $V_{ad} = V_{ab} + V_{bc} + V_{bd}$

(2) $V_{ad} = iR_1$; $V_{dc} = iR_2$; $V_{cd} = iR_3$

(3) Substituting from (2) into (1), $V_{ad} =$ _____.

★ ★ ★ ★ ★

$iR_1 + iR_2 + iR_3$

17. Panel 27, Fig. 1.

(1) $V_{ad} = iR_1 + iR_2 + iR_3.$

(2) Let R be a single resistance which will have an effect equivalent to this series combination. In terms of R and i, $V_{ad} =$ _____.

★ ★ ★ ★ ★

iR

18. Panel 27, Fig. 1.

(1) $V_{ad} = iR$, where R is the single resistance which is equivalent to R_1, R_2, and R_3 combined in a *series* circuit.

(2) $V_{ad} = iR + iR_2 + iR_3.$

(3) Let the right-hand member of (1) and (2) be equal to each other, divide by i, and $R =$ _____.

★ ★ ★ ★ ★

$iR = iR_1 + iR_2 + iR_3$

$R = R_1 + R_2 + R_3$

19. We have shown that the combined resistance of a group of resistors in a _____ circuit is the _____ of the individual resistors.
★　★　★　★　★

series ; sum

20. Panel 27, Fig. 1. If $R_1 = 10$ ohms, $R_2 = 5$ ohms, and $R_3 = 15$ ohms, $R =$ _____ ohms. Suppose $\mathscr{E}$ maintains a potential difference of 90 volts from a to d. Compute i for the circuit.
★　★　★　★　★

$R = 30$ ohms

$V_{ad} = iR$

$$i = \frac{V_{ad}}{R} = \frac{90 \text{ volts}}{30 \text{ ohms}} = 3 \text{ amp.}$$

21. Panel 27, Fig. 1. Using the data of the previous frame, the current in R_2 is _____ amp. The current in R_3 is _____ amp.
★　★　★　★　★

3 ; 3 (Because the current is the same in each resistor.)

22. Panel 27, Fig. 1. V_{ab} is the electric potential difference across ($R_1/R_2/R_3$).
★　★　★　★　★

R_1

23. Panel 27, Fig. 1, Let $i = 3$ amp and $R_1 = 10$ ohms. The potential difference across R_1 is _____ volts. If $R_2 = 5$ ohms, the potential difference across $R_2 =$ _____ volts.
★　★　★　★　★

$V_{ab} = (3)(10) - 30$ volts

$V_{bc} = (3)(5) = 15$ volts

24. Panel 27. Refer to Fig. 2. This (is/is not) a series circuit. Explain your answer.
★　★　★　★　★

is (Because all the current at any part of the circuit must pass through all other parts of the circuit; there is only one conducting path.)

25. Panel 27, Fig. 2. Write an equation for the combined resistance of this circuit. $R =$ _____. $R =$ _____ ohms.
★　★　★　★　★

$R_1 + R_2 + R_3 + R_4$

$R = 2 + 10 + 3 + 25 = 40$ ohms

26. Panel 27, Fig. 2. $\mathscr{E}$ maintains a potential difference of 100 volts from a to b around the circuit. Compute the current i in R_1.

★　★　★　★　★

$$i = \frac{V_{ab}}{R} = \frac{100 \text{ volts}}{40 \text{ ohms}} = 2.5 \text{ amp}$$

27. Panel 27, Fig. 2. What is the current in R_3?

★　★　★　★　★

2.5 amp

28. Panel 27, Fig. 2. Compute the potential differences across R_1, R_2, R_3, and R_4 using the current calculated for $V_{ab} = 100$ volts.

$V_1 = $ _____ volts $V_3 = $ _____ volts

$V_2 = $ _____ volts $V_4 = $ _____ volts

★　★　★　★　★

$V_1 = iR_1 = (2.5)(2) = 5 \text{ volts}$

$V_2 = iR_2 = (2.5)(10) = 25 \text{ volts}$

$V_3 = iR_3 = (2.5)(3) = 7.5 \text{ volts}$

$V_4 = iR_4 = (2.5)(25) = 62.5 \text{ volts}$

(A good check on your work is to add these and see if their sum is $V_{ab} = 100$ volts.)

29. The product iR is often called either the *drop in potential* across a resistor or the *iR-drop* across the resistor. The iR-drop across a resistor is measured in (amps/ohms/coulombs/joules/volts).

★　★　★　★　★

volts

30. When a seat of EMF maintains a current i in an external circuit, it must also maintain that current internally. A certain amount of work must be done (inside/outside) a battery to move (+) charges from its (−) to its (+) terminal.

★　★　★　★　★

inside

31. Panel 27. Refer to Fig. 3. A battery drives current through (an external circuit only/an internal circuit only/both external and internal circuits).

★　★　★　★　★

both external and internal circuits

32. Panel 27. The box in the circuit drawn in Fig. 3 contains the seat of EMF and the (external/internal) resistance through which i must flow. R and r (constitute/do not constitute) a series combination.

★   ★   ★   ★   ★

internal ; constitute

33. Panel 27, Fig. 3. The combined resistance of this circuit is the sum _____. (*Use letters.*)

★   ★   ★   ★   ★

$R + r$

34. Panel 27, Fig. 3. $\mathscr{E}$ is the potential difference maintained around the whole circuit. Here it is equivalent to the (sum/difference) of the potential drops across r and R.

$\mathscr{E} =$ _____ (*In terms of the current and the internal and external resistances*).

★   ★   ★   ★   ★

sum ; $\mathscr{E} = ir + iR$

35. Panel 27, Fig. 3. $\mathscr{E} = ir + iR$. iR is the potential drop across the (internal/external) circuit. ir is the potential drop across the (internal/external) circuit.

★   ★   ★   ★   ★

external ; internal

36. Panel 27. In Fig. 2, $\mathscr{E}$ (is/is not) equivalent to the sum of the iR drops across R_1, R_2, and R_3. An additional potential is used to move a current through the _____ resistance of the battery.

★   ★   ★   ★   ★

is not ; internal

37. $\mathscr{E} = ir + iR$. Note that as i increases, the potential drop across the internal resistance (increases/decreases/remains the same) and (a greater/a lesser/the same) amount of the potential difference provided by the battery is required to overcome internal resistance.

★   ★   ★   ★   ★

increases ; a greater

38. Panel 27, Fig. 3. $\mathscr{E} = ir + iR$. The product iR here is called the *terminal voltage* of the battery; it represents the potential difference used to move a current i around the (internal/external/entire) circuit.

★   ★   ★   ★   ★

external

39. Panel 27, Fig. 3. Let $R = 10$ ohms and $i = 0.3$ amp. The terminal voltage of the battery used in this circuit is _____ volts.

★   ★   ★   ★   ★

$V_{\text{term}} = iR = (0.3)(10) = 3$ volts

40. Panel 27, Fig. 3. $\mathscr{E} = ir + iR$. The EMF of a battery is the sum of the potential drops across the _____ resistance of the battery plus the _____ voltage of the battery.

★　★　★　★　★

internal ; terminal

41. Panel 27, Fig. 3.

(1) $\mathscr{E} = ir + iR$
(2) $\mathscr{E} = i(r + R)$
(3) $i =$ _____ (*Solve* (2) *for i.*)

★　★　★　★　★

$$\frac{\mathscr{E}}{R + r}$$

42. Panel 27, Fig. 3. Let $\mathscr{E} = 6.6$ volts, $r = 0.5$ ohm, and $R = 5$ ohms. Compute i.

★　★　★　★　★

$$i = \frac{\mathscr{E}}{r + R} = \frac{6.6}{0.5 + 5} = \frac{6.6}{5.5} = 1.2 \text{ amp}$$

43. Panel 27. Fig. 3.

$\mathscr{E} = 6.6$ volts　　　　　　　　　$R = 5$ ohms
$r = 0.5$ ohm　　　　　　　　　　$i = 1.2$ amp

Compute the terminal voltage of the battery under these conditions.

★　★　★　★　★

$V_{\text{term}} = iR = (1.2)(5) = $ **6 volts**

44. Panel 27. Refer to Fig. 4. In this figure, the external resistances are represented by _____; the internal resistances are represented by

_____.

★　★　★　★　★

R_1, R_2, R_3 ; r_a, r_b

45. Panel 27, Fig. 4. Which of the following is true (*a*/*b*/*c*)?
(*a*) The external resistances are *not* connected in series; the internal resistances are in series.
(*b*) The external resistances are in series; the internal resistances are not.
(*c*) The external resistance and the internal resistance are each in series and in series with each other.

★　★　★　★　★

(*c*)

46. Panel 27, Fig. 4. The combined *external* resistance is $R =$ _____ (*symbols*). $R =$ _____ ohm(s). The combined *internal* resistance is $r =$ _____ (*Symbols*). $r =$ _____ ohm(s).

$R_1 + R_2 + R_3$; 99 ohms

$r_a + r_b$; 1 ohm

47. Panel 27, Fig. 4. $\mathscr{E}_A = $ _____ volts; $\mathscr{E}_B = $ _____ volts. $\mathscr{E}_A$ and $\mathscr{E}_B$ tend to move (+) charges in (the same direction/opposite directions). The EMF for the circuit is $\mathscr{E} = $ _____ volts.
10 volts ; 7 volts ; opposite ; 10 volts − 7 volts = **3 volts**

48. Panel 27, Fig. 4. We can find the current i in this circuit with the equation:
$i = $ _____ (*In terms of $\mathscr{E}$, r, and R*). $i = $ _____ amp.

$$\frac{\mathscr{E}}{r + R} ; \frac{\mathscr{E}}{r + R} = \frac{3 \text{ volts}}{1 \text{ ohm } + 99 \text{ ohms}} = 0.03 \text{ amp}$$

49. Panel 27, Fig. 4. The iR drops across R_1, R_2, and R_3 are _____ volt, _____ volt, and _____ volts, respectively.

$iR_1 = (0.03)(25) = 0.75$ volt

$iR_2 = (0.03)(30) = 0.90$ volt

$iR_3 = (0.03)(44) = 1.32$ volt

50. Panel 27. Refer to Fig. 5. Here several batteries are connected with the negative terminal of one attached to the positive terminal of another by a wire conductor. Let n be the number of batteries and $\mathscr{E}$ the EMF of each battery. The total EMF is $\mathscr{E} + \mathscr{E} + \mathscr{E} + \cdots$ to n terms or the product

_____.
$n\mathscr{E}$

51. Panel 27. Batteries arranged as those in Fig. 5 are said to be in series. Their internal resistances are also in series. If $r = $ the internal resistance of one battery, the combined internal resistance of n batteries in series is the product _____.
nr

52. Panel 27, Fig. 5. There are n batteries, each with an EMF $\mathscr{E}$ and an internal resistance r, arranged in series, i.e., the (+) terminal of one connected to the [(+)/(−)] terminal of another. The total resistance of the circuit is the sum _____. The current in the circuit is $i = $ _____. (Use $\mathscr{E}$, i, n, r, and R.)

$*$ $*$ $*$ $*$ $*$

$(-)$; $nr + R$; $i = \dfrac{n\mathscr{E}}{nr + R}$

53. Suppose there are 10 batteries, each with an EMF of 1.5 volts and internal resistance of 0.5 ohm. Compute the current i, if the external resistance is 45 ohms.

$*$ $*$ $*$ $*$ $*$

$$i = \dfrac{n\mathscr{E}}{nr + R} = \dfrac{(10)(1.5)}{(10)(0.5) + 45} = \dfrac{15}{50} = \textbf{0.3 amp}$$

Section 7. Parallel Resistors

$$\dfrac{1}{R} = \dfrac{1}{R_1} + \dfrac{1}{R_2} + \dfrac{1}{R_3} + \cdots + \dfrac{1}{R_n}$$

$$i = i_1 + i_2 + i_3 + \cdots + i_n$$

1. Refer to Panel 28. The letter in the upper right-hand corner is _____.
$*$ $*$ $*$ $*$ $*$

W

2. Panel 28. Refer to Fig. 1. Here 1 kg steel balls are dropped from the same height through liquids which offer different resistance to their motion. The gravitational potential energies of the balls at the top are (equal/unequal).
$*$ $*$ $*$ $*$ $*$

equal

3. Panel 28, Fig. 1. We can say that these balls undergo (equal/unequal) potential energy changes as they move from top to bottom of their columns. The one which encounters the least resistance will be moving (fastest/slowest) when it reaches the bottom of its column.
$*$ $*$ $*$ $*$ $*$

equal ; fastest

4. Panel 28, Fig. 1. Of the three balls under consideration, the ball which encounters least resistance will transform the (most/least/same) amount of its potential energy to heat.
$*$ $*$ $*$ $*$ $*$

least

5. Panel 28. Refer to Fig. 2. This (is/is not) a series combination of resistors.
$*$ $*$ $*$ $*$ $*$

is not (Because there is more than one conducting path. Charge may move through R_1, R_2, or R_3.)

6. Panel 28. Refer to Fig. 2. We have assumed and will continue to assume that the resistance of wires joining resistors in an electric circuit is (negligible/ not negligible). This means that the electric potential difference from a to b in this circuit (depends/does not depend) on whether we consider path R_1, path R_2 or path R_3.

★　★　★　★　★

negligible ; does not depend

7. Panel 28, Fig. 2. R_1, R_2, and R_3 are unequal resistors. The *potential differences* across R_1, R_2, and R_3 in this circuit are (equal/unequal).

★　★　★　★　★

equal

8. Panel 28, Fig. 2. The rate with which charge moves through R_1, R_2, and R_3 (depends/does not depend) on the resistances of R_1, R_2, and R_3. (Consider the analogous situation in Fig. 1.)

★　★　★　★　★

depends

9. Panel 28, Fig. 2. Resistances across which the identical potential difference is applied are said to be *parallel* resistors. R_1, R_2, and R_3 in this circuit (are/are not) parallel resistors.

★　★　★　★　★

are

10. In (I), R_1, R_2, and R_3 are (series/parallel) resistors. In (II), R_1, R_2, and R_3 are (series/parallel) resistors.

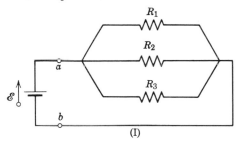

(I)

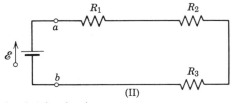

(II)

★　★　★　★　★

parallel ; series

11. Refer to figures in Frame 10. R_1, R_2, and R_3 are unequal resistors. In (I), the potential differences across R_1 and R_2 are (unequal/identical). In (II), the potential differences across R_1 and R_2 are (unequal/identical).

★ ★ ★ ★ ★

identical ; unequal

12. Refer to figures in Frame 10. In (I), if R_1 and R_2 are unequal, the currents in R_1 and R_2 are (equal/unequal). In (II), if R_1 and R_2 are unequal, the currents in R_1 and R_2 are (equal/unequal).

★ ★ ★ ★ ★

unequal ; equal

13. Panel 28, Fig. 2. The current entering a (or leaving b) must be the sum of the currents in R_1, R_2, and R_3. Using the symbols in the figure: $i =$ _____.

★ ★ ★ ★ ★

$i_1 + i_2 + i_3$

14. Panel 28, Fig. 2. Let V be the potential difference from a to b. Then by our definition of resistance:

$R_1 =$ _____. $R_2 =$ _____. $R_3 =$ _____.

★ ★ ★ ★ ★

$\dfrac{V}{i_1} ; \dfrac{V}{i_2} ; \dfrac{V}{i_3}$

15. Panel 28, Fig. 2. Let R be the combined resistance of R_1, R_2, and R_3 in this circuit. By definition of resistance in terms of current entering a and leaving b and the potential difference from a to b: $R =$ _____.

★ ★ ★ ★ ★

$\dfrac{V}{i}$

16. Panel 28, Fig. 2.

(1) $i = i_1 + i_2 + i_3$.

(2) $R = \dfrac{V}{i}$; $R_1 = \dfrac{V}{i_1}$; $R_2 = \dfrac{V}{i_2}$; $R_3 = \dfrac{V}{i_3}$.

(3) Solve each equation in (2) for the current: $i =$ _____; $i_1 =$ _____; $i_2 =$ _____; $i_3 =$ _____.

(4) Substitute the right hand member of each equation in (3) for its equivalent in (1): $\dfrac{V}{R} =$ _____.

★ ★ ★ ★ ★

$$i = \frac{V}{R} \; ; \; i_1 = \frac{V}{R_2} \; ; \; i_2 = \frac{V}{R_2} \; ; \; i_3 = \frac{V}{R_3}$$

$$\frac{V}{R} = \frac{V}{R_1} + \frac{V}{R_2} + \frac{V}{R_3}$$

17. Panel 28, Fig. 2.

(1) $\dfrac{V}{R} = \dfrac{V}{R_1} + \dfrac{V}{R_2} + \dfrac{V}{R_3}$

(2) Divide each term in (1) by V. The result is: $\dfrac{1}{R} = $ _____ .

★ ★ ★ ★ ★

$$\frac{1}{R_1} + \frac{1}{R_2} + \frac{1}{R_3}$$

18. $\dfrac{1}{R} = \dfrac{1}{R_1} + \dfrac{1}{R_2} + \dfrac{1}{R_3}$.

This equation enables us to compute the _____ resistance R of resistors R_1, R_2, and R_3 when R_1, R_2, and R_3 are arranged in (series/parallel).

★ ★ ★ ★ ★

combined ; parallel

19. Resistances R_x and R_y are arranged in *series*. The combined resistance R is found by the equation: _____ . When R_x and R_y are arranged in *parallel*, their combined resistance is found by the equation: _____ .

★ ★ ★ ★ ★

$$R = R_x + R_y$$

$$\frac{1}{R} = \frac{1}{R_x} + \frac{1}{R_y}$$

20. Panel 28. In Fig. 2. $R_1 = 3$ ohms, $R_2 = 6$ ohms, $R_3 = 12$ ohms. Compute the combined resistance R.

★ ★ ★ ★ ★

$$\frac{1}{R} = \frac{1}{R_1} + \frac{1}{R_2} + \frac{1}{R_3}$$

$$\frac{1}{R} = \frac{1}{3} + \frac{1}{6} + \frac{1}{12}$$

$12 = 4R + 2R + R \; ; \; 12 = 7R \; ; \; R = \frac{12}{7}$ ohms $= 1.71$ ohms

21. From the previous frame:

$R_1 = 3\,\Omega$ $R_3 = 12\,\Omega$

$R_2 = 6\,\Omega$ $R = 1.71\,\Omega$

Note that the combined resistance of this (parallel/series) arrangement is (less/greater) than any individual resistance in the arrangement.

⋆   ⋆   ⋆   ⋆   ⋆

parallel ; less

22. Panel 28, Fig. 2. Compute the current entering a and leaving b if the potential difference between a and b is 48 volts, and R_1, R_2, and R_3 have the resistance given in Frame 21.

⋆   ⋆   ⋆   ⋆   ⋆

$$i = \frac{V}{R} = \frac{48 \text{ volts}}{12/7 \text{ ohms}} = 28 \text{ amp}$$

23. Panel 28, Fig. 2.

$R_1 = 3 \text{ ohms}$ $R_3 = 12 \text{ ohms}$

$R_2 = 6 \text{ ohms}$ $V = 48 \text{ volts}$

Compute i_1, i_2, and i_3. Add the results and compare to answer to previous frame.

⋆   ⋆   ⋆   ⋆   ⋆

$$i_1 = \frac{V}{R_1} = \frac{48 \text{ volts}}{3 \text{ ohms}} = 16 \text{ amp}$$

$$i_2 = \frac{V}{R_2} = \frac{48 \text{ volts}}{6 \text{ ohms}} = 8 \text{ amp}$$

$$i_3 = \frac{V}{R_3} = \frac{48 \text{ volts}}{12 \text{ ohms}} = 4 \text{ amp}$$

$i_1 + i_2 + i_3 = 28 \text{ amp}$, which checks with $i = 28 \text{ amp}$ from previous frame.

24. Panel 28, Fig. 2. From the previous frame:

$i_1 = 16 \text{ amp}$ $i_3 = 4 \text{ amp}$

$i_2 = 8 \text{ amp}$ $i = 28 \text{ amp}$

The current in the wires leading to and leaving a parallel arrangement of resistors is (less than/equal to/greater than) the current in any single resistor.

⋆   ⋆   ⋆   ⋆   ⋆

greater than

25. The current in the wires leading to and leaving a *series* arrangement of resistors is (less than/equal to/greater than) the current in any individual resistor.

* * * * *

equal to

26. Given resistors R_1, R_2, and R_3 with *unequal* resistances. If R_1, R_2, and R_3 are arranged in *series*, the current in each resistor is (equal/unequal) to that in the others. If R_1, R_2, and R_3 are arranged in parallel, the current in each resistor is (equal/unequal) to that in the others.

* * * * *

equal ; unequal

27. Given resistors R_1, R_2, and R_3 with unequal resistance. When R_1, R_2, and R_3 are arranged in series, the drop in potential (is/is not) the same across each resistor. When R_1, R_2, and R_3 are arranged in parallel, the drop in potential (is/is not) the same across each resistor.

* * * * *

is not ; is

28. Panel 28. Refer to Fig. 3. This is a circuit which contains a group of resistors arranged in (series/parallel). The potential difference from *a* to *b* is 5 volts. The potential difference across R_2 is _____ volts.

* * * * *

parallel
5 volts

29. Panel 28, Fig. 3. We can expect the combined resistance of the parallel arrangement to be (greater/less) than 5 ohms. Compute the combined resistance.

* * * * *

less

$$\frac{1}{R} = \frac{1}{5} + \frac{1}{10} + \frac{1}{25}$$

$$50 = 10R + 5R + 2R$$

$$17R = 50$$

$$R = \frac{50}{17} \text{ ohms} = 2.9 \text{ ohms}$$

30. Panel 28, Fig. 3. Compute the current in each resistor and the current in the wires leading to *a* and leaving *b*.

$i_1 =$ _____ ; $i_2 =$ _____ ; $i_3 =$ _____ ;
$i =$ _____. (Check Frame 28 for V.)

* * * * *

Parallel Resistors 139

$$i_1 = \frac{V}{R_1} = \frac{5 \text{ volts}}{5 \, \Omega} = 1 \text{ amp}$$

$$i_2 = \frac{V}{R_2} = \frac{5 \text{ volts}}{10 \, \Omega} = 0.5 \text{ amp}$$

$$i_3 = \frac{V}{R_3} = \frac{5 \text{ volts}}{25 \, \Omega} = 0.2 \text{ amp}$$

$$i = i_1 + i_2 + i_3 = 1.7 \text{ amp } \textit{ or } i = \frac{V}{R} = \frac{5}{50/17} = 1.7 \text{ amp}$$

31. Refer to Panel 29. The letter in the upper right-hand corner is _____.
★   ★   ★   ★   ★

Y

32. Panel 29. Read Problem 1. Sketch this circuit using a battery as a seat of EMF and R_1, R_2, R_3 as resistors.
★   ★   ★   ★   ★

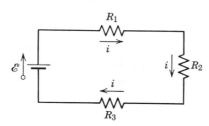

33. Panel 29, Problem 1. Compute the combined resistance R as required in part (a). $R =$ _____ ohms.
★   ★   ★   ★   ★

$R = 2 + 4 + 8 = 14$ ohms

34. Panel 29, Problem 1. The current in each resistor in a series arrangement is (the same/different) for each resistor.
★   ★   ★   ★   ★

the same

35. Panel 29, Problem 1(b). Let $V =$ the total potential difference across the series of resistors and $R =$ the combined resistance. Then the current in any resistor is $i =$ _____ (*symbols*). $i =$ _____ amp.
★   ★   ★   ★   ★

$$i = \frac{V}{R} ; i = \frac{70 \text{ volts}}{14 \text{ ohms}} = 5 \text{ amp}$$

36. Panel 29, Problem 1(c). Let the potential difference across the 4-ohm resistor be V_2. The current in the 4-ohm resistor is _____ amp. $V_2 =$ _____ volts.
★   ★   ★   ★   ★

5 amp

$V_2 = iR_2 = (5 \text{ amp})(4 \text{ ohm}) = \textbf{20 volts}$

37. Panel 29, Problem 1(*d*). Sketch this circuit labeling the new resistor R_4.
★ ★ ★ ★ ★

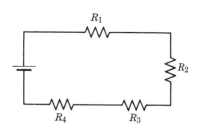

(R_4 can be added anywhere as long as it is in series with R_1, R_2, and R_3.)

38. Panel 29, Problem 1(*d*). The combined resistance now is _____
ohms. The current in each resistor is _____ amp. The
potential difference across the 4-ohm resistor is _____ volts.
★ ★ ★ ★ ★

$R = 2 + 4 + 8 + 14 = \textbf{28 ohms}$

$$i = \frac{V}{R} = \frac{70 \text{ volts}}{28 \text{ ohms}} = 2.5 \text{ amp in each resistor}$$

$V_2 = iR_2 = (2.5 \text{ amp})(4 \text{ ohm}) = 10 \text{ volts}$

39. As we add resistors to a series arrangement, the combined resistance
(increases/decreases/remains the same) and the current in each resistor
(increases/decreases/remains the same). No matter what the combined
resistance, the current in any one series resistor is (equal/unequal) to the
current in any other resistor in the series.
★ ★ ★ ★ ★

Increases ; decreases ; equal

40. Panel 29. Read Problem 2. Sketch this circuit, using a battery as a source
of EMF and label resistors R_1, R_2, and R_3.
★ ★ ★ ★ ★

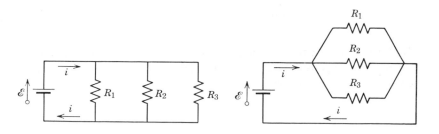

41. Panel 29, Problem 2. Compute the combined resistance R of these resistors arranged in parallel. $R =$ _____ ohms.

★   ★   ★   ★   ★

$$\frac{1}{R} = \frac{1}{2} + \frac{1}{4} + \frac{1}{8}$$

$$8 = 4R + 2R + R$$

$$7R = 8$$

$$R = \tfrac{8}{7} \text{ ohm} = 1.14 \text{ ohms}$$

42. Panel 29, Problem 2(*b*). The current in each resistor of a parallel arrangement (depends on/is independent of) the resistance of the individual resistor.

★   ★   ★   ★   ★

depends on

43. Panel 29, Problem 2(*b*). Let i_3 be the current in the 8-ohm resistor. $i_3 =$ _____ amp.

★   ★   ★   ★   ★

$$i_3 = \frac{V}{R_3} = \frac{70 \text{ volts}}{8 \text{ ohms}} = 8.75 \text{ amp}$$

44. Panel 29, Problem 2. Let $i_1 =$ the current in the 2-ohm resistor, and $i_2 =$ the current in the 4-ohm resistor.

$i_1 =$ _____ amp $i_2 =$ _____ amp

The current which enters and leaves the parallel arrangement is $i =$ _____ amp.

★   ★   ★   ★   ★

$$i_1 = \frac{70 \text{ volts}}{2 \text{ ohms}} = 35 \text{ amp}$$

$$i_2 = \frac{70 \text{ volts}}{4 \text{ ohms}} = 17.5 \text{ amp}$$

$$i = i_1 + i_2 + i_3 = 35 + 17.5 + 8.75 = 61.25 \text{ amp}$$

$$\text{or } i = \frac{V}{R} = \frac{70}{8/7} = 61.25 \text{ amp}$$

45. Panel 29, Problem 2(*c*). The potential differences across the resistors in a parallel arrangement are (identical/unequal). The potential difference across the 4-ohm resistor is _____ volts.

★   ★   ★   ★   ★

identical ; 70

46. Panel 29, Problem 2. Sketch the circuit described in part (d). Use R_4 to represent the new resistor.

★ ★ ★ ★ ★

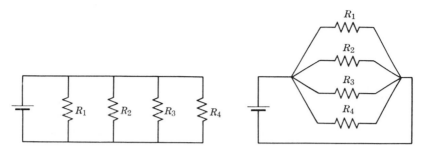

These are two possible arrangements. The important thing is that R_4, when added, is parallel to the other resistors.

47. Panel 29, Problem 2(d). When the 14-ohm resistor is added to this circuit, the combined resistance becomes _____ ohms.

★ ★ ★ ★ ★

$$\frac{1}{R} = \frac{1}{R_1} + \frac{1}{R_2} + \frac{1}{R_3} + \frac{1}{R_4}$$

$$\frac{1}{R} = \frac{1}{2} + \frac{1}{4} + \frac{1}{8} + \frac{1}{14}$$

$$56 = 28R + 14R + 7R + 4R$$

$$53R = 56$$

$$R = \tfrac{56}{53} \text{ ohm} = 1.06 \text{ ohms}$$

(Compare this to answer in part (a) of this problem.)

48. Panel 29, Problem 2(d). Compute the current in the 8-ohm resistor: $i_3 = $ _____ amp. Does it change when a resistor is added in parallel? (Yes/No).

★ ★ ★ ★ ★

$$i_3 = \frac{V}{R_3} = \frac{70 \text{ volts}}{8 \text{ ohms}} = 8.75 \text{ amp}$$

No!

49. Panel 29, Problem 2(d). The potential difference across the 4-ohm resistor (is/is not) changed by the addition of a resistor in parallel. $V_3 = $ _____ volts.

★ ★ ★ ★ ★

is not ; 70

50. Panel 29, Problem 2(d). Compute the current entering and leaving the arrangement described in d.

* * * * *

$$i = \frac{V}{R} = \frac{70 \text{ volts}}{56/53 \text{ ohms}} = 66.25 \text{ amp}$$

(Compare this with 61.25 amp before the 14-ohm resistor was added.)

51. It is a property of parallel arrangements of resistors that the addition of a resistor in parallel (increases/decreases/has no effect on) the combined resistance. It follows from this that the current entering and leaving the parallel arrangement of resistors (increases/decreases/remains the same) as we add resistors in parallel.

* * * * *

decreases ; increases

52. Fuses in house circuits burn out when the current in the line becomes so large that the heat developed in the wires melts a low melting point strip of metal in the fuse. This happens when we add too many appliances to a house line. This indicates that house circuits are wired in (series/parallel).

* * * * *

parallel

Section 8. Review and Problems

1. Refer to Panel 28. Examine Fig. 4. We have an equation which relates the internal resistance of this battery to the combined resistance of the external circuit, $\mathcal{E}$ and i. $i =$ _____ (Symbols).

* * * * *

$$\frac{\mathcal{E}}{r + R}$$

2. Panel 28, Fig. 4. $i = \dfrac{\mathcal{E}}{r + R}$. i is the current flowing into and out of the parallel arrangement. The current in r is (greater than/less than/equal to) i. The current in R_1 is (greater than/less than/equal to) i. R is the combined resistance of the resistors in the (external/internal) circuit. We relate R to R_1, R_2, and R_3 in the equation: _____.

* * * * *

equal to ; less than ; external ; $\dfrac{1}{R} = \dfrac{1}{R_1} + \dfrac{1}{R_2} + \dfrac{1}{R_3}$

3. Panel 28, Fig. 4. Compute R from the data in this figure: $R =$ _____ ohms. Compute i from the data in the figure: $i =$ _____ amp.

★ ★ ★ ★ ★

$$\frac{1}{R} = \frac{1}{R_1} + \frac{1}{R_2} + \frac{1}{R_3} = \frac{1}{15} + \frac{1}{15} + \frac{1}{15}$$

$$15 = 3R$$

$$R = \textbf{5 ohms}$$

$$i = \frac{\mathscr{E}}{r + R} = \frac{11 \text{ volts}}{0.5\ \Omega + 5\ \Omega} = \frac{11}{5.5} = \textbf{2 amp}$$

4. Panel 28, Fig. 4. The potential difference from a to b over the external circuit is the _____ voltage of the battery.

★ ★ ★ ★ ★

terminal

5. Panel 28, Fig. 4. $\mathscr{E} = ir + iR$.
($\mathscr{E}/ir/iR$) is the terminal voltage of the battery in this circuit.

★ ★ ★ ★ ★

iR

6. Panel 28, Fig. 4. Use i computed earlier and data from the figure to compute the potential difference V_{ab} across the external circuit: $V_{ab} =$ _____ volts.

★ ★ ★ ★ ★

$V_{ab} = iR = (2 \text{ amp})(5 \text{ ohm}) = 10 \text{ volts}$

7. Panel 28, Fig. 4. The potential difference across $R_1 =$ _____ volts. The potential difference across $R_2 =$ _____ volts.

★ ★ ★ ★ ★

10 ; 10

8. Panel 8, Fig. 4. Compute the current in R_1.

★ ★ ★ ★ ★

$$i_1 = \frac{V_{ab}}{R_1} = \frac{10 \text{ volts}}{15 \text{ ohms}} = 0.67 \text{ volt}$$

9. Panel 28, Fig. 3. An *ammeter* is a device used to measure electric current. It is placed in *series* with that part of a circuit in which we want to measure the current. To measure the current in R_1 we should place the ammeter at (a/x).

★ ★ ★ ★ ★

x

10. Place an ammeter (label it (A)) in this circuit to measure the current in *R*.

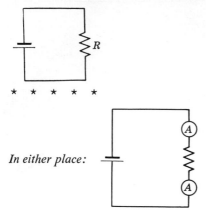

In either place:

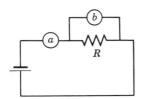

11. An ammeter is a device to measure electric _____. It is placed in (series/parallel) with the part of the circuit it is meant to measure.

★ ★ ★ ★ ★

current ; series

12. A voltmeter is a device used to measure potential difference between two points in a circuit. It is connected in *parallel* with that part of the circuit it is

measuring. (a) and (b) are voltmeters. Which is wired to measure the potential difference across *R*?

★ ★ ★ ★ ★

b

13. We will use the symbol —(V)— to represent a voltmeter in an electric circuit and —(A)— to represent an ammeter. —(V)— should be connected in (series/parallel) to the element across which the potential difference is measured; —(A)— is connected in (series/parallel) to the element through which the current is measured.

★ ★ ★ ★ ★

parallel ; series

146 CURRENT ELECTRICITY

14. An ammeter is calibrated to give readings in units like (volts/ohms/amperes). A voltmeter is calibrated to give readings in units like (volts/ohms/amperes).

★   ★   ★   ★   ★

amperes ; volts

15. Panel 29. Read Problem 3. Resistors R_1 and R_2 constitute a (series/parallel) arrangement. R_3 and the combined resistance of R_1 and R_2 constitute a (series/parallel) arrangement.

★   ★   ★   ★   ★

parallel ; series

16. Panel 29. Problem 3. Compute the combined resistance R of R_1 and R_2: $R =$ _____ ohms. Compute the combined resistance R' of R and R_3: $R' =$ _____ ohms.

★   ★   ★   ★   ★

$$R = \frac{1}{R_1} + \frac{1}{R_2} = \frac{1}{3} + \frac{1}{6}$$
$$6 = 2R + R$$
$$3R = 6$$
$$R = 2 \text{ ohms}$$
$$R' = R + R_3 = 2 + 5 = 7 \text{ ohms}$$

17. Panel 29, Problem 3. The potential difference from a to b is _____ volts. The reading in —(V_1)— is _____ volts.

★   ★   ★   ★   ★

12 ; 12

18. Panel 29, Problem 3. The current in R_1 is $i_1 =$ _____ amp. The reading in —(A_1)— is _____ amp.

★   ★   ★   ★   ★

$$i_1 = \frac{V_{ab}}{R_1} = \frac{12 \text{ volts}}{6 \text{ ohms}} = 2 \text{ amp} \text{ ; } 2$$

19. Panel 29, Problem 3. The current in R_2 is $i_2 =$ _____ amp. The current entering a and leaving b is _____ amp.

★   ★   ★   ★   ★

$$i_2 = \frac{V_{ab}}{R_2} = \frac{12 \text{ volts}}{3 \text{ ohms}} = 4 \text{ amp}$$
$$i = i_1 + i_2 = 2 \text{ amp} + 4 \text{ amp} = 6 \text{ amp} \text{ or}$$
$$i = \frac{V}{R} = \frac{12 \text{ volts}}{2 \text{ ohms}} = 6 \text{ amp}$$

20. Panel 29, Problem 3. There is(are) _____ path(s) from b to c in this circuit. The current in R_3 and the reading in —(A₂)— is _____ amp.

★ ★ ★ ★ ★

one ; 6

21. Panel 29, Problem 3. The potential difference across R_3 and the reading in —(V₂)— is _____ volts.

★ ★ ★ ★ ★

$V_3 = iR_3 = (6\text{ amp})(5\text{ ohm}) = 30$ volts

22. Panel 29, Problem 3. The total potential difference in the external circuit is _____ volts. This is also (the terminal voltage of the battery/the potential difference across the internal resistance of the battery).

★ ★ ★ ★ ★

$V_{ab} = 12$ volts $V_{bc} = 30$ volts $V_{ac} = \mathbf{42}$ **volts**

terminal voltage of the battery

23. Panel 29, Problem 4. $\mathscr{E} = iR' + ir$. ($\mathscr{E}/ir/iR'$) is the potential difference across the internal resistance of the battery.

★ ★ ★ ★ ★

ir

24. Panel 29, Problem 3. Compute the potential difference across the internal resistance.

★ ★ ★ ★ ★

$\mathscr{E} = ir + iR'$

$iR' = 42$ volts

$\mathscr{E} = 45$ volts

$ir = 45 - 42 = 3$ volts.

25. An atom which has lost or gained one or more electrons is called an

_____.

★ ★ ★ ★ ★

ion

26. The graph of current versus potential difference across an ionized gas

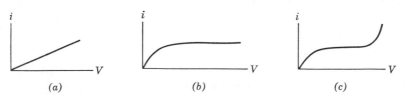

(a)   (b)   (c)

is likely to look like [(a)/(b)/(c)].

★ ★ ★ ★ ★

(c)

27. A device which maintains a potential difference between two points at which it is connected is called _____ (*Complete*).

★ ★ ★ ★ ★

a seat of EMF

28. In a liquid solution the charge carriers are (ions/electrons). The charge carriers in a metal are (ions/electrons).

★ ★ ★ ★ ★

ions ; electrons

29. By convention, an electric current flows in the direction a $[(+)/(-)]$ charge flows under the influence of an electric field.

★ ★ ★ ★ ★

$(+)$

30. We can "boil" electrons off a metal filament by heating the filament. This is known as _____ emission.

★ ★ ★ ★ ★

thermionic

31. The electrons which are free to move in a metallic solid are called _____ electrons. When an electric field exists in a metal, these electrons move (parallel/antiparallel) to the field.

★ ★ ★ ★ ★

conduction ; antiparallel

32. Conduction electrons moving under the influence of an electric field collide with an array of ions called a _____. The external effect of these collisions constitutes what we call an electric _____.

★ ★ ★ ★ ★

lattice ; resistance

33. A charge of 15 coulombs passes through a cross section of conducting wire in 3 sec. The current, *i*, through the wire is _____ amp.

★ ★ ★ ★ ★

$$i = \frac{Q}{t} = \frac{15 \text{ coul}}{3 \text{ sec}} = \frac{5 \text{ coul}}{\text{sec}} = 5 \text{ amp}$$

34. The current passing through a cross-sectional area of 2.5×10^{-6} m² of copper wire is 10 amperes. Compute the current density *j*.

★ ★ ★ ★ ★

$$j = \frac{i}{A} = \frac{10 \text{ amp}}{2.5 \times 10^{-6} \text{ m}^2} = 4 \times 10^6 \text{ amp/m}^2$$

35. The drift velocity of electrons in a wire is of the order of magnitude of $(10^{-2}/10^2/10^6)$ cm/sec.

★ ★ ★ ★ ★

10^{-2}

36. When an electric potential of 20 volts is placed across two points on a wire conductor, the current in the wire is 0.5 amp. Compute the resistance in the wire.

★ ★ ★ ★ ★

$$R = \frac{V}{i} = \frac{20\text{ volts}}{0.5\text{ amp}} = 40\text{ ohms } or \text{ } 40\ \Omega$$

37. The resistivity of a metal is 2.0×10^{-7} ohm-meter. Compute the resistance of a wire made from this metal if it is 25 m long and has a cross-sectional area of 0.5×10^{-6} m^2.

★ ★ ★ ★ ★

$$R = \rho\frac{l}{A} = \frac{(2.0 \times 10^{-7})(25)}{0.5 \times 10^{-6}} = 10\ \Omega$$

38. The resistivity of *most* metals (increases/decreases) as temperature increases.

★ ★ ★ ★ ★

increases

39. A current of 5 amp flows through a resistance of 8 ohms for 3 hours. Compute the power used in *watts*.

★ ★ ★ ★ ★

$$P = i^2R = (25)(8) = 200\text{ watts}$$

40. Compute the heat energy developed in joules in the resistor described in the previous frame.

★ ★ ★ ★ ★

3 hours $= (3 \times 3600)$ sec

$$H = i^2Rt = (25)(8)(3 \times 3600) = 2,160,000\text{ joules}$$

41. The power used in an element of an electric circuit is the amount of electric _____ _____ changed into some other form of _____ per unit time in that element.

★ ★ ★ ★ ★

potential energy ; energy

PROBLEMS

1. Compare the conduction in a copper wire, a salt solution and a vacuum tube containing a heated filament and a plate.

2. If 8×10^6 electrons pass through an ionizing flame in 5 sec, what is the current?

3. If in Panel 21, Fig. 4, a charge of 2000 coulombs passes through area A in 2 hours, what is the current?

4. What is the charge in coulombs if in Panel 21, Fig. 4, the current i is 0.25 amp and the time is 30 sec?

5. What is current density in a wire 0.05 cm² in cross section and carrying a current of 2 amp?

6. If the current density in a wire is 300 amp/cm² and the cross-sectional area is 0.5 cm², what is the current?

7. The potential difference across a part of a circuit is 20 volts and 10 amp flow. What is the resistance?

8. What is the current i and resistance r if 500 coulombs flow past a point in a conductor in 20 minutes with a potential difference of 20 volts?

9. What is the resistivity of copper for a rise from 20°C to 23°C when the resistivity of copper at 20°C is 1.77 microohms-cm. (1 microohm $= 10^{-6}$ ohm)

10. What is the power used in operating an electric motor that consumes 100 joules per hour?

11. How many watts are consumed in Problem 10?

12. What is the power consumed by an electric heater operating at 120 volts and 10 amperes for 1 hour?

13. What is the power consumed by an electric iron that has a resistance of 5 ohms and draws 15 amp?

14. What is the heat energy in joules developed in 10 sec when the power is 20 watts?

15. What is the heat energy developed in a resistance in 10 minutes with a potential difference of 10 volts and a current of 5 amp?

16. What is the heat developed in a 6-ohm resistance if the current is 5 amp?

17. What is the total resistance of 5-, 10-, and 25-ohm resistors in series?

18. What is the total resistance of the following resistors in parallel: 10, 15, and 20 ohms?

19. If in a circuit the clockwise potential difference is 30 volts and the counterclockwise potential difference is 40 volts, what is the effective EMF?

20. If a series circuit is made up of three resistances of 5, 10, and 15 ohms and the current in the 15-ohm resistance is 3 amp, what is the current in all three resistances?

21. What is the potential difference across each of the following four resistances in series: 1, 2, 3, 4 ohms when connected to a dry cell that supplies 1.5 volts?

Chapter Four

THE MAGNETIC FIELD

OBJECTIVES

Upon successful completion of this chapter, the student should be able to:

1. Describe magnetic fields.
2. Describe the magnetic effects of electric currents; compute the fields at the center of loops and around straight conductors.
3. Describe and compute the magnetic forces on current-carrying conductors; use the right-hand rule to determine the directions of magnetic forces and fields.
4. Compute magnetic forces on charged particles moving in magnetic fields.
5. Describe the electron gun and Thomson's measurement of q/m for the electron.
6. Describe the principles associated with the operation of the mass spectrometer, the cyclotron, the moving coil ammeter, and the electric motor; describe the transverse Hall effect.
7. Describe magnetic domains and use the concept of amperian current to explain magnetic effects.

INTRODUCTORY NOTE

We have encountered two kinds of field in our study of physics. Masses are influenced by forces when they are in the vicinity of other masses. This influence which appears to radiate from masses on other masses is called the gravitational field. Electric charges influence other electric charges; this kind of influence is called an electric field. The field concept is one of the most important in modern physical theory, and in this chapter we will associate the influence which a magnet exerts on certain objects (pieces of iron, current-carrying conductors, compass needles, etc.) with a *magnetic* field. We will see that magnetic fields are closely associated with electric *currents* (in fact, with any electric charge in motion).

Section 1. Magnets, Magnetic Poles, Magnetic Fields, Magnetic Field Lines

1. An ore of iron, called magnetite, attracts small iron filings and, when suspended so that it can rotate freely around a vertical axis, lines up generally in a north-south direction. We call a sample of this substance or any object that acts this way a _____.
★　★　★　★　★
magnet

2. If one end of a magnet is marked in some way and we allow the magnet to rotate freely (isolated from the influence of other magnets) we find that one end tends to point always in a southerly direction. We call this the _____ pole of the magnet. We call the other end the _____ _____ of the magnet.
★　★　★　★　★
south ; north pole

3. Think of your experience with magnets. (Each/Only the north) pole of a magnet attracts bits of iron filing, iron nails, etc.
★　★　★　★　★
Each

4. When two north poles of magnets are brought close to each other, they repel. When two south poles of magnets are brought close to each other, they (attract/repel).
★　★　★　★　★
repel

5. In general, (like/unlike) magnetic poles attract; (like/unlike) magnetic poles repel.
★　★　★　★　★
unlike ; like

6. The phrases "north pole" and "south pole" applied to the ends of magnets refer to specific geographic locations only when a magnet is allowed to rotate freely. Packed in a case, lying on a table, or under the influence of other magnets, a magnet may point east-west, northeast-southwest, etc. We will, therefore, refer to the ends of a magnet as N-pole and S-pole from now on. The important characteristic of a S-pole is, therefore, _not_ the fact that it is pointing in a specific geographical direction, but that, when two S-poles are brought close to each other, they (attract/repel) each other. When the N-poles of two magnets are brought close to each other, they tend to (attract/repel) each other.

★ ★ ★ ★ ★

repel ; repel

7. A piece of iron which is not itself a magnet is (attracted/repelled/unaffected) by the N-pole of a magnet. It is (attracted/repelled/unaffected) by the S-pole of a magnet.

★ ★ ★ ★ ★

attracted ; attracted

8. The fact that a sample of a metal is attracted to one pole of a magnet (is/is not) sufficient evidence that the sample is itself a magnet.

★ ★ ★ ★ ★

is not

9. Suppose one end of a sample of a metal is attracted to the N-pole of a magnet but repelled by the S-pole of the magnet. This indicates that *this* end of the sample is itself the (S-pole/N-pole) of a magnet.

★ ★ ★ ★ ★

S-pole

10. We would expect the other end of this sample of metal to be (attracted/ repelled) by the N-pole of the magnet and to be (attracted/repelled) by the S-pole of the magnet.

★ ★ ★ ★ ★

repelled ; attracted.

11. Materials like iron, steel, cobalt, nickel, etc., which are attracted by magnets can be *magnetized*, i.e., made into magnets themselves. A *compass needle* is a small, light piece of steel which has been magnetized and can be suspended so that it is free to rotate around a vertical axis. When it is isolated from other magnets, we can expect a compass needle to point in a (random/ north-south/east-west) direction.

★ ★ ★ ★ ★

north-south

12. A compass needle (is/is not) itself a magnet. Brought close to a magnet, (each end/only one end) will be attracted to the N-pole of the magnet.

★ ★ ★ ★ ★

is ; only one end

13. We explain the roughly north-south alignment of an isolated compass needle by saying that it reacts this way to the *magnetic field* of the Earth. A magnetic field exerts a force on objects that have been _____.

An electric field exerts a force on objects that have been _____.
* * * * *
magnetized (made into magnets) ; charged.

14. All magnets tend to align compass needles brought near them into definite directions. This means that there are _____ _____ around all magnets.
* * * * *
magnetic fields.

15. A compass needle (N-pole at arrow tip; S-pole at the tail) placed *above*

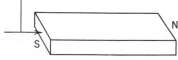

the center of a bar magnet is aligned in the field of the magnetic so that its N-pole points in the direction of the (N-pole/S-pole) of the magnet.
* * * * *
S-pole

16. When the compass needle is placed at the right hand end of this bar

magnet, it is aligned in the field so that its N-pole points (toward/away from) the N-pole of the magnet.
* * * * *
away from

17. When a compass needle is placed at the left end of this bar magnet, it is

aligned in the _____ _____ of the magnet so that its N-pole points (toward/away from) the S-pole of the magnet.
* * * * *
magnetic field ; toward

18. A magnetic field, like an electric field, is a _____ quantity. We agree by convention that the direction of the magnetic field at any point is the direction in which the N-pole of a compass needle points when it is placed

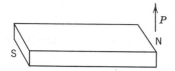

at that position. The direction of the magnetic field at P is (parallel/perpendicular) to the magnet and (away from/toward) the N-pole of the magnet.
★   ★   ★   ★   ★

vector ; perpendicular ; away from

19. We map the magnetic field at a set of positions in the space around a magnet by moving a _____ _____ through these positions

and noting how it is aligned at each point. The figure shows that the magnetic field runs from the (N-/S-) pole to the (N-/S-) pole in the space around the magnet.
★   ★   ★   ★   ★

compass needle ; N- ; S-

20. We used electric field lines to represent the electric field in the space around one or more electric charges. We can trace the lines followed by the N-pole of a compass needle as we move it around in the space around a magnet. By analogy we call these _____ _____ lines.
★   ★   ★   ★   ★

magnetic field

21. Refer to Panel 30. The letter in the upper right-hand corner is _____.
★   ★   ★   ★   ★

A

22. Panel 30. Examine Fig. 1 and read the descriptive paragraph. Iron filings sprinkled over the space around a bar magnet align themselves in the _____ _____ of the magnet. The filings suggest paths in the space around the magnet which begin at the _____-pole of the magnet and end at the _____-pole of the magnet.
★   ★   ★   ★   ★

magnetic field ; N ; S

23. Panel 30. Refer to Fig. 2. It is a sketch of some magnetic field lines around a bar magnet. We interpret magnetic field lines in the same manner as we have interpreted electric field lines. The magnetic field is, therefore, strongest where the lines are (most/least) bunched.

★ ★ ★ ★ ★

most

24. Panel 30, Fig. 2. The magnetic field is (stronger/weaker) at A than it is at B.

★ ★ ★ ★ ★

weaker

25. Panel 30. Refer to Fig. 3. This is a picture of the magnetic field lines in the space between (like/unlike) magnetic poles. The magnetic field is (uniform/nonuniform) except at the edges.

★ ★ ★ ★ ★

unlike ; uniform

26. Panel 30, Fig. 3. The magnetic fields at P and T are (unequal in magnitude and direction/unequal in magnitude but parallel in direction/equal in magnitude only/equal in magnitude and direction). The magnetic fields at P and X are (equal/unequal) in magnitude and direction.

★ ★ ★ ★ ★

equal in magnitude and direction ; unequal

27. Panel 30, Fig. 3. This magnetic field should remind you of an electric field with similar properties. Describe the electric field.

★ ★ ★ ★ ★

The field between two large parallel plates with equal but opposite charges. This field is uniform except at the edges.

28. Magnetic field lines run from (N-pole to S-pole/S-pole to N-pole) in a magnetic field.

★ ★ ★ ★ ★

N-pole to S-pole

Section 2. *Magnetic Fields Around Current-Carrying Conductors Loops and Long Straight Wires Right-Hand Rules for Direction of Field and Current*

1. A compass needle isolated from other magnetized objects aligns itself in a generally north-south direction. This is because it is under the influence of the _____ _____ of the _____.

★ ★ ★ ★ ★

magnetic field ; Earth

2. A compass needle brought near a magnetized bar of iron aligns itself in a definite direction relative to the poles of the magnetized bar. It does this because it is under the influence of the _____ _____ of the magnetized iron bar.

★ ★ ★ ★ ★

magnetic field

3. Compared with the magnetic fields of most magnetized objects like bar magnets the magnetic field of the Earth is quite weak. Hence a compass needle aligns itself with the magnetic field of the Earth only when it (is isolated from/is close to) other magnetized objects.

★ ★ ★ ★ ★

is isolated from

4. The magnetic field of the Earth is very (strong/weak) compared to the fields of iron bar magnets and other magnetized objects.

★ ★ ★ ★ ★

weak

5. So far we have considered only the magnetic fields around materials like pieces of iron or steel which have been magnetized or the magnetic field associated with the Earth. However, we will assume that a magnetic field exists anywhere that a compass needle which is free to rotate assumes a definite alignment in space. Therefore, we will assume that a magnetic field exists in any region of space in which a compass needle free to rotate assumes a (random/definite) alignment.

★ ★ ★ ★ ★

definite

6. Refer to Panel 31. The letter in the upper right-hand corner is _____.

Z

7. Panel 31. In Fig. 1 a compass needle is placed at the center of a loop of wire. When a current i flows through the wire in the direction shown, the compass needle rotates until it is aligned along an axis which is (perpendicular/parallel) to the plane of the loop.

★ ★ ★ ★ ★

perpendicular

8. Panel 31, Fig. 1. This alignment of the compass needle in a specific direction is evidence that a _____ _____ exists at the center of the loop when there (is/is no) electric current in the loop.

★ ★ ★ ★ ★

magnetic field ; is

9. Experiment shows that there is a magnetic field in the space around a loop of wire *while* a current flows through the loop. In Figs. 1*b* and *c* of Panel 31, the current moves in (the same direction/opposite directions) and the compass needles point in (the same direction/opposite directions).

★   ★   ★   ★   ★

opposite directions ; opposite directions.

10. Panel 31, Fig. 1. The direction of the magnetic field at any given location is the direction in which the _____-pole of a compass needle points when the compass needle is put at that location. In (*a*), the direction of the magnetic field at the center of the loop is (into/out of) the page.

★   ★   ★   ★   ★

N ; out of

11. There is a simple rule for determining the direction of the magnetic field at the center of a loop of wire carrying a current. Make the fingers of your

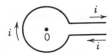

right hand form a loop with the tips pointing in the direction the current moves around the loop. The extended thumb of your right hand indicates the direction of the magnetic field at the center of the loop. The magnetic field at O is directed (into/out of) the page.

★   ★   ★   ★   ★

into

12. We frequently want to represent vectors like magnetic fields moving into or out of the page. We represent a vector going *into* the page by a cross (×) mark. We use a dot (·) to represent a vector which is directed *out of* the page. In this figure, the evenly-spaced ×'s represent a (uniform/nonuniform) field (into/out of) the page.

×   ×   ×
×   ×   ×
×   ×   ×
×   ×   ×

★   ★   ★   ★   ★

uniform ; into

13. Use the right-hand rule to determine the direction of the magnetic field produced at the center of the loop by *i*. Put (×) or (·) in the circle to indicate

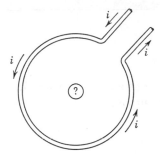

whether the field moves out of or into the page.

★   ★   ★   ★   ★

a dot ⊙

14. Indicate by using a dot or cross in the circle the direction of the magnetic field.

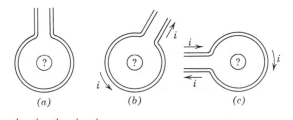

(*a*)   (*b*)   (*c*)

★   ★   ★   ★   ★

(*a*) Nothing ; there is no current in the loop. (*b*) ⊙ ; (*c*) ⊗

15. In this figure, the direction of the magnetic field is indicated by the ×.

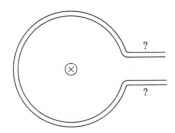

Use the right-hand rule to determine the direction of the current. The current flows around the loop in a (clockwise/counterclockwise) direction.

★   ★   ★   ★   ★

clockwise (Thumb of right hand points into the page, and tip of fingers wrap around the loop in direction of current.)

16. We have seen that there is a magnetic field in the space around a loop of wire when _____.
(*Complete this sentence.*)
★   ★   ★   ★   ★

a current flows through the wire.

17. Panel 31. Refer to Fig. 2. (a) shows that there (is a/is no) magnetic field around a long, straight wire carrying an electric current.
★   ★   ★   ★   ★

is a

18. Panel 31, Fig. 2. Examine (*b*). When the current in the wire is emerging

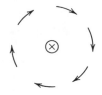

out of the page, the magnetic field around the wire rotates in a (clockwise/counterclockwise) direction. Sketch the compass needle pattern you would expect when the current is moving *into* the page.
★   ★   ★   ★   ★

clockwise

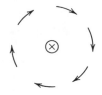

19. Panel 31. Figure 2(*c*) shows that the magnetic field lines around a long straight wire carrying a current are concentric _____s with their common center at the center of the wire. Note that the magnitude of the field (increases/decreases/remains constant) as we get farther from the wire.
★   ★   ★   ★   ★

circles ; decreases (Because the field lines are spread farther apart.)

20. To determine the direction in which a magnetic field around a long, straight wire rotates, we have another right-hand rule: Grasp the wire with the thumb pointing in the direction of the current; the fingers then curl around the wire in the direction in which the magnetic field rotates. This is a cross section of a long, straight wire in which current is moving in a direction out of

the page. Using the right-hand rule, your thumb would point (into/out of) the page and your fingers would curl around the wire in a (clockwise/counter-clockwise) direction.

★   ★   ★   ★   ★

out of ; counterclockwise

21. This is a section of a long straight wire in which there is a current *i* as indicated. Applying the right-hand rule to determine the manner in which the

magnetic field rotates around the wire, you grasp the wire so that your thumb points (left/right). The magnetic field (comes out of/goes into) the page *above* the wire and (comes out of/goes into) the page *beneath* the wire.

★   ★   ★   ★   ★

right ; comes out of ; goes into

22. The direction of the magnetic field at a given point on a magnetic field line is the direction in which the _____-pole of a compass needle would point

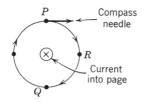

if placed there. At *P* the magnetic field is (vertical up/vertical down/horizontal right/horizontal left). At *Q* the magnetic field is (vertical up/vertical down/horizontal right/horizontal left). At *R* the field is (vertical up/vertical down/horizontal right/horizontal left).

★   ★   ★   ★   ★

N ; horizontal right ; horizontal left ; vertical down.

23. A straight line which touches a circle at one point is called a tangent.

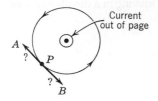

Which tangent (PA/PB) represents the magnetic field at P.
⋆ ⋆ ⋆ ⋆ ⋆

PB

24. This is a section of a long, straight wire which carries the current i. The magnetic field produced by i rotates around the wire so that it comes out of

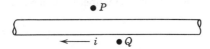

the page (above/below) the wire and goes into the page (above/below) the wire. At P the field points (out of/into) the page. At Q, the field points (out of/into) the page.
⋆ ⋆ ⋆ ⋆ ⋆

below ; above ; into ; out of

25. Use the right-hand rule for long, straight wire conductors to determine whether the current is (into/out of) the page. The arrows indicate the direction

of the field at points indicated.
⋆ ⋆ ⋆ ⋆ ⋆

out of (Grasp wire with finger tips in direction of rotation of field. Thumb gives the direction of current.)

Section 3. Magnetic Force on Current-Carrying Wire

$$\vec{F}_B \perp i$$

$$\vec{F}_B \perp \vec{B}$$

Right-Hand Rule to Determine Direction of $\vec{F}_B$

1. Refer to Panel 32. The letter in the upper right-hand corner is _____.
★ ★ ★ ★ ★

D

2. Panel 32. In each figure, a uniform magnetic field, which we will call *B*, is represented by evenly-spaced dots or crosses. In Fig. 1, *B* is directed (into/out of) the page. In each figure, a conductor is placed across the field. The section *PQ* of the conductor is flexible and in Fig. 1 and 3 it sags under the influence of its w_____.
★ ★ ★ ★ ★

into ; weight

3. Panel 32. In each figure the dots or crosses representing $\vec{B}$ are evenly spaced. This means that $\vec{B}$ is (uniform/nonuniform) in magnitude. The direction of $\vec{B}$ in Fig. 5 is (into/out of) the page.
★ ★ ★ ★ ★

uniform ; out of

4. Panel 32. Note that in each figure the magnetic field is (parallel/perpendicular) to the plane of the page and that the conductor is (parallel/perpendicular) to the plane of the page. In every case, the magnetic field and the conductor are (parallel/perpendicular) to each other.
★ ★ ★ ★ ★

perpendicular (Because it goes into or out of the page.) ; parallel (Because it goes along the surface of the page.) ; perpendicular.

5. Panel 32. In Fig. 1, there (is a/is no) current flowing in the conductor.
★ ★ ★ ★ ★

is no

6. Panel 32. In Fig. 2, there (is a/is no) current in the conductor, and the section *PQ* (sags/does not sag) under the influence of its weight. This means that $\vec{B}$ exerts (a force/no force) on the conductor when there is a current flowing in the conductor.
★ ★ ★ ★ ★

is a ; does not sag ; a force.

7. Panel 32. In Fig. 3, there (is a/is no) current in PQ, and $\vec{B}$ exerts (a force/ no force) on PQ.

★   ★   ★   ★   ★

is no ; no force

8. Panel 32. In Fig. 4, the magnetic field exerts (a force/no force) on PQ because there is a _____ in the conductor.

★   ★   ★   ★   ★

a force ; current

9. Panel 32. Compare the magnetic forces on PQ in Figs. 4 and 5. They have (the same direction/opposite directions).

★   ★   ★   ★   ★

opposite directions

10. Panel 32. Examine Figs. 4 and 5. How do you account for the change in direction of the magnetic force on PQ?

★   ★   ★   ★   ★

The *direction* of the magnetic field $\vec{B}$ has been changed so that it is opposite what it was in Fig. 4.

11. Panel 32. Examine Figs. 4 and 6, and account for the fact that the magnetic forces PQ have opposite directions.

★   ★   ★   ★   ★

The current is moving in the *opposite* direction.

12. Refer to Panel 33. The letter in the upper right-hand corner is _____.

★   ★   ★   ★   ★

G

13. Panel 33. Figure 1 is a three-dimensional sketch of Fig. 6 in Panel 32. It shows that the magnetic force $\vec{F}_B$ produced when an _____ _____ passes through a conductor in a _____ _____ is (parallel/perpendicular) to both i and $\vec{B}$.

★   ★   ★   ★   ★

electric current ; magnetic field ; perpendicular

14. We have seen that an electric field $\vec{E}$ exerts an electric force $\vec{F}_E$ on a charge q. We write $\vec{F}_E = \vec{E}q$, and this tells us that $\vec{F}_E$ and $\vec{E}$ are (parallel/ perpendicular) to each other.

★   ★   ★   ★   ★

parallel

15. Panel 33, Fig. 1. We now see that a magnetic field $\vec{B}$ exerts a magnetic force $\vec{F}_B$ on a conductor carrying a _____ through the field. $\vec{F}_B$ and $\vec{B}$ are always (parallel/perpendicular) to each other.

★ ★ ★ ★ ★

current ; perpendicular

16. We have also seen (in Panel 32, Figs. 4 and 6) that the direction of $\vec{F}_B$ depends upon the direction of _____ as well as the direction of $\vec{B}$.

★ ★ ★ ★ ★

the current in PQ (or i)

17. Panel 33. In Fig. 2 we have a three-dimensional representation of the situation shown in Fig. 2 of Panel 32. $\vec{F}_B$ is (parallel/perpendicular) to the current and is (parallel/perpendicular) to the magnetic field.

★ ★ ★ ★ ★

perpendicular ; perpendicular

18. To determine the exact direction of $\vec{F}_B$ we use yet another *right-hand* rule which relates $\vec{F}_B$ to $\vec{B}$ and i. This rule is applied to Fig. 2 of Panel 33. Read the descriptive paragraph. If the magnetic field happens to be supplied by the poles of magnets. The tips of the fingers would be extended toward the _____pole of the magnet.

★ ★ ★ ★ ★

S- (Because this is the direction the N-pole of a compass needle would point.)

19. Panel 33. For practice, apply the right-hand rule to Fig. 1. Then apply it to the figure in this frame. $\vec{F}_B$ will be directed (up/down/right/left/into the

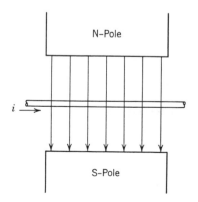

page/out of the page). (Perhaps you will understand why this kind of problem leads to dislocated wrists!)

★　★　★　★　★

into the page (Fingers down, thumb to the right. The palm of your right hand should then face into the page.)

20. Here $\vec{F}_B$ is (parallel to $\vec{B}$/antiparallel to $\vec{B}$/perpendicular to $\vec{B}$ and upward/ perpendicular to $\vec{B}$ and downward).

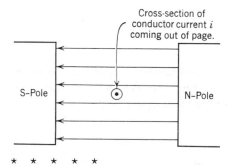

★　★　★　★　★

perpendicular to $\vec{B}$ and downward

21. Use the right-hand rule to determine $\vec{F}_B$ in figures (*a*) and (*b*). Note the directions of the currents indicated by $\odot$ and $\otimes$. In Fig. (*a*), $\vec{F}_B$ has the same

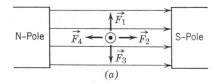

(*a*)

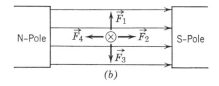

(*b*)

direction as $(\vec{F}_1/\vec{F}_2/\vec{F}_3/\vec{F}_4)$. In Fig. (*b*), $\vec{F}_B$ has the same direction as $(\vec{F}_1/\vec{F}_2/\vec{F}_3/ \vec{F}_4)$.

★　★　★　★　★

$\vec{F}_1$; $\vec{F}_3$

22. The existence of a magnetic force on a piece of wire depends on the

_____ in the wire and the _____ _____ in which the wire is placed.

★   ★   ★   ★   ★

current ; magnetic field.

23. The electric force on a charge is always (parallel/perpendicular) to the *electric* field in which the charge is placed. The magnetic force on a length of current-carrying conductor immersed in a magnetic field is always (parallel/ perpendicular) to the magnetic field. Its exact direction also depends on the _____ in the conductor.

★   ★   ★   ★   ★

parallel ; perpendicular ; current

Section 4. Magnetic Forces (Continued)
  Magnetic Force on Length l of Wire: $F_B = Bil$
  Field near Long Straight Wire: $B = k\dfrac{i}{d}$
  Magnetic Force between Two Long Parallel Wires
  $F_B = k\dfrac{i_1 i_2 l}{d}$; $k = 2 \times 10^{-7}$ newton/amp²
  Field at Center of Loop: $B = 2\pi \times 10^{-7}\dfrac{i}{r}$

1. Refer to Panel 34. The letter in the upper right-hand corner is _____.

★   ★   ★   ★   ★

J

2. Panel 34. Refer to Fig. 1. We want to establish a relationship between F_B and $\vec{B}$, *l*, and *i*. *l* is the length of the section of the conductor which is immersed in the magnetic field. The current in *l* flows from (left to right/right to left) in the plane of the page. $\vec{B}$ is directed (into/out of) the plane of the page.

★   ★   ★   ★   ★

right to left ; out of

3. Panel 34, Fig. 1. Experiment shows that the magnitude of $\vec{F}_B$ is directly proportional to the product of *B*, *i*, and *l*. Let *k* be a suitable constant of proportionality. Then F_B = _____. The direction of $\vec{F}_B$ is (the same as the direction of *B*/the same as the direction of *i*/perpendicular to both *i* and *B*).

★   ★   ★   ★   ★

$F_B = kBil$; perpendicular to both $\vec{B}$ and *i*

4. $F_B = kBil$ is strictly true only when $\vec{B}$ and l are perpendicular to each other. Although $\vec{F}_B$ is always perpendicular to *both* l (or the direction of i in

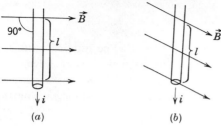

(a)   (b)

the field) and $\vec{B}$, it is *not* necessarily true that $\vec{B}$ and l are perpendicular to each other. In (a) l and $\vec{B}$ (are/are not) perpendicular. In (b) l and $\vec{B}$ (are/are not) perpendicular.
★   ★   ★   ★   ★

are ; are not

5. In (a) $\vec{B}$ and l (are/are not) perpendicular. In (b) $\vec{B}$ and l (are/are not) perpendicular.

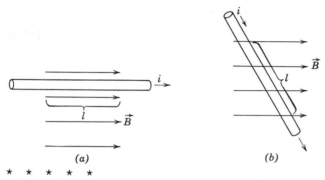

(a)   (b)
★   ★   ★   ★   ★

are not ; are not

6. In general, we use the equation $F_B = kBil \sin \theta$ to find the magnetic force on a length of wire l carrying a current i, where θ is the angle between $\vec{B}$ and l. When $\vec{B}$ and l are perpendicular, $\theta =$ _____°; When $\vec{B}$ and l are parallel [see Frame 5, Fig. (b)], the angle between $\vec{B}$ and l is _____°.
★   ★   ★   ★   ★

90 ; 0

7. $\sin 90° = 1$ $\sin 0° = 0$ $F_B = kBil \sin \theta$
When B and l are perpendicular, this equation becomes: $F_B =$ _____
When B and l are parallel to each other, F_B becomes _____.
★   ★   ★   ★   ★

$kBil$; 0 *or* zero

170 THE MAGNETIC FIELD

8. Unless otherwise specified, we will consider only situations where $\theta = 90°$. Thus we will use the simpler equation: $F_B = kBil$. We can simplify this equation further if we decide upon a unit to measure magnetic field which will make $k = 1$. When we do this the equation for magnetic force in terms of B, i, and l becomes _____.

★　★　★　★　★

$F_B = Bil.$

9. We define our unit of magnetic field as follows: it is that amount of field which when 1 *meter* of wire carrying a current of 1 *ampere* is immersed in it at right angles exerts a force of 1 *newton* on the wire.

(1) $F_B = Bil.$

(2) Solving for B: $B =$ _____ (*Symbols*).

Substitute the units given in the definition above into (2) and derive the unit of magnetic field which is _____.

★　★　★　★　★

$B = \dfrac{F_B}{il}$; $B = $ newton/ampere-meter

10. We now have a unit with which to measure the magnitude of magnetic fields; it is the _____ per _____-_____.

★　★　★　★　★

newton (per) ampere-meter

11. Panel 34, Fig. 1. Suppose $F_B = 0.05$ newton, $l = 0.25$ meter and $i = 10$ amp. Compute the magnitude of $\vec{B}$.

★　★　★　★　★

$F_B = Bil.$

$B = \dfrac{F_B}{il} = \dfrac{0.05 \text{ newton}}{(10 \text{ amp})(0.25 \text{ m})} = 2 \times 10^{-2}$ ncwton/amp-m

12. Panel 34, Fig. 1. Compute the magnetic force on the wire if $l = 1.5$ meter, $i = 5$ amp and the magnitude of the magnetic field is 3×10^{-3} newton/amp-meter.

★　★　★　★　★

$F_B = Bil = (3 \times 10^{-3} \text{ newton/amp-m})(5 \text{ amp})(1.5 \text{ m}) = 2.25 \times 10^{-2}$ newton

13. Panel 34, Fig. 1. $B = 2 \times 10^{-3}$ newton/amp-meter　　　$l = 0.75$ meter
$i = 3$ amp　　　$\vec{F}_B = $ _____ magnitude and direction
(up/down/right/left/into page/out of page).

★　★　★　★　★

$F_B = Bil = (2 \times 10^{-3} \text{ nt/amp-m})(3 \text{ amp})(0.75 \text{ m}) = 4.50 \times 10^{-3}$ newton
up

14. We have defined a unit of B called the _____.
To use the equation $F_B = Bil$ correctly with this unit, i must be measured in
_____ and l in _____.

★ ★ ★ ★ ★

newton/amp-meter ; amperes ; meters.

15. $l = 10$ cm $B = 10$ newtons/amp-m $i = 25$ amp
$\vec{F}_B =$ _____.

★ ★ ★ ★ ★

$F_B = Bil$
$l = 10$ cm $= 0.10$ m
$F_B = (10$ newtons/amp-m$)(25$ amp$)(0.10$ m$) = 25$ newtons

16. In Section 2 of this chapter and Panel 31 we learned that a current in a
long, straight wire produces a _____ _____ which radiates
out from the wire in concentric circles.

★ ★ ★ ★ ★

magnetic field

17. Experiment shows that the magnitude of the magnetic field around a long
straight wire carrying a current is directly proportional to the current in the
wire and (look at Fig. 2c of Panel 31)(directly/inversely) proportional to the
distance from the wire.

★ ★ ★ ★ ★

inversely

18. Let k be a suitable constant of proportionality. Then at P, $B =$ _____
(*In terms of i, d, etc.*)

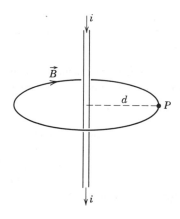

★ ★ ★ ★ ★

$B = k\dfrac{i}{d}$

19. Panel 34. Refer to Fig. 2. These are two long parallel wires carrying currents in (the same direction/opposite directions). Each current produces a _____ _____ which radiates out into space and exerts a _____ _____ on the other wire.

★ ★ ★ ★ ★

same direction ; magnetic field ; magnetic force.

20. Panel 34, Fig. 2. The magnetic field $\vec{B}$ from i_1 is (parallel/perpendicular) to i_2 where it passes through l. The magnetic force this field exerts on i_2 is such that the two wires (attract/repel) each other.

★ ★ ★ ★ ★

perpendicular ; attract

21. Panel 34, Fig. 2.
(1) The force F_B exerted on a section l of the wire carrying i_2 by the field $\vec{B}$ produced by i_1 is $F_B = $ _____.
(2) The magnitude of B produced by i_1 at a distance d is $B = k$ _____.

★ ★ ★ ★ ★

$F_B = Bi_2l$; $B = k \dfrac{i_1}{d}$

22. Panel 34, Fig. 2.

(1) $F_B = Bi_2l$.

(2) $B = k\dfrac{i_1}{d}$.

(3) Substitute the right-hand member of (2) for B in (1). Then $F_B = $ _____.

★ ★ ★ ★ ★

$k \dfrac{i_1 i_2 l}{d}$

23. Panel 34, Fig. 2. $F_B = k\dfrac{i_1 i_2 l}{d}$.

This is an equation for the magnetic force between long, straight (parallel/ perpendicular) wires a distance (l/d) apart. If i_1 and i_2 have the same direction, the wires (attract/repel) each other; if i_1 and i_2 have opposite directions, the wires (attract/repel) each other.

★ ★ ★ ★ ★

parallel ; d ; attract ; repel

24. Panel 34, Fig. 2. $F_B = k\dfrac{i_1 i_2 l}{d}$

k is a constant which can be determined by experiment. If i_1 and i_2 are measured in amperes, F_B in newtons and d and l in meters, solve for k and determine its units.

★ ★ ★ ★ ★

$$k = \frac{F_B d}{l i_1 i_2} = \frac{\text{(newtons)}(\cancel{\text{meters}})}{(\cancel{\text{meters}})(\text{amperes})^2} = \text{newtons/amp}^2$$

25. Panel 34, Fig. 2. When F, d, l, and i are measured in newtons, meters, meters, and amperes respectively, the constant of proportionality is determined by experiment to be $k = 2 \times 10^{-7}$ newtons/amp². Suppose $i_1 = 10$ amp and $d = 0.5$ m. Then the magnetic field produced by i_1 at l is _____ newton/amp-m.

★ ★ ★ ★ ★

$$B = k \frac{i_1}{d} = (2 \times 10^{-7} \text{newton/amp}^2) \left(\frac{10 \text{ amp}}{0.5 \text{ m}} \right) = 4.0 \times 10^{-6} \text{newton/amp-m}$$

26. Panel 34, Fig. 2. Let $i_1 = 10$ amp and $i_2 = 15$ amp. If $d = 0.5$ m and $l = 2$m, compute the magnitude of F_B on l.

★ ★ ★ ★ ★

$$F_B = k \frac{i_1 i_2 l}{d} = \frac{(2 \times 10^{-7})(10)(15)(2)}{0.5} = 1.2 \times 10^{-4} \text{newton}$$

27. Experiment shows that the magnitude of the magnetic field $\vec{B}_l$ at the center of a *loop* of wire is directly proportional to the current, i, in the wire and inversely proportional to the radius, r, of the wire. Use k_l as the constant of proportionality and write and equation for B_l: _____.

★ ★ ★ ★ ★

$$B_l = k_l \frac{i}{r}$$

28. k_l has been determined by experiment to be $2\pi \times 10^{-7}$ newton/amp², k for a long, straight wire we found to be _____ newton/amp²

★ ★ ★ ★ ★

2×10^{-7}

29. Use $\pi = 3.14$. A loop of wire, 0.05 meter in radius carries a current of 1.2 amperes. Compute the magnitude of the magnetic field $\vec{B}_l$, at its center.

$$B_l = k_l \frac{i}{r} = 2\pi \times 10^{-7} \text{newton/amp}^2 \frac{(1.2 \text{ amp})}{(0.05 \text{ m})}$$

$$= \frac{(2)(3.14)(10^{-7})(1.2)}{0.05} \text{ newton/amp-m} = 1.51 \times 10^{-5} \text{newton/amp-m}$$

30. Refer to Panel 35. The letter in the upper right-hand corner is _____.

★ ★ ★ ★ ★

M

31. Panel 35. Read Problem 1. In part (a), the field produced by loop 1 at the center of the loops is _____ (*Number*).

★   ★   ★   ★   ★

zero *or* 0

32. Panel 35, Problem 1. In part (a), compute the magnetic field, $\vec{B}_3$, produced by i_3 in loop 3 at 0. Use the right-hand rule for loops to determine its direction. $\pi = 3.14$.

$\vec{B}_3 =$ _____ newton/amp-m (up/down/into the page/ out of the page).

★   ★   ★   ★   ★

$$B_3 = k_l \frac{i_3}{r_3} = (2\pi \times 10^{-7}) \frac{(10)}{(0.10)}$$

$$= (2)(3.14)(10^{-5}) = 6.28 \times 10^{-5} \text{ newton/amp-m}$$

(Wrapping your right hand around loop 3 in the direction of the current, your thumb should point *down*.)

33. Panel 35, Problem 1(*a*). $\vec{B}_2 =$ _____ (*magnitude and direction*).

★   ★   ★   ★   ★

$$\vec{B}_2 = k_l \frac{i_2}{r_2} = 2\pi \times 10^{-7} \frac{(10)}{0.25} = 2.51 \times 10^{-5} \text{ newton/amp-m ; up}$$

34. Panel 35, Problem 1(*a*). The resultant magnetic field $\vec{B}$ at 0 is the _____ _____ of B_3 and B_2.

$\vec{B} =$ _____ (*magnitude and direction*).

★   ★   ★   ★   ★

vector sum

$\vec{B}_3 = 6.28 \times 10^{-5}$ newton/amp-m ; down

$\vec{B}_2 = 2.51 \times 10^{-5}$ newton/amp-m ; up

$\vec{B} = 3.77 \times 10^{-5}$ newton/amp-m ; down

35. Panel 35, Problem 1. Let $\vec{B} = \vec{B}_2 + \vec{B}_3$ and let $\vec{B}'$ represent the resultant field at 0 when $i_1 = 10$ amp. If $\vec{B}_1$ is the magnetic field at 0 due to i_1, then $\vec{B}' =$ _____ + _____. The right-hand rules indicates that the direction of $\vec{B}_1$ is (up/down/into the page/out of the page).

★   ★   ★   ★   ★

$\vec{B} + \vec{B}_1$; into the page

36. Panel 35, Problem 1(*b*). In part (*a*) we found that the direction of $\vec{B}$ is

(up/down/into the page/out of the page). $\vec{B}$ and $\vec{B}_1$ are (parallel/antiparallel/perpendicular).
★   ★   ★   ★   ★

down ; perpendicular

37. Panel 35, Problem 1(b). Since $\vec{B}_1$ and $\vec{B}$ are perpendicular, we use the _____ theorem to find the magnitude of their vector sum.
First, $B_1 =$ _____ newton/amp-m
Then $B' =$ _____ newton/amp-m
★   ★   ★   ★   ★

Pythagorean

$$B_1 = k_l \frac{i_1}{r_1} = 2.51 \times 10^{-5} \text{ newton/amp-m}$$

$$(B')^2 = (B)^2 + (B_1)^2 = (3.77 \times 10^{-5})^2 + (2.51 \times 10^{-5})^2 = 20.5 \times 10^{-10}$$

$$B' \approx 4.5 \times 10^{-5} \text{ newton/amp-m}$$

38. Panel 35. Read Problem 2. We consider first the sides AB and DC of the rectangle. The average magnetic force on AB is (equal/unequal) to the average magnetic force on DC in magnitude. The current in AB runs (parallel/anti-parallel/perpendicular) to the current in DC. The average magnetic forces on AB and DC have (the same direction/opposite directions).
★   ★   ★   ★   ★

equal ; antiparallel ; opposite directions

39. Panel 35, Problem 2. The vector sum of the magnetic forces in AB and DC (is/is greater than) zero.
★   ★   ★   ★   ★

is

40. Panel 35, Problem 2. Now consider sides AD and BC. The magnetic field, $\vec{B}_1$, produced by the current in the long straight wire is:
(a) Parallel to the current in AD.
(b) Antiparallel to the current in AD.
(c) Perpendicular to the current in AD and into the page.
(d) Perpendicular to the current in AD and out of the page.
★   ★   ★   ★   ★

(c)

41. Panel 35, Problem 2. Use the right-hand rule for determining the direction of magnetic forces to determine the magnetic force on AD. F_B on AD is directed (up/down/left/right).
★   ★   ★   ★   ★

Fingers into the page, thumb up leaves the palm of right hand facing **left.**

42. Panel 35, Problem 2. The magnetic force F_B on a length l of a wire carrying current i_2 by a parallel wire carrying current i_1 a distance d away is given by the equation: $F_B = $ _____.

★ ★ ★ ★ ★

$$F_B = k \frac{i_1 i_2 l}{d}$$

43. Panel 35, Problem 2. The magnetic force on AD is _____ newton(s) _____ (*Direction*).

★ ★ ★ ★ ★

$$F_B = \frac{(2 \times 10^{-7})(20)(10)(0.30)}{0.10} = 12 \times 10^{-5} \text{ newton left}$$

44. Panel 35, Problem 2. Consider the magnetic force on side BC of the rectangle. Use the right-hand rule to determine its direction (up/down/right/left).

★ ★ ★ ★ ★

When fingers are into the page, thumb down, the palm of the right hand is facing **right**.

45. The magnetic force exerted on BC by the current in the long, straight wire is _____ newton(s) _____ (*Direction*).

★ ★ ★ ★ ★

$$F_B = k \frac{i_1 i_2 l}{d} = \frac{(2 \times 10^{-7})(20)(10)(0.30)}{(0.20)} = 6 \times 10^{-5} \text{ newton right}$$

46. Panel 35, Problem 2. Compute the resultant magnetic force of i_1 on the rectangular loop. $\vec{F}_B = $ _____ (*Magnitude and direction*).

★ ★ ★ ★ ★

6×10^{-5} newton *right* and 12×10^{-5} newton *left* gives a vector sum of 6×10^{-5} newton **left**

Magnetic Force on Charged Particle: $F_B = Bvq$
Centripetal Acceleration of Charged Particle in Uniform
Magnetic Field
Invariance of Period with Velocity
Use of Electric and Magnetic Fields as Velocity
Selector: $v = \dfrac{E}{B}$

1. In Section 4 of this chapter, we found that a length of wire l carrying a current i in a field $\vec{B}$ undergoes a magnetic force. Write an equation for the

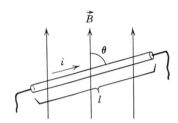

magnitude of this force in terms of i, l, B, and θ as shown in this figure. Use k as a constant of proportionality.

★　★　★　★　★

$F_B = kBil \sin \theta$

2. (1) $F_B = kBil \sin \theta$. If B is measured in _____ (*Units*), then $k = 1$. If l and B are perpendicular, then $\sin \theta =$ _____ (*Number*) and equation (1) becomes _____.

★　★　★　★　★

newton/amp-m ; 1 ; $F_B = Bil$

3. Refer to figure in Frame 1. When there is no current in l, there (is a/is no) magnetic force on l.

★　★　★　★　★

is no

4. A current is a measure of the amount of _____ that passes through a given cross section per unit _____. In symbols, $i =$ _____.

★　★　★　★　★

charge ; time ; $\dfrac{Q}{t}$

5. (1) $F_B = Bil$. (2) Since $i = \dfrac{Q}{t}$, (3) substitute the right-hand member of (2) for i in (1), and

$F_B =$ _____.

★ ★ ★ ★ ★

$$B \frac{Q}{t} l$$

6. (1) $F_B = Bil$. (2) $i = \frac{Q}{t}$. (3) $F_B = B\frac{Q}{t}l = BQ\frac{l}{t}$.

(4) $\frac{l}{t}$ is the _____ with which charged particles move through a length l of wire.

★ ★ ★ ★ ★

speed *or* velocity

7. (1) $F_B = Bil$. (2) $i = \frac{Q}{t}$. (3) $F_B = BQ\frac{l}{t}$. (4) $v = \frac{l}{t}$

(5) ∴ $F_B = $ _____ (*In terms of B, v, and Q*).

★ ★ ★ ★ ★

BvQ

8. If a charge Q is moving through a magnetic field B, it undergoes a magnetic force F_B which is (directly/inversely) proportional to its speed and directly/inversely) proportional to its charge.

★ ★ ★ ★ ★

directly ; directly

9. We derived $F_B = BvQ$ from $F_B = Bil$. Recall the conditions under which we derived the latter equation. B must be measured in _____ (*Units*), i in _____ (*Units*), and l in _____ (*Units*). This means that $F_B = BvQ$ can be used only when B is in _____, v in _____, and Q in _____.

★ ★ ★ ★ ★

newton/amp-m ; amperes ; meters ; newton/amp-m ; m/sec ; coulombs

10. $F_B = Bil$ also assumes that l and B are (parallel/perpendicular) to each other.

★ ★ ★ ★ ★

perpendicular

11. $F_B = BvQ$ can be used only when v and B are (parallel/perpendicular) to each other. When the angle between l and B is θ, $F_B = Bil$ _____.

★ ★ ★ ★ ★

perpendicular ; sin θ

12. Write an equation for $\vec{F}_B$ here in terms of B, v, Q, and θ.

★ ★ ★ ★ ★

$F_B = BvQ \sin \theta$

13. In general, if a charge Q measured in coulombs is moving at a velocity $\vec{v}$ through a magnetic field $\vec{B}$, the magnetic force exerted on the charge by the field is $F_B =$ _____ where θ is the angle between _____ and _____. (*Use symbols.*)

★ ★ ★ ★ ★

$BvQ \sin \theta$; $\vec{B}$ and $\vec{v}$.

14. Recall that when l and $\vec{B}$ are parallel, $\sin \theta =$ _____ (*Number*) and the magnetic force on l is _____ (*Number*).

★ ★ ★ ★ ★

0 ; 0 *or* zero ; zero

15. If a charge Q moves at a velocity $\vec{v}$ parallel to $\vec{B}$, it undergoes (a force/ no force) due to magnetic field.

★ ★ ★ ★ ★

no force (Because $\sin \theta = 0$.)

16. Unless otherwise stated, we will assume that $F_B = Bvq$ is adequate for our problems. In other words, we assume that $\sin \theta =$ _____, which is true only if the velocity of the charge and the magnetic field are (parallel/perpendicular).

★ ★ ★ ★ ★

1 ; perpendicular

17. A particle with a charge 12.8×10^{-19} coulomb moves into a magnetic field $B = 3 \times 10^{-3}$ newton/amp-m at a speed $v = 6 \times 10^5$ m/sec. Compute the magnitude of the magnetic force F_B on Q.

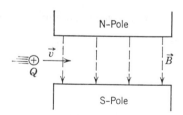

★ ★ ★ ★ ★

$F_B = BvQ = (3 \times 10^{-3}$ newton/amp-m$)(6 \times 10^5$ m/sec$)(12.8 \times 10^{-19}$ coulomb$)$

$= 2.3 \times 10^{-15} \dfrac{\text{newton coulomb}}{\text{amp. sec.}} = 2.3 \times 10^{-15} \dfrac{\text{newton } \cancel{\text{coulomb}}}{\cancel{\text{coulomb/sec.}} \cdot \cancel{\text{sec})}}$

$= 2.3 \times 10^{-15}$ newton

18. We apply the following right-hand rule to determine the direction of $\vec{F}_B$ in frame 17: Extend the fingers of the right hand in the direction of the field with the thumb in the direction of the motion of (+) charge. The direction of $\vec{F}_B$ then extends out from the palm of the hand. $\vec{F}_B$ in the previous frame is directed (up/down/into the page/out of the page).

★　★　★　★　★

into the page

19. Here a charge $Q = 3 \times 10^{-15}$ coulomb moves into a magnetic field

$\vec{B} = 4 \times 10^{-6}$ newton/amp-m directed into the page. Its velocity $v = 2 \times 10^6$ m/sec.
$\vec{F}_B =$ _____ [*magnitude and direction* (up/down/into page/out of page)].

★　★　★　★　★

$\vec{F}_B = BvQ = (4 \times 10^{-6})(2 \times 10^6)(3 \times 10^{-15}) = 2.4 \times 10^{-14}$ newton

For direction: fingers of right hand into page, thumb to the left, leaves palm of right hand facing **down.**

20. Q is a charge of -6×10^{-15} coulomb moving at velocity $v = 5 \times 10^5$ m/sec into field $\vec{B} = 5 \times 10^{-5}$ newton/amp-m. Compute the magnitude of $\vec{F}_B$. (Ignore the sign of Q for the time being.)

★　★　★　★　★

$\vec{F}_B = BvQ = (5 \times 10^{-5})(5 \times 10^5)(6 \times 10^{-15}) = 1.5 \times 10^{-13}$ newton

21. To find the direction of $\vec{F}_B$ in the previous frame, we alter the right-hand rule as follows for *negative* charges: The thumb points in the *opposite* direction to the velocity of the particle. The fingers of the right-hand are still extended in the direction of the field, and the final position of the palm indicates the direction of $\vec{F}_B$. The direction of $\vec{F}_B$ in the previous frame is (up/down/into the page/out of the page)

★ ★ ★ ★ ★

down (Because fingers extend into the page ; thumb points to the left ; palm of hand faces down.)

22. Think over the results of applying the right-hand rule to determine the direction of $\vec{F}_B$ on charge moving at velocity $\vec{v}$ in a magnetic field $\vec{B}$. The rule indicates that $\vec{F}_B$ is always (parallel to $\vec{B}$ and perpendicular to $\vec{v}$/parallel to $\vec{v}$ and perpendicular to $\vec{B}$/perpendicular to both $\vec{v}$ and $\vec{B}$/parallel to both $\vec{B}$ and $\vec{v}$).

★ ★ ★ ★ ★

perpendicular to both $\vec{B}$ and $\vec{v}$

23. Panel 34, Fig. 3. A charged particle moving in a *uniform* magnetic field is continuously accelerated by a force (parallel/perpendicular) to its velocity. We learn in mechanics that such a force (increases/decreases/does not affect) the speed of the object to which it is applied; it changes the direction of the velocity in such a way that the particle moves in a (straight line/circular path).

★ ★ ★ ★ ★

perpendicular ; does not affect ; circular

24. A *uniform* magnetic field exerts a force on a charge moving in it which produces (uniform/centripetal) acceleration. Under the influence of this field the charge moves at a (constant/variable) speed in a (straight line/ circular) path.

★ ★ ★ ★ ★

centripetal ; constant ; circular

25. As the electron enters this strong magnetic field, which path (1/2/3) will it follow?

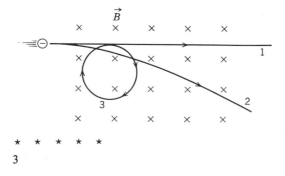

★ ★ ★ ★ ★

3

26. The magnetic force on a charged particle moving in a magnetic field is centripetal if the magnetic field is (uniform/nonuniform).

★ ★ ★ ★ ★

uniform

27. Panel 35. Read Problem 3. Once the electron is in this magnetic field, it will follow the path of a _____ under the influence of the magnetic field.

★ ★ ★ ★ ★

circle (See Panel 34, Fig 3.)

28. Panel 35, Problem 3. Apply the right-hand rule to this *electron* as it enters the field. Which of these [(a)/(b)] circular paths will it follow?

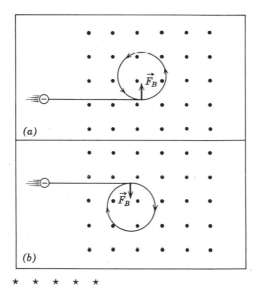

(a)

(b)

★ ★ ★ ★ ★

The initial F_B is upward; therefore, the electron will follow path shown in (a).

29. Panel 35, Problem 3. The charge on an electron is _____ elem. chge. In coulombs this is _____.

★ ★ ★ ★ ★

-1 ; -1.6×10^{-19}

30. Panel 35, Problem 3. Compute the magnetic force on the electron.

★ ★ ★ ★ ★

$F_B = BvQ$

$F_B = (1 \times 10^{-2})(4 \times 10^7 \,\text{m/sec})(1.6 \times 10^{-19} \,\text{coulomb}) = 6.4 \times 10^{-14} \,\text{newton}$

31. Panel 35, Problem 3. Considered as a *magnetic* force $F_B = BvQ$. Considered as a centripetal force, $F_B =$ _____ (*In terms of m, v, and r*).

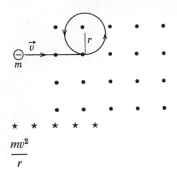

$$\frac{mv^2}{r}$$

32. Refer to figure in Frame 31.

(1) $F_B = BvQ$.

(2) $F_B = \dfrac{mv^2}{r}$

(3) From (1) and (2): $BvQ =$ _____.

(4) Solving (3) for r: $r =$ _____.

★ ★ ★ ★ ★

$$\frac{mv^2}{r} \; ; BvQ = \frac{mv^2}{r} \; ; r = \frac{mv}{BQ}$$

33. Panel 35, Problem 3. Compute the radius of the electron path in the magnetic field. $r =$ _____ meter.

★ ★ ★ ★ ★

$$r = \frac{mv}{BQ} = \frac{(9 \times 10^{-31})(4 \times 10^7)}{(1 \times 10^{-2})(1.6 \times 10^{-19})} = 2.25 \times 10^{-2}\,\text{m}$$

34. Panel 35, Problem 3. Let T be the period of revolution of the electron in this circular path. In terms of r and v, $T =$ _____.

★ ★ ★ ★ ★

$$\frac{2\pi r}{v}$$

35. Panel 35, Problem 3. Compute the period of revolution of the electron's motion in this field. $T =$ _____ sec.

★ ★ ★ ★ ★

$$T = \frac{2\pi r}{v} = \frac{2(3.14)(2.25 \times 10^{-2})}{4 \times 10^7} = 3.53 \times 10^{-9}\,\text{sec}$$

36. (1) $r = \dfrac{mv}{BQ}$. (2) $T = \dfrac{2\pi r}{v}$.

(3) Substitute the right-hand member of (1) for r in (2). Then $T =$ _____.

★ ★ ★ ★ ★

$$T = \frac{2\pi}{v}\frac{mv}{BQ} = \frac{2\pi m}{BQ}$$

37. $T = \dfrac{2\pi m}{BQ}$. This equation shows that the time for one complete revolution of the charge Q in uniform field B (depends on/is independent of) the speed of the particle.

★ ★ ★ ★ ★

is independent of

38. Panel 35, Problem 3. $r = \dfrac{mv}{BQ}$. This indicates that the radius of the path of a charge Q in a uniform field B (increases/decreases) with an increase in the speed of the particle.

★ ★ ★ ★ ★

increases

39. Fast particles require (large/small) circles; slower particles require (larger/smaller) circles. $T = \dfrac{2\pi m}{BQ}$ shows us that fast particles require (more time than/less time than/the same time as) slower particles to make one complete revolution in the field.

★ ★ ★ ★ ★

large ; smaller ; the same time as

40. Panel 35. Read Problem 4. Determine the directions of $\vec{F}_B$ and $\vec{F}_E$. $\vec{F}_B$ is directed (up/down/into the page/out of the page/left/right). $\vec{F}_E$ is directed (up/down/into the page/out of the page/left/right). $\vec{F}_B$ and $\vec{F}_E$ are (parallel/antiparallel/perpendicular) to each other.

★ ★ ★ ★ ★

up ; down ; antiparallel

41. Panel 35, Problem 4. Q is *undeflected* if the magnitudes of $\vec{F}_B$ and $\vec{F}_E$ are (equal/unequal).

★ ★ ★ ★ ★

equal

42. Panel 35, Problem 4.

(1) If Q is undeflected, than $F_B = F_E$.

(2) $F_B = BvQ$ and $F_B = EQ$.

(3) If Q is undeflected, from (3) $BvQ =$ _____.

(4) $\therefore$ $v =$ _____ (*in terms of B and E*) when Q is undeflected.

  ★   ★   ★   ★   ★

EQ ; Since $BvQ = EQ$, $v = \dfrac{E}{B}$

43. Panel 35, Problem 4. Compute the velocity in m/sec at which Q will be undeflected by this combination of magnetic and electric fields.

  ★   ★   ★   ★   ★

$$v = \frac{E}{B} = \frac{1.5 \times 10^3 \text{ newtons/coulomb}}{2.0 \times 10^{-2} \text{ newton/amp-m}} = 7.5 \times 10^4 \text{ amp-m/coulomb}$$

$$= 7.5 \times 10^4 \, \frac{\text{coul}}{\text{sec}} \cdot \frac{\text{m}}{\text{coul}} = 7.5 \times 10^4 \text{ m/sec}$$

44. Panel 35, Problem 4. The combination of magnetic and electric fields shown in this problem is sometimes used as a *velocity* selector. Only those charged particles moving at a speed given by the ratio _____ will pass through this device _____.

  ★   ★   ★   ★   ★

$\dfrac{E}{B}$; undeflected.

Section 6.   Electron Gun; Thomson's Experiment:
Measurement of $\dfrac{q_e}{m_e}$

Note. We have seen that both electric and magnetic fields exert forces on charged particles. The effect of a magnetic field is limited to charges in motion nonparallel to the field. In the following sections we examine some of the experiments and devices which utilize magnetic and electric forces to investigate physical phenomena. Among these are the electron gun (used in TV cameras), the cyclotron, and the mass spectroscope.

1. Refer to Panel 36. The letter in the upper right-hand corner is _____.

  ★   ★   ★   ★   ★

L

2. Panel 36. Refer to Fig. 1. This device is a vacuum tube. On the left a battery A heats a *filament*. When the filament is heated to a high temperature, it "boils" off _____. This is known as th_____ emission.

★ ★ ★ ★ ★ ★

electrons ; thermionic

3. Panel 36. Fig. 1. *P* is a metal plate with a hole through which electrons may pass into the right-hand chamber of the tube. Battery *B* maintains a high potential difference *V* between this plate and the f_____.
Let q_e be the charge on an electron. An electron which starts from rest at *F* and moves across the field under the influence of *V* has a kinetic energy equal to _____ in terms of *V* and q_e when it reaches the plate.

★ ★ ★ ★ ★

filament ; $q_e V$

4. Panel 36, Fig. 1. Suppose the potential difference provided by *V* is 5,000 volts. The charge on an electron is 1.6×10^{-19} coulomb. An electron from *F* has a kinetic energy of _____ joule as it passes through the hole in *P*.

★ ★ ★ ★ ★

$E_k = q_e V = (1.6 \times 10^{-19}$ coulomb$)(5000$ volts$) = 8 \times 10^{-16}$ joule

5. Panel 36, Fig. 1. This combination of batteries *A* and *B*, filament, and plate constitutes a device called an *electron gun*. The electron gun provides electrons with a specific amount of _____ energy to be used in experiments in the right-hand chamber of the tube.

★ ★ ★ ★ ★

kinetic

6. Panel 35, Fig. 1. (1) In terms of the mass *m* of an electron and its speed *v* when it reaches the hole *P*, its kinetic energy $E_k = $ _____.
(2) In terms of the potential difference *V* maintained in the electron _____ and the charge q_e on an electron, the kinetic energy of an electron when it reaches the hole in *P* is $E_k = $ _____.

★ ★ ★ ★ ★

$\frac{1}{2}mv^2$; gun ; $q_e V$

7. Panel 36, Fig. 1.

(1) $E_k = \frac{1}{2}mv^2$.

(2) $E_k = q_e V$

(3) Equate the right-hand members of (1) and (2) to each other. Solving for *v*,
$v = $ _____.

★ ★ ★ ★ ★

$\frac{1}{2}mv^2 = q_e V$ $v^2 = \dfrac{2q_e V}{m}$ $v = \sqrt{2q_e V/m}$

8. Panel 36, Fig. 1. Compute the speed of an electron leaving the electron gun if the potential difference maintained by battery B is 2000 volts and the charge on an electron is 1.6×10^{-19} coulomb. Use $m = 9 \times 10^{-31}$ kg.

★ ★ ★ ★ ★

$$v = \sqrt{\frac{2q_e V}{m}} = \sqrt{\frac{(2)(1.6 \times 10^{-19})(2000)}{9 \times 10^{-31}}}$$

$$= \sqrt{\frac{64 \times 10^{14}}{9}} = \frac{8}{3} \times 10^7 = 2.67 \times 10^7 \text{ m/sec}$$

9. Panel 36, Fig. 1. To the right of the electron gun is a set of parallel plates. If these plates are *un*charged, then an electron from the gun (is/is not) deflected and follows the path (NK/NG) to the screen.

★ ★ ★ ★ ★

is not ; NK

10. Panel 36, Fig. 1. When the top plate is positively charged and the bottom plate negatively charged, an electron from the gun is (deflected/undeflected) and follows the path (NG/NK).

★ ★ ★ ★ ★

deflected ; NG

11. Panel 36, Fig. 1. When a field E exists between the plates, there is an electric force on an electron which acts (parallel/perpendicular) to the electron's horizontal path as it leaves the gun.

★ ★ ★ ★ ★

perpendicular

12. Panel 36. Refer to Fig. 2. This is a blow-up of that part of the vacuum tube which contains the parallel plates. The electric force on an electron while it is between the plates (changes/does not change) the component of velocity of the electron parallel to the plates.

★ ★ ★ ★ ★

does not change

13. Panel 36, Fig. 2. Let $\vec{v}$ be the horizontal component of velocity of an electron from the gun. The time interval, Δt, during which an electric force acts perpendicular to $\vec{v}$, depends on v and the distance l through the space between the plates, or $\Delta t =$ _____ (*In terms of v and l*).

★ ★ ★ ★ ★

$\dfrac{l}{v}$ or $\dfrac{\text{distance}}{\text{speed}}$

14. Panel 36, Fig. 2. (1) The electric force, $F_e =$ _____ in terms of E and q_e.

(2) F_e produces an acceleration a which is (perpendicular/parallel) to $\vec{v}$.
★   ★   ★   ★   ★

Eq_e ; perpendicular

15. Panel 36, Fig. 2.

(1) $F_e = Eq_e$.

(2) According to Newton's second law, $F_e =$ _____ (*In terms of mass m of electron and perpendicular acceleration a*).

(3) Equate the right-hand members of (1) and (2) and solve for a. $a =$ _____.
★   ★   ★   ★   ★

ma ; $Eq_e = ma$; $a = \dfrac{Eq_e}{m}$

16. Panel 36, Fig. 2. The deflection y is the result of a (uniform/nonuniform) force. The distance the electron is deflected by this force is $y =$ _____ (*In terms of a and Δt*).
★   ★   ★   ★   ★

uniform ; $y = \frac{1}{2}a(\Delta t)^2$ (Because this is a form of uniformly accelerated motion.)

17. Panel 36, Fig. 2. (1) $y = \frac{1}{2}a(\Delta t)^2$.

(2) $a =$ _____ (*In terms of E, q_e, and m*) and $(\Delta t)^2 =$ _____ (*In terms of v and l*).(3) $y =$ _____(*In terms of E, l, q_e, m, and v*).
★   ★   ★   ★   ★

$a = \dfrac{Eq_e}{m}$

$\Delta t = \dfrac{l}{v}$ and $(\Delta t)^2 = \dfrac{l^2}{v^2}$

$y = \frac{1}{2}a(\Delta t)^2 = \frac{1}{2}\dfrac{Eq_e}{m}\cdot\dfrac{l^2}{v^2}$; $y = \dfrac{Eq_el^2}{2mv^2}$

18. Panel 36. Refer to Fig. 3 and read the descriptive paragraph. The electric field here is directed (up/down/right/left/into the page/out of the page). The magnetic field when it is applied is directed (up/down/right/left/into the page/out of the page).
★   ★   ★   ★   ★

up ; into the page

19. Panel 36, Fig. 3. Use the right-hand rule to determine the effect of the magnetic field on an electron from the gun. It deflects an electron (up/down/right/left/into the page/out of the page).
★   ★   ★   ★   ★

down (fingers into the page, thumb *opposite* the direction of electron motion, palm facing down)

20. The effects of the electric field and the magnetic field when they are both applied are in (the same direction/opposite directions). When *neither* field is applied, the electrons from the gun strike the screen at _____. When only E is applied, electrons from the gun strike the screen at _____.

⋆   ⋆   ⋆   ⋆   ⋆

opposite directions ; K ; G

21. Panel 36, Fig. 3. When the field E is applied across the plates, we have derived an equation, $y = \dfrac{Eql^2}{2mv^2}$, for the deflection it produces in the path of an electron passing between the plates (Fig. 2). Thomson could measure the distance GK on the screen and from this could compute y. He did not know q_e or m and wanted to compute the ratio $\dfrac{q_e}{m}$. He solved the equation given above for this ratio and got $\dfrac{q_e}{m} = $ _____.

⋆   ⋆   ⋆   ⋆   ⋆

$\dfrac{2yv^2}{El^2}$

22. Panel 36, Fig. 3. $\dfrac{q_e}{m} = \dfrac{2yv^2}{El^2}$.

In this equation, E, y, and l are easy to measure from the geometry and structure of the vacuum tube. Thomson could not measure v directly. However, when he adjusted B to a value where the beam again struck K, he knew that the effects of E and B (canceled/renforced) each other.

⋆   ⋆   ⋆   ⋆   ⋆

canceled

23. Panel 36, Fig. 3. Let B_0 be the magnetic field which exactly cancels E. When B_0 and E are both applied to electrons from the gun, the electrons (are deflected to G/are deflected below K/are undeflected). In this case, $v = $ _____ (*In terms of B_0 and E*).

⋆   ⋆   ⋆   ⋆   ⋆

are undeflected ; $\dfrac{E}{B_0}$

24. Panel 36, Fig. 3.

(1) $\dfrac{q_e}{m} = \dfrac{2yv^2}{El^2}$.

(2) $v = \dfrac{E}{B_0}$

(3) $\dfrac{q_e}{m} = $ _____ (*In terms of E, B_0, l, and y*).

$$\frac{q_e}{m} = \frac{2yv^2}{El^2} = \frac{2y}{El^2}\left(\frac{E^2}{B_0{}^2}\right)$$

$$\frac{q_e}{m} = \frac{2yE}{l^2 B_0{}^2}$$

25. $\dfrac{q_e}{m} = \dfrac{2yE}{l^2 B_0{}^2} = 1.7 \times 10^{11}$ coulomb/kg according to Thomson's experiment. Thomson knew neither q_e nor m. He was trying to find the ratio of the _____ of an electron to the _____ of an electron. We know today that $m = 9.1 \times 10^{-31}$ kg and $q_e = 1.6 \times 10^{-18}$ coulomb. Compute $\dfrac{q_e}{m}$ from this data and compare with Thomson's experimental value.

★ ★ ★ ★ ★

charge ; mass ; $\dfrac{1.6 \times 10^{-19} \text{ coulomb}}{9.1 \times 10^{-31}} = 1.76 \times 10^{11}$ coulomb/kg

Thomson's accuracy was quite good.

Section 7.   Mass Spectrometer $R = m\left(\dfrac{E}{B^2 q}\right)$

1. Refer to Panel 37. The letter in the upper right-hand corner is _____.
★ ★ ★ ★ ★

P

2. Panel 37. Refer to Fig. 1. (Positive/negative) ions are introduced into this device through slit S_1. Ions are atoms which have lost or gained one or more

_____.

★ ★ ★ ★ ★

Positive ; electrons

3. Panel 37, Fig. 1. The ions which enter S_1 came from a chamber in which atoms have (lost/gained) electrons.
★ ★ ★ ★ ★

lost

4. Panel 37, Fig. 1. A device which is in principle like an electron gun, but which accelerates positive ions instead of electrons, sends ions at *varying* speeds through S_1. P_1 and P_2 are parallel plates with opposite electric charges.

They provide a uniform _____ field across the space between S_1 and S_2.

$\star$　$\star$　$\star$　$\star$　$\star$

electric

5. Panel 37, Fig. 1. The $\times$ marks represent a uniform magnetic field $\vec{B}$ (into/out of) the page. In the space between S_1 and S_2 the electric field $\vec{E}$ and the magnetic field $\vec{B}$ are (parallel/perpendicular) to each other. $\vec{E}$ tends to deflect a positive ion moving down through this space (up/down/right/left/ into the page/out of the page). $\vec{B}$ tends to deflect a positive ion moving down through this space (up/down/right/left/into the page/out of the page).

$\star$　$\star$　$\star$　$\star$　$\star$

into ; perpendicular ; left ; right

6. Panel 37, Fig. 1. Positive ions enter S_1 at varying speeds. Only those ions which have a speed equal to the ratio _____ will pass through the chamber *undeflected*.

$\star$　$\star$　$\star$　$\star$　$\star$

$$\frac{E}{B}$$

7. Panel 37, Fig. 1. Ions which enter S_1 at speeds greater or less than $\dfrac{E}{B}$ (are/ are not) deflected and (pass through the hole in S_2/crash into S_2).

$\star$　$\star$　$\star$　$\star$　$\star$

are ; crash into S_2.

8. Panel 37, Fig. 1. Ions which pass through the space between S_1 and S_2 undeflected have (the same velocity/different velocities).

$\star$　$\star$　$\star$　$\star$　$\star$

the same velocity

9. Panel 37, Fig. 1. Suppose $\vec{B} = 2 \times 10^{-2}$ newton/amp-m and $\vec{E} = 2 \times 10^3$ newtons/coulomb in space between S_1 and S_2. The speed of any ion which emerges from S_2 is _____ m/sec.

$\star$　$\star$　$\star$　$\star$　$\star$

$$v = \frac{E}{B} = \frac{2 \times 10^3 \text{ newtons/coulomb}}{2 \times 10^{-2} \text{ newton/amp-m}} = 10^5 \text{ m/sec}$$

10. Panel 37, Fig. 1. That part of this device in this figure between S_1 and S_2 is called a *velocity selector*. It is constructed in such a way that the _____ of ions which pass through it undeflected is determined by the _____ and _____ _____s placed across it.

$\star$　$\star$　$\star$　$\star$　$\star$

speed ; *in either order:* magnetic, electric fields

11. Panel 37, Fig. 1. After an ion emerges from S_2 it is under the influence of ($\vec{B}$ and $\vec{E}/\vec{B}$ only/$\vec{E}$ only/neither B nor E).

$\star$ $\quad$ $\star$ $\quad$ $\star$ $\quad$ $\star$ $\quad$ $\star$

$\vec{B}$ only

12. Panel 37, Fig. 1. An ion emerging from the _____ selector in this device enters a (uniform/nonuniform) _____ field. The effect of this field on a moving charge is to pull it into a (straight-line/circular) path. In other words, the force exerted by this field acts as a (gravitational/centripetal) force.

$\star$ $\quad$ $\star$ $\quad$ $\star$ $\quad$ $\star$ $\quad$ $\star$

velocity ; uniform ; magnetic ; circular ; centripetal

13. Panel 37, Fig. 1. Let m and q be the mass and charge, respectively, on an ion which emerges from S_2. If v is its speed and R is the radius of its path under the influence of $\vec{B}$, then:

(1) $F_B =$ _____ (*In terms of field, charge, and speed*).

(2) $F_B =$ _____ (*In terms of mass, radius and speed*).

(3) $R =$ _____ (*In terms of mass, charge, field, and speed*).

$\star$ $\quad$ $\star$ $\quad$ $\star$ $\quad$ $\star$ $\quad$ $\star$

(1) $F_B = Bvq$

(2) $F_B = \dfrac{mv^2}{R}$

(3) $Bvq = \dfrac{mv^2}{R}$; $R = \dfrac{mv}{Bq}$

14. Panel 37, Fig. 1.

(1) $R = \dfrac{mv}{Bq}$

(2) $v =$ _____ in terms of the electric and magnetic fields in the selector.

(3) $R =$ _____ in terms of E, B, m and q.

$\star$ $\quad$ $\star$ $\quad$ $\star$ $\quad$ $\star$ $\quad$ $\star$

$v = \dfrac{E}{B}$

$R = \dfrac{m(E/B)}{Bq} = \dfrac{mE}{B^2q}$

15. Panel 37, Fig. 1. $R = m\left(\dfrac{E}{B^2q}\right)$.

The values of E and B are determined by the device and can be held constant.

Assume that the charge on all positive ions entering the device is the same. Then R is (directly/inversely) proportional to the _____ of the ion.

★ ★ ★ ★ ★

directly ; mass

16. Panel 37, Fig. 1. Assume that only positively charged hydrogen ions enter S_1. Since a hydrogen atom can lose only one electron, hydrogen ions entering S_1 have (the same charge/different charges). If all hydrogen ions have the same mass, then we expect hydrogen ions emerging from S_2 to strike (the same point/different points) on the photographic plate.

★ ★ ★ ★ ★

the same charge ; the same point

17. Panel 37, Fig. 1. $R = m\left(\dfrac{E}{B^2q}\right)$.

If hydrogen ions emerging from S_2 strike the photographic plate at points M_1 and M_2, then we have evidence that all hydrogen ions (have/do not have) the same mass.

★ ★ ★ ★ ★

do not have

18. Panel 37, Fig. 1. $R = m\left(\dfrac{E}{B^2q}\right)$. The hydrogen ions which expose the photographic plate at M_1 have a mass which is (equal to/less than/greater than) the mass of ions which expose the plate at M_2.

★ ★ ★ ★ ★

greater than (Because it is on the semicircle which has the greater radius.)

19. Panel 37, Fig. 1. Experiment does in fact show that ions of hydrogen expose the plate at two positions. Atoms of the *same* element which have *different* masses are called *isotopes* of that element. Experiment shows that there are at least _____ (*Number*) isotopes of hydrogen.

★ ★ ★ ★ ★

two *or* 2.

20. It is relatively easy to ionize atoms of any given element in such a way that each ion has the same charge. This means that the number of exposures on the photographic plate for ions of any given element is an indication of the number of _____ of that element that exist.

★ ★ ★ ★ ★

isotopes

21. Panel 37. Refer to Fig. 2. The black smudges indicate points at which the photographic plate in Fig. 1 has been exposed. There are at least _____

isotopes of germanium, and at least six isotopes of _____.
* * * * *
five *or* 5 ; selenium

22. Panel 37, Fig. 2 shows that atoms of copper occur with _____ different _____. These atoms are called _____ of _____.
* * * * *
two *or* 2 ; masses ; isotopes (of) copper

23. Isotopes are _____ of (the same element/different elements) which have (the same mass/different masses).
* * * * *
atoms ; the same element ; different masses

24. Panel 37, Fig. 1. The device shown here is called a *mass spectrometer*. It enables us to separate _____ of the same element which have different _____.
* * * * *
isotopes ; masses

25. A mass _____ is a device which enables us to separate ions of the same element which have different masses. The photographs in Fig. 2 of Panel 37 are mass _____ of the elements copper, germanium and selenium.
* * * * *
spectrometer ; spectra

26. In a mass spectroscope, $R = m\left(\dfrac{E}{B^2 q}\right)$. E, B, q, and R are known or can be measured. We can use this equation to compute the _____ of the different _____ of any given element.
* * * * *
masses ; isotopes

27. In an experiment with a mass spectroscope, the distance between the center of an ion's path and the point at which it exposes the plate is d. Write an equation for m in terms of B, E, q, and d.
* * * * *
$$R = m\left(\frac{E}{B^2 q}\right)$$
$$R = d$$
$$m = \frac{dB^2 q}{E}$$

Section 8.   The Cyclotron

1. Refer to Panel 38. The letter in the upper right-hand corner is _____.
★   ★   ★   ★   ★

C

2. Panel 38. Refer to Fig. 1. This is a drawing of a device called a _____.
It consists of two half-cylinders called _____ because of their shape. They
are immersed in a uniform _____ field which is (parallel/per-
pendicular) to their bases.
★   ★   ★   ★   ★

cyclotron ; Dees ; magnetic ; perpendicular

3. Panel 38, Fig. 1. The Dees are (placed in contact with each other/separated
by a gap). The whole device is placed in a chamber from which the air has
been removed. The space around and inside the Dees (is/is not) a vacuum.
★   ★   ★   ★   ★

separated by a gap ; is

4. Panel 38, Fig. 1. Each Dee is connected to a terminal of a device which
maintains an electric potential difference between the Dees. This device is
called a _____   _____   _____.
★   ★   ★   ★   ★

high frequency oscillator

5. Panel 38, Fig. 1. The high frequency oscillator maintains an electric
potential difference across the gap between the Dees by placing a positive
charge on one Dee when it is placing a negative charge on the other. In Fig.
2, when D_1 is (+), D_2 is [(+)/(−)].
★   ★   ★   ★   ★

(−)

6. Panel 38, Fig. 2. The high frequency oscillator *alternates* the charge on
D_1 from (+) to (−) after a specific time interval T. Then after another interval
equal to T, it changes the charge on D_1 from (−) to (+). During the time T
that D_1 is (+), D_2 is [(+)/(−)]. When D_1 becomes negatively charged, D_2
becomes (positively/negatively) charged.
★   ★   ★   ★   ★

(−) ; pos tively

7. Panel 38, Figs. 1 and 2. The function of the high frequency oscillator is to
_____ the charges on D_1 and D_2 every T sec. It is called a "high
frequency" oscillator because it does this *very rapidly*. T is therefore a (long/
short) interval of time.
★   ★   ★   ★   ★

alternate (change, vary, etc.) ; short

8. Panel 38. Suppose a positive ion is released from source S into the gap between the Dees when D_1 is negative. The electric field in the gap between the Dees pushes the ion in the direction of (D_1/D_2).

⋆   ⋆   ⋆   ⋆   ⋆

D_1

9. Panel 38, Fig. 2. The positive ion moves in the direction of D_1. Once it is inside the D_1, there (is an/is no) electric field force on it, because the field inside a charged hollow conductor is _____ (*Number*).

⋆   ⋆   ⋆   ⋆   ⋆

is no ; zero

10. Panel 38. While an ion is in the gap between the Dees, there (is an/is no) electric force acting upon it. While the ion is in the gap, an electric force (does/ does no) work on it, and its kinetic energy (increases/decreases/remains constant).

⋆   ⋆   ⋆   ⋆   ⋆

is an ; does ; increases

11. Panel 38. Inside D_1, there (is an/is no) electric force on the ion. There (is a/ is no) magnetic force on the ion inside D_1.

⋆   ⋆   ⋆   ⋆   ⋆

is no/is a

12. Panel 38. A magnetic force is always perpendicular to the velocity of a charged particle. This means that there (is a/is no) change in the speed of the ion inside D_1 and that its kinetic energy inside D_1 (increases/decreases/remains constant).

⋆   ⋆   ⋆   ⋆   ⋆

is no ; remains constant

13. Panel 38. The effect of the magnetic field is to pull the moving ion into a _____ path. The (magnetic/electric) field does not increase the speed or the kinetic energy of the ion. The (magnetic/electric) field is used to increase the speed and the kinetic energy of the ion.

⋆   ⋆   ⋆   ⋆   ⋆

circular ; magnetic ; electric

14. Panel 38. Consider what happens when the positive ion has moved in a semicircular path and is about to leave D_1 and reenter the gap between the Dees. If D_1 remains ($-$) and D_2 remains ($+$), the electric field in the gap acts in such a way as to (increase/decrease) the speed of the ion as it moves toward D_2.

★ ★ ★ ★ ★

decrease (Because the positive ion will be repelled by a positive charge on D_2, i.e., the electric force of such a field acts on a positive ion in the direction of D_1, against the motion of the ion.)

15. Panel 38. If, however, the high frequency oscillator switches the signs of the charges D_1 and D_2 to ($+$) and ($-$) respectively at the moment the ion is reentering the gap, then the new electric field across the gap acts to (increase/decrease) the kinetic energy of the ion. Explain your answer.
★ ★ ★ ★ ★

increase ; D_2 becomes ($-$) and D_1 becomes ($+$). The ion is now attracted towards D_2 ; it is acted upon by a force which increases its speed.

16. Panel 38. The ion then moves across the gap from D_1 to D_2. When it enters D_2 it has a kinetic energy which is (greater than/less than/the same as) it had when it left D_1. While it is in D_2 it moves in a _____ path because of the effect of the _____ field inside the Dee.
★ ★ ★ ★ ★

greater than ; circular *or* semicircular ; magnetic field

17. Panel 38. This time the radius of the semicircular path is (larger/smaller) than it was in D_1 because the _____ and _____ _____ of the ion when it enters D_2 is greater than it was when it entered D_1.
★ ★ ★ ★ ★

larger ; speed ; kinetic energy

18. Panel 38. When the ion is about to enter the gap between the Dees again, our oscillator conveniently switches the signs of the charges on the Dees so that D_1 is again ($-$) and D_2 is ($+$). If the oscillator can do this each time the ion is ready to cross the gap, then each time the ion crosses the gap, its kinetic energy (increases/decreases).
★ ★ ★ ★ ★

increases

19. Panel 38. The effect of the alternating electric field across the Dees is to increase the _____ _____ of the ion every time the ion crosses the gap. The purpose of the magnetic field is to twist the path of the ion in such a way that it has to cross the gap many times. The magnetic field (changes/does not change) the speed of the ion.
★ ★ ★ ★ ★

kinetic energy ; does not change

20. Panel 38. The ion does not travel in a single circular path because each time it enters a Dee it is traveling (faster/slower) than it was traveling the last time it entered that Dee. This means that the radii of successive semicircular trips inside the Dees are (larger/smaller/the same size). The over-all path of the ion is that of a (circle/spiral/straight line).

*   *   *   *   *

faster ; larger ; spiral

21. The purpose of a cyclotron is to increase the kinetic energies of ions moving through it. One of the basic problems of cyclotron operation is to make sure the oscillator changes the signs of the charges on the Dees at exactly the right time. If the oscillator changes the charges on the Dees to

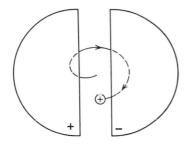

what they are in this figure at a moment when the ion is near the middle of the gap, the ion (loses/gains) kinetic energy as it moves the rest of the way. This (is/is not) an effective use of the cyclotron.

*   *   *   *   *

loses ; is not

22. An oscillator changes the signs of the charges on the Dees *periodically;* this means that it does so at (equal/unequal) intervals of time.

*   *   *   *   *

equal

23.

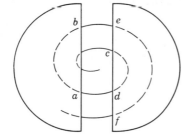

If an oscillator is going to change the signs of charges on these Dees at the most effective instants, then we must be sure that the ion will travel semi-circular paths like *ab*, *cd*, and *ef* in (equal/unequal) time intervals.

*   *   *   *   *

equal

24. Refer to figure in previous frame. The ion will travel the semicircular paths *ab*, *cd*, *ef*, etc. in equal time intervals T, if T is (directly proportional to/ inversely proportional to/independent of) the radius of the semicircular path.

★ ★ ★ ★ ★

independent of

25. The magnetic force on an ion while it is in a Dee is a _____ force because it moves the ion in a (semi)circular path.

$F_B = $ _____ in terms of B, q, and v.

$F_B = $ _____ in terms of m, v, and R.

★ ★ ★ ★ ★

centripetal ; Bvq ; $\dfrac{mv^2}{R}$

26. Panel 38. (1) $F_B = Bvq$, (2) $F_B = \dfrac{mv^2}{R}$.

(3) $\dfrac{mv^2}{R} = Bvq$ or $v = $ _____

★ ★ ★ ★ ★

$mv^2 = Bvq$

$v = \dfrac{BqR}{m}$

27. Panel 38.

(1) The speed of the ion whenever it is inside a Dee is given by the equation: $v = $ _____. This indicates that the larger the semicircular radius, the (faster/ slower) the ion is moving.

(2) Let $T = $ the time it takes for an ion to move through its semi-circular path in a Dee. πR is the distance it travels in a Dee. Therefore $v = $ _____ in terms of T, π, and R.

★ ★ ★ ★ ★

$\dfrac{BqR}{m}$; faster ; $\dfrac{\pi R}{T}$ (Because πR represents half a circumference.)

28. (1) $v = \dfrac{BqR}{m}$. (2) $v = \dfrac{\pi R}{T}$.

(3) Set the right-hand members of (1) and (2) equal to each other and solve for T: $T = $ _____.

★ ★ ★ ★ ★

$\dfrac{BqR}{m} = \dfrac{\pi R}{T}$

$T = \dfrac{\pi \cancel{R} m}{Bq\cancel{R}} = \dfrac{\pi m}{Bq}$

29. Panel 38. $T = \dfrac{\pi m}{Bq}$. T is the _____ it takes an ion in a cyclotron to move through its semicircular path in a Dee. Note that T is (directly proportional to/inversely proportional to/independent of) the radius of such a path.

★   ★   ★   ★   ★

time ; independent of

30. Panel 38. We have shown that the time it takes an ion to move the semicircular distance ab is (greater than/less than/equal to) the time it takes the same ion to move the semi-circular distance ef.

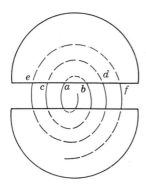

★   ★   ★   ★   ★

equal to

31. Panel 38. The high-frequency oscillator must be set to switch the signs of the charges on D_1 and D_2 in (equal/unequal) time intervals. The time interval can be calculated from the equation: $T =$ _____.

★   ★   ★   ★   ★

equal ; $\dfrac{\pi m}{Bq}$

32. $T = \dfrac{\pi m}{Bq}$. The efficient operation of a cyclotron depends upon the fact that T is (dependent on/independent of) the radius of the path of an ion being accelerated in it.

★   ★   ★   ★   ★

independent of

33. $T = \dfrac{\pi m}{Bq}$. The frequency oscillator must be set according to the charge on the ion and the magnetic field of the device. q is not likely to change and B is built into the structure of the device and can be regulated very precisely. It appears then that our oscillator will become ineffective only if there is a change in the _____ of an ion. (Examine the equation.)

⋆　⋆　⋆　⋆　⋆　⋆

mass

34. The special theory of relativity tells us that the masses of objects increase appreciably when they are moving at speeds of 90 to 99⁺% the speed of light. At such speeds T (increases/decreases/remains constant), and an oscillator alternating Dee-charges at a constant frequency (remains efficient/becomes less effective).

⋆　⋆　⋆　⋆　⋆

increases ; becomes less effective

35. The cyclotron described in Panel 38 (is/is not) an effective accelerator of charged particles to speeds very close to the speed of light ($\sim 3 \times 10^8$ m/sec).

⋆　⋆　⋆　⋆　⋆

is not

36. Other devices, similar in some respects to the cyclotron in Panel 38, have been and are being developed to accelerate ions to speeds near the speed of light. Examples are the synchrocyclotron, the synchrotron, cosmotron, etc. They are all similar to the cyclotron in as much as they use _____ fields to increase the _____ _____ of *charged* particles and _____ fields to control their paths.

⋆　⋆　⋆　⋆　⋆

electric ; kinetic energy ; magnetic

37. Devices like the cyclotron, which utilize electric and magnetic fields to increase the kinetic energies and the _____ of particles, are effective on (charged particles only/uncharged particles only/on both charged and uncharged particles.)

⋆　⋆　⋆　⋆　⋆

speeds ; charged particles only

38. A cyclotron is an effective accelerator of which of the following particles?

(*a*) a hydrogen atom   (*d*) an alpha particle
(*b*) a neutron   (*e*) an electron
(*c*) a hydrogen ion   (*f*) a chlorine atom

⋆　⋆　⋆　⋆　⋆

(*c*), (*d*), (*e*) (These are the only charged particles in the group given.)

39. Panel 38. The increased kinetic energy of the ion which has spiraled its way through the cyclotron is used to provide energy for interactions of ions with selected targets, e.g., thin metal sheets, photographic emulsions, etc. This means that we have to get the ions out of the Dee when it is approaching

the wall of the Dee. This is done by a deflecting plate which can be charged at the right time to alter the path of the ion and direct it at a target. In Fig. 3, the deflecting plate requires a [(+)/(−)] charge to aim the ion beam at the target.
★　★　★　★　★

— (The ion is positive)

40. A device like a cyclotron is often called a *particle accelerator*. The particles referred to are ions or electrons, i.e., they are small _____ particles. "Accelerator" refers to the fact that such devices increase the _____ of these particles, thereby increasing their _____ energies.
★　★　★　★　★

charged ; speeds *or* velocities ; kinetic

41. Any device which increases the kinetic energy of charged particles is called a particle _____.
★　★　★　★　★

accelerator

42. The mass spectrometer described in Section 7 of this chapter (is/is not) a particle accelerator in this particular sense.
★　★　★　★　★

is not (It does, in fact, accelerate ions inasmuch as it changes their direction, but it does *not* increase their speeds and kinetic energies.)

Section 9. The Hall Effect

1. Refer to Panel 39. The letter in the upper right-hand corner is _____.
★　★　★　★　★

A

2. Panel 39. Examine Figs. 1 and 2. The current arrows indicate the direction charge carriers would move if they were (positive/negative). A positive charge carrier would move in (the same direction as *i*/a direction opposite *i*). A negative charge carrier would move in (the same direction as *i*/a direction opposite *i*).
★　★　★　★　★

positive ; the same direction as *i* ; a direction opposite *i*

3. Panel 39. Apply the right-hand rule to determine the effect of the magnetic field on the positive charge carrier in Fig. 1. The direction of the field is (into/out of) the page. The positive charge is moving (up/down). The magnetic force on the positive charge tends to move it to the (right/left).

★ ★ ★ ★ ★

into ; down ; (Fingers into the page ; thumb down. This leaves palm of right hand facing **right**.)

4. Panel 39, Fig. 1. The effect of the magnetic field in Fig. 1 is to accumulate (positive/negative) charge on the (right/left) side of the sheet.
★ ★ ★ ★ ★

positive ; right

5. Panel 39. *If* Fig. 1 is a true picture of what constitutes an electric current in a metallic conductor like copper, then it is (positive/negative) charge carriers which move in a conductor. This means that point *a* in this experiment will be at a (higher/lower) electric potential than point *b*.
★ ★ ★ ★ ★

positive ; lower

6. Panel 39. Suppose Fig. 2 represents what actually happens when a current flows in a metallic conductor. Apply the right-hand rule to determine the effect of this magnetic field on a *negative* charge carrier. The magnetic force tends to push this charge carrier to the (right/left).
★ ★ ★ ★ ★

right (Fingers into the page ; thumb *down*, i.e., in a direction opposite the motion of negative charge ; palm of right hand faces to the right.)

7. Panel 39. If negative charge carriers account for electric currents in metallic conductors, then there is a tendency for (positive/negative) charge to accumulate on the right side of this sheet. This means that point *a* should be at a (higher/lower) electric potential than point *b*.
★ ★ ★ ★ ★

negative ; higher

8. The experiment described in Panel 39 was devised by E. H. Hall in 1879 to determine the sign of charge carriers in a metallic conductor. If the charge carriers are positive, we except the electric potential from *b* to *a* to be (positive/negative). If the charge carriers are negative, we expect the electric potential form *b* to *a* to be (positive/negative).
★ ★ ★ ★ ★

positive ; negative

9. Panel 39. Measurement shows that the *b* is at a lower electric potential than *a*, i.e., that the electric potential from *b* to *a* is negative. This is known as the *Hall effect*, and indicates that in fact the charge carriers in metals are (positive/negative).
★ ★ ★ ★ ★

negative

10. Panel 39. The result of this experiment is that (positive/negative) charge tends to acculalate on the right hand side of the sheet. This makes the electric _____ at *b* lower than it is at *a*. This result is called the _____ effect and shows that the carriers in a _____ are in fact negative.

★　★　★　★　★

negative ; potential ; Hall ; metal *or* metallic conductor

11. The convention that electric current moves from $[(+)/(-)]$ to $[(+)/(-)]$, i.e., in the direction a $[(+)/(-)]$ charge would move in an electric field was settled on many years before Hall's experiment. Hall showed that in metallic substances the charges which actually moved were those which moved (in the same direction on the electric field/in a direction opposite to the electric field).

★　★　★　★　★

$(+)$; $(-)$; $(+)$; in a direction opposite to the electric field

12. A positive charge moving in one direction is equivalent *in almost all external effects* to a negative charge moving in the opposite direction. The Hall effect (is/is not) one of those external effects which are the same whether the charge carriers are positive or negative.

★　★　★　★　★

is not

13. Our explanation of the Hall effect requires that we refer (only to the direction of the electric current/consider the actual motion of charge carriers).

★　★　★　★　★

consider the actual motion of charge carriers

14. The external effect of charges moving through a resistor is an increase in the temperature of the resistor. This effect depends only upon the fact that charges are moving and is (the same/different) whether we think of positive charge carriers moving in one direction or electrons moving in the other. Our explanation of the heating efiect of an electric current in a resistor requires that we ((*a*) refer only to the existence of a current/(*b*) consider the direction in which charges carriers are actually moving) in the resistor.

★　★　★　★　★

the same ; (*a*)

15. It is on the basis of experiments like the _____ _____ that we know that the charge carriers in metals are negatively charged particles called

_____.

★　★　★　★　★

Hall effect ; electrons

Section 10.   Moving Coil Ammeter
Electric Motor

1. Refer to Panel 40. The letter in the upper right hand corner is _____.
★   ★   ★   ★   ★

T

2. Panel 40. Refer to Fig. 1. A rectangular loop of wire placed between the poles of a magnet is free to move around the axis *RW*. When a current flows through the loop in the direction indicated, the section *KP* moves (into/out of) the page and *TM* moves (into/out of) the page. (Use right-hand rule.)
★   ★   ★   ★   ★

into (Fingers pointing right ; thumb up ; palm of hand faces into the page.)
out of (Fingers pointing right ; thumb up ; palm of hand faces out of page.)

3. Panel 40, Fig. 1. Looking down on the loop from *R*, when a current is flowing through the coil in the direction indicated, the loop twists in a (clockwise/counterclockwise) direction.
★   ★   ★   ★   ★

clockwise

4. Panel 40. Examine Figs. 2 and 3. When the current in the loop is reversed. the loop twists in a (clockwise/counterclockwise) direction as viewed from *R*,
★   ★   ★   ★   ★

counterclockwise

5. Panel 40. When there is no current in the loop, there (is/is no) magnetic force tending to _____ it around the axis *RW*.
★   ★   ★   ★   ★

is no ; twist *or* turn, rotate

6. Panel 40. In principle, then, the effect of the magnetic field on this loop of wire (can/cannot) be used to detect the existence of a current in the loop.
★   ★   ★   ★   ★

can

7. Panel 40. The direction in which the loop rotates around the axis *RW* is an indication of the _____ of the current in the loop.
★   ★   ★   ★   ★

direction

8. Panel 40. The force which tends to twist this loop around the axis *RW* is a _____ force. If the length of *KP* is *l*, an equation for the force *F* which tends to twist K into the page is given by the equation: $F =$ _____, in terms of l, i, and B.

★ ★ ★ ★ ★

magnetic ; Bil

9. Panel 40. The force tending to produce rotation of the loop is (directly proportional to/inversely proportional to/independent of) the current.

★ ★ ★ ★ ★

directly proportional to

10. Panel 40. If a coil spring is attached (see Fig. 4) to the loop in such a way as to exert a restoring force on the loop, the loop rotates until this spring restoring force just balances the _____ force making the loop twist in the magnetic field.

★ ★ ★ ★ ★

magnetic

11. Panel 40. In Fig. 4, a pointer has been attached to the loop in such a way that the point moves along a calibrated scale as the loop rotates in the magnetic field. When there is no current in the loop, the loop and pointer are held at the center of the scale by the _____ _____ attached to the loop.

★ ★ ★ ★ ★

coil spring

12. Panel 40. Fig. 4. When there is a current in the loop, the pointer moves to the right or left until the _____ force on the loop is balanced by the _____ force of the coil spring. As the current (increases/decreases) the pointer swings farther to the left or right.

★ ★ ★ ★ ★

magnetic ; restoring ; increases

13. Panel 40, Fig. 4. Whether the pointer swings right or left depends on the (magnitude/direction) of the current in the loop. How far the pointer swings in either direction depends on (the magnitude/direction) of the current in the loop.

★ ★ ★ ★ ★

direction ; magnitude

14. Panel 40. Careful selection of springs and calibration of the scale in *amperes* enables us to use this device to detect and measure electric _____

★ ★ ★ ★ ★

currents

15. Panel 40. The device described here is called a *moving coil ammeter*. The "coil" does *not* refer to the coil spring; it refers to the fact that practical devices of this sort require *many* loops of wire rather than one. These loops are wrapped close together in a wire coil; it is this coil which _____ when a current flows through it. The coil spring, on the other hand, acts to _____ the wire loops coil to its original position.

★　★　★　★　★

moves *or* twists, rotates, turns ; restore *or* return, bring back, etc.

16. Panel 40. A moving _____ _____ is a device used to detect and measure electric currents. Its operation depends upon the fact that a current-carrying conductor undergoes a _____ when it is in a _____ field.

★　★　★　★　★

coil ammeter ; force ; magnetic

17. Panel 40. The direction in which the pointer of a moving coil ammeter rotates (depends/does not depend) upon the direction in which the current flows in its coil. The amount of rotation is (directly/inversely) proportional to the current.

★　★　★　★　★

depends ; directly

18. Refer to Panel 41. The figure in the upper right-hand corner is _____.

★　★　★　★　★

K

19. Panel 41. Examine Fig. 1 and read the descriptive paragraph. When current from the battery enters the loop through the split-ring commutator, the interaction between the current and the _____ field causes the loop to _____.

★　★　★　★　★

magnetic ; rotate *or* turn, twist, move

20. Panel 41. When the loop and the split-ring commutator have made a half-rotation, the split-ring supplying section *a* of the lope with current is in contact with the [(+)/(−)] of the battery.

★　★　★　★　★

(+)

21. Panel 41, Fig. 1. When sections *a* and *b* have exchanged positions because the loop has moved through a half rotation, the current flows in the loop in such a way that the loop (reverses its direction of rotation/continues to rotate in the same direction).

★　★　★　★　★

continues to rotate in the same direction

22. Panel 41, Fig. 1. The purpose of the split-ring commutator in an electric motor is to provide _____ to the loop in such a way as to maintain its rotation in the same direction.

★ ★ ★ ★ ★

current

23. Panel 41, Fig. 1. A shaft attached to the loop transmits energy from the rotary motion of the loop to outside machinery it is used to operate. An electric motor is a device which transforms _____ energy into mechanical energy.

★ ★ ★ ★ ★

electric

24. A resistor is a device in which electric potential energy from a source of EMF is changed into _____ energy. An electric motor changes electric potential energy into _____ energy.

★ ★ ★ ★ ★

heat ; mechanical

25. Both the moving coil ammeter and the electric motor depend on the fact that (an electric/a magnetic) field exerts a force on (stationary/moving) charges.

★ ★ ★ ★ ★

magnetic ; moving

Section 11.   A Theory of Magnetism

1. A solenoid is a wire conductor wound into a coil. A solenoid like the one in the figure consists of many loops. When current flows in the solenoid there is in the space in and around each loop a _____ field.

★ ★ ★ ★ ★

magnetic

2. When an electric current flows in a solenoid the magnetic fields of the individual loops are additive. If the current flows in the same direction in each loop, then the solenoid (has/does not have) a magnetic field around it when a current flows through it.

★   ★   ★   ★   ★

has

3. Figure (*a*) is a sketch of the magnetic field lines around a bar magnet. Figure (*b*) is a sketch of the magnetic field lines around a _____.

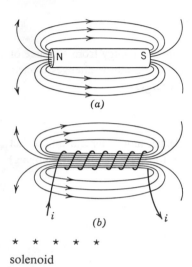

(*a*)

(*b*)

★   ★   ★   ★   ★

solenoid

4. Refer to figure in previous frame. The *external* magnetic fields of a bar magnet and a solenoid in which there is an electric current (are/are not) similar.

★   ★   ★   ★   ★

are

5. A solenoid has a magnetic field similar to the magnetic field of a bar magnet only when it (the solenoid)_____.
(*Complete.*)

★   ★   ★   ★   ★

has an electric current in its loops

6. Early in the 19th century the French physicist Ampère suggested that the magnetic field around a bar magnet is due to the same general causes as the field around a solenoid. Ampère meant that the external magnetic effects of a bar magnet were the result of the existence of a _____ somewhere inside or on the surface of the magnet.

★   ★   ★   ★   ★

current

7. To achieve the observed field which is similar to that around a solenoid, this *amperian* current would have to flow as indicated in Fig. [(a)/(b)].

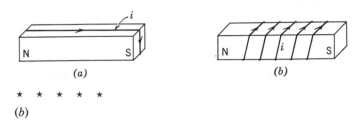

(a)   (b)

★   ★   ★   ★   ★

(b)

8. We can account for the existence of currents in magnets if we recall that a current is constituted by the motion of _____.

★   ★   ★   ★   ★

charges *or* charged particles

9. Suppose a charge is placed on the rim of a wheel. In (a), the wheel is stationary; in (b) it is rotating in the direction shown. In (a) there (is a/is no) magnetic field due to the charge because the charges (are/are not) moving.

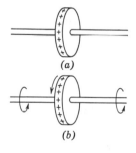

(a)

(b)

★   ★   ★   ★   ★

is no ; are not

10. Refer to figure in Frame 9. In (b) the rotation of the charges constitutes an electric _____ and there (is a/is no) magnetic field due to the charges on the wheel.

★   ★   ★   ★   ★

current ; is a

11. We now know that electrons in atoms can be thought of as orbiting the nucleus of the atom in much the same way that the earth orbits the sun.

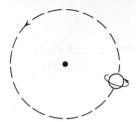

Furthermore, an electron spins on its own axis as the Earth rotates on its axis. An electron in an atom (has/does not have) a magnetic field around it.
*   *   *   *   *
has

12. We can account for the amperian current which produces the magnetic field around a bar magnet by reference to the motions of _____ in atoms.
*   *   *   *   *
electrons

13. Refer to panel 42. The letter in the upper right-hand corner is _____.
*   *   *   *   *
G

14. Panel 42. Refer to Fig. 1. Each square loop represents the current produced by the motion of the electrons in a single atom of the material in a bar magnet. This current loop produces a _____ _____ which points (into/out of) the page.
*   *   *   *   *
magnetic field ; out of

15. Panel 42, Fig. 1. The face (i.e., the surface enclosed by the square and facing out of the page) of each of the square loops in this figure acts like a (N-/S-) pole.
*   *   *   *   *
N-

16. Panel 42, Fig. 1. Note that the current in sections *a* and *b* of these current loops placed next to each other move in (the same direction/opposite directions). This means that the magnetic effects of *a* and *b* tend to (cancel/reinforce).
*   *   *   *   *
opposite directions ; cancel

17. Panel 42, Fig. 1. In a solid the atoms are packed together closely. If the square loops in Fig. 1 represent such close-packed atoms, the magnetic effects of sections *a* and *b* cancel, and the net magnetic effect of these two square loops is that represented by the stage r_____ loop.

★ ★ ★ ★ ★

rectangular

18. Panel 42. In Fig. 2, in the two atomic loops represented by the squares, the magnetic effects of sections c and b (cancel/reinforce) and the external magnetic effect (is/is not) that of a single current loop.

★ ★ ★ ★ ★

cancel ; is

19. Panel 42. Figure 3 represents all the atomic current loops at the N-pole end of a bar magnet. Note that the magnetic effects of all internal current sections (remain uncancelled/cancel each other out), which those current sections which are on the outside (remain uncancelled/cancel each other out).

★ ★ ★ ★ ★

cancel each other out ; remain uncancelled

20. Panel 42. The net external magnetic effects of all the *atomic* current loops at the left of the figure is represented by the one *amperian* current loop on the right. The amperian current loops (account for/do not account for) the magnetic field around a bar magnet.

★ ★ ★ ★ ★

account

21. Panel 42. The rectangular loop on the right in Fig. 3 is an _____ current loop. It is the net effect of all the _____ current loops on the left, and it accounts for the _____ _____ we find in the space around a bar magnet.

★ ★ ★ ★ ★

amperian ; atomic ; magnetic field

22. Most atoms, especially those of solid substances, contain many electrons moving in different directions, so in general we expect to find that the magnetic effects of electron orbits tend to (cancel/reinforce) each other.

★ ★ ★ ★ ★

cancel

23. Thus we find that (most/very few) substances are strongly magnetic in character.

★ ★ ★ ★ ★

very few

24. Paramagnetic and diamagnetic substances are those which exhibit such extremely weak reactions to external magnetic fields that they are not considered to be magnetic in our daily experiences because their reactions to fields are not readily observable. Iron (is/is not) a paramagnetic or a diamagnetic substance.

* * * * *

is not

25. Substances whose reactions to magnetic fields are strong enough to be observed in our daily experience are called *ferromagnetic* substances. Substances like iron, cobalt, nickel, and a variety of alloys of these and other metals are readily observed to be magnetic in our daily experience. These (are/are not) ferromagnetic substances.

* * * * *

are

26. Whenever we talk about magnetic substances in this course we will refer to those substances which exhibit a strong tendency to align themselves in an external magnetic fields. Technically, such substances are said to be _____.

* * * * *

ferromagnetic

27. It has been shown in recent years that substances like iron, cobalt and nickel contain atoms whose electron orbits and spins are oriented in such a manner that their magnetic fields do not cancel. Atoms of ferromagnetic substances have net atomic currents (greater than/equal to) zero.

* * * * *

greater than

28. Iron is a _____ substance. An atom of iron (has/does not have) a net magnet field which is due to the orbital motions and spins of its own electrons.

* * * * *

ferromagnetic ; has

29. One iron nail does not necessarily attract another iron nail, although both will be attracted by a magnet. The individual atoms of a sample of a ferromagnetic substance (are/are not) magnets; the sample itself (is/is not) necessarily a magnet.

* * * * *

are ; is not

30. Since the atoms of a ferromagnetic material are magnets, they respond to an external magnetic field and a sample of a ferromagnetic material (can/cannot) be magnetized.

★ ★ ★ ★ ★

can

31. A ferromagnetic material is magnetized (i.e., made to act like a magnet) when the magnetic fields of its atoms are aligned in (the same direction/different directions).

★ ★ ★ ★ ★

the same direction

32. Experiments show that any sample of a ferromagnetic material consists of large *groups of atoms* called *domains* where the magnetic fields of the atoms are rigidly aligned in the same direction. Each domain (has/does not have) its own magnetic field since the magnetic fields of the atoms in a domain (cancel/reinforce) each other.

★ ★ ★ ★ ★

has ; reinforce

33. Panel 42. Refer to Fig. 4 and read the descriptive paragraph. The arrows represent the magnetic fields of individual domains in the sample. The dimensions of an atom are about 10^{-10} m; the dimensions of a domain in this sample is about _____ m. Each domain consists, therefore, of (a few/very many) atoms whose magnetic fields are aligned in the same direction. In this sample, the domains themselves (are/are not) aligned in the same direction.

★ ★ ★ ★ ★

10^{-5} ; very many $\left(\dfrac{10^{-5}}{10^{-10}} \approx 10^5 \text{ atoms} \right)$; are not

34. Panel 42, Fig. 4. The separate domains in the sample are oriented in such a manner as to produce a (strong/negligible) magnetic field in the space around the sample. Each domain consists of _____ whose _____ _____ are all aligned in the same direction.

★ ★ ★ ★ ★

negligible ; atoms ; magnetic fields

35. A ferromagnetic substance consists, therefore, of regions called _____ which are groups of atoms aligned to produce a cumulative magnetic field in that region. When these regions are randomly oriented with respect to each other, their cumulative magnetic effect (is/is not) negligible.

★ ★ ★ ★ ★

domains ; is

36. Panel 42. Refer to Fig. 5. The arrows represent the magnetic fields of the separate domains (designated by letters) of this ferromagnetic sample. When the sample is immersed in an external magnetic field $\vec{B}$, we find that those domains whose fields are oriented generally in the direction of $\vec{B}$ grow at the expense of those domains whose fields are oriented generally opposite to $\vec{B}$. Thus we expect in time that domains (*f*), (*c*), and (*a*) will (grow/diminish) in size while domains (*b*), (*d*), and (*e*) will (grow/diminish) in size.
★　★　★　★　★
diminish ; grow

37. Panel 42. Figure 6 shows what happens to the sample in Fig. 5 as the external field $\vec{B}$ is applied. The boundaries of the separate domains in the sample (change/remain fixed).
★　★　★　★　★
change

38. Panel 42, Figs. 5 and 6. Those domains which are favorably oriented with respect to $\vec{B}$ (grow/diminish) while others (grow/diminish) as $\vec{B}$ is applied for longer period of time.
★　★　★　★　★
grow ; diminish

39. The arrows in these figures represent domains in a sample of ferromagnetic material. Each domain represents a group of _____ whose magnetic fields are oriented (randomly/in the same direction).

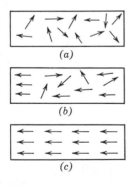

(a)

(b)

(c)

★　★　★　★　★
atoms ; in the same direction

40. Refer to figure in Frame 39. Which sample [(*a*)/(*b*)/(*c*)] exhibits the strongest external magnetic effects? Which sample [(a)/(b)/(c)] exhibits negligible external magnetic effects?

★ ★ ★ ★ ★

(c) ; (a)

41. A substance which contains magnetic domains is said to be _____ (or, in our daily experience, just *magnetic*). A substance in which the magnetic domains have been aligned in the same direction by an external magnetic field is said to be *magnetized*. The sample shown in Fig. 4, Panel 42 (is/is not) magnetic; it (is/is not) magnetized.

★ ★ ★ ★ ★

ferromagnetic ; is ; is not

42. An iron nail (is/is not) magnetic. An iron nail is magnetized only if its _____ are aligned in the same direction.

★ ★ ★ ★ ★

is ; domains *or* magnetic domains

43. Panel 42. The domains represented in Fig. 4 (are/are not) affected by external magnetic fields. This means that they (can/cannot) be aligned in the same direction by the application of an external magnetic field.

★ ★ ★ ★ ★

are ; can

44. The arrows in (a) represent magnetic domains in an iron bar. In (a), the bar is (magnetized/magnetic), but it is not (magnetized/magnetic). In (b), the

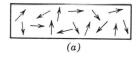

(a)

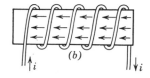

(b)

same iron bar has been placed in a solenoid through which a current *i* flows. The magnetic _____ of the solenoid aligns the _____ of the bar in such a way that the bar becomes (magnetic/magnetized).

★ ★ ★ ★ ★

magnetic ; magnetized ; field ; domains ; magnetized (Because it is already magnetic by nature of the fact that it contains domains.)

45. Samples of magnetic materials can be magnetized by the application of an external _____ _____ which tends to align their domains _____. (*How?*)

★ ★ ★ ★ ★

magnetic field ; in the same direction

46. Ampère's theory and the theory of domains explain our observations and experiments with magnets. For instance, if the bar magnet in (*a*) is broken

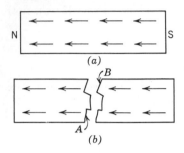

into two parts and care is taken not to disturb the orientation of the magnetic domains, we expect end *A* to be a (N-/S-) pole, and end *B* to be a (N-/S-) pole.

★ ★ ★ ★ ★

S- ; N- (Since the magnetic domains remained aligned, we now have two magnets each with its own set of poles.)

47. Experiment confirms theory on this point. The bar magnet shown in (1) is broken into the three sections shown in (2). When end (*b*) is brought near the

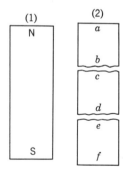

S-pole of a compass needle, it (repels/attracts) the needle. When end *e* is brought close to the S-pole of a compass needle, it (repels/attracts) the needle.

★ ★ ★ ★ ★

repels (like poles repel) ; attracts (unlike poles attract)

48. Part (2) of the figure in Frame 47 is repeated here. Mark the points a, b, c, d, e, and f, with an N or an S to indicate their polarity.

```
a
b
```
```
c
d
```
```
e
f
```

★ ★ ★ ★ ★

```
N
S
```
```
N
S
```
```
N
S
```

49. Our theory of magnetic substances also predicts that for each ferro-magnetic substance above a specified temperature, called the Curie tempera-ture, the vibration of the atoms in the crystal lattice is so great that the orientation of the magnetic field of atoms with each other will become ran-dom. The Curie temperature for iron is about 770°C. Above this temperature magnetic domains (cease/continue) to exist in iron; below this temperature, magnetic domains (cease/continue) to exist in iron.
★ ★ ★ ★ ★

cease ; continue

Section 12. Review and Problems

1. According to Ampère's theory, magnetic fields in the space around bar magnets are due to electric _____ inside the magnets which we associate today with the motion and spin of _____ in their _____.
★ ★ ★ ★ ★

currents ; electrons ; atoms

2. A bar magnet consists of many small atomic currents with their magnetic fields oriented (randomly/in antiparallel directions/in the same direction). Inside the magnet, adjacent sections of current (refer to Figs. 1 to 3 of Panel 42) (reinforce/cancel) each other. The external effect is the same we expect when a current flows around the (inside/surface) of the magnet. This theory is suggested by the similar magnetic fields of a bar magnet and a ———————————.

* * * * *

in the same direction ; cancel ; surface ; solenoid

3. Cobalt is a ferromagnetic material. This means that a sample of cobalt at ordinary temperatures contains groups of ——————— whose ———————— ——————— are aligned in the same direction. These groups are called ———————.

* * * * *

atoms ; magnetic fields ; domains

4. The domains of a sample of a ferromagnetic substance can be aligned. When such alignment occurs, we say that the sample has been ———————.

* * * * *

magnetized

5. The N-pole of a compass needle is repelled by one end of a bar of metal. This is evidence that this end of the bar is a (N-/S-) pole.

* * * * *

N-

6. The magnetic field lines in the space around a magnet start at the (N-/S-) pole and end at the (N-/S-) pole of the magnet. The direction of the magnetic field at any point in the space around a magnet is the direction assumed by the (N-/S-) pole of a ——————— ——————— placed at that point.

* * * * *

N- ; S- ; N- ; compass needle

7. Apply the appropriate right-hand rule to determine the direction of the magnetic field at c. The direction of the field is (up/down/left/right/into the page/out of the page).

* * * * *

out of the page

8.

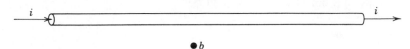

The magnetic field due to the current in this long, straight wire rotates in such a way that it points (out of/into) the page at *a* and (out of/into) the page at *b*.

★ ★ ★ ★ ★

out of ; into

9. The ○ in this figure represents an electric current in a long straight wire emerging from the plane of the page. A magnetic field rotates around the

wire in a (clockwise/counterclockwise) direction.

★ ★ ★ ★ ★

counterclockwise

10. The concentric circles represent the magnetic field around a long, straight wire carrying a current. Using the appropriate right-hand rule, we see that the current is moving (into/out of) the page.

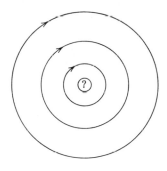

★ ★ ★ ★ ★

into

11. In order for a magnetic force to be exerted on a conductor, the conductor [(*a*) need have only a current/(*b*) need only be placed in a magnetic field/(*c*) must carry a current and also be placed in a magnetic field].

★ ★ ★ ★ ★

(*c*)

12. The direction of the magnetic force on a current i in a magnetic field $\vec{B}$ depends on (i only/$\vec{B}$ only/both i and $\vec{B}$)

★ ★ ★ ★ ★

both i and $\vec{B}$

13. The magnetic force on this conductor is directed (up/down/left/right/ into the page/out of the page).

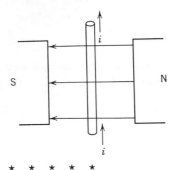

★ ★ ★ ★ ★

out of the page

14. The direction of $\vec{F}_B$ on this conductor is (up/down/into the page/out of the page/left/right).

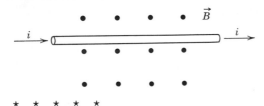

★ ★ ★ ★ ★

down

15. This particle will be deflected (up/down/into the page/out of the page) by the magnetic field.

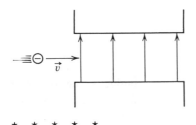

★ ★ ★ ★ ★

into the page

222 THE MAGNETIC FIELD

16. This particle will be deflected (up/down/into the page/out of the page) by the magnetic field.

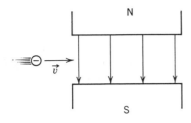

★ ★ ★ ★ ★

out of the page

17. For the problems which follow you may want to review Section 4 of this chapter for the equations required. Compute the magnitude of the magnetic field at the center of a loop of wire 0.08 meter in radius and carrying a current of 12 amp.

★ ★ ★ ★ ★

$$B = k_l \frac{i}{r} = (2\pi \times 10^{-7})\left(\frac{12}{0.08}\right)$$

$$= 3\pi \times 10^{-5} \text{ newton/amp-m } or \text{ } 9.42 \times 10^{-5} \text{ newton/amp-m}$$

18. Two long, straight wires are hung parallel to each other 2 meters apart. They carry currents of 5 amp in *opposite* directions. Compute the magnetic force exerted by the magnetic field of one wire on a 25-meter length of the other. Indicate whether the force is attracting or repelling.

★ ★ ★ ★ ★

$$F_B = k \frac{i_1 i_2 l}{d} = \frac{(2 \times 10^{-7})(5)(5)(25)}{2} = 6.25 \times 10^{-5} \text{ newton repelling}$$

19. Compute the magnetic field at a point 2 m from a long straight wire which carries a current of 3 amp.

★ ★ ★ ★ ★

$$B = k \frac{i}{d} = \frac{(2 \times 10^{-7})(3 \text{ amp})}{2} = 3 \times 10^{-7} \text{ newton/amp-m}$$

20. A 10-meter length of wire carries a current of 3 amp and is immersed at right angles to a magnetic field of 5×10^{-2} newton/amp-m. Compute the magnetic force on this length of wire.

★ ★ ★ ★ ★

$$F_B = Bil = (5 \times 10^{-2} \text{ newton/amp-m})(3 \text{ amp})(10 \text{ m}) = 1.5 \text{ newtons}$$

21. If a 10-meter length of wire carrying a current of 7 amp is placed *parallel* to a magnetic field, $B = 3 \times 10^{-2}$ newton/amp-m, the magnetic force on it is _____ newton.

★ ★ ★ ★ ★

0 *or* zero

22. An alpha particle, which has a charge of $+2$ elem. chge., enters at right angles to a magnetic field of 3×10^{-2} newton/amp-m at a speed of 4×10^4 m/sec. Compute the magnetic force on it.

★ ★ ★ ★ ★

2 elem. chge. $= 2 \times (1.6 \times 10^{-19}$ coulomb$) = 3.2 \times 10^{-19}$ coulomb

$F_B = Bvq = (3 \times 10^{-2})(4 \times 10^4)(3.2 \times 10^{-19}) = 3.84 \times 10^{-16}$ newton

23. Refer to problem in Frame 22. Compute the radius of the path of the alpha particle while it is in the magnetic field if the mass of the alpha particle is given as 6.8×10^{-27} kg.

★ ★ ★ ★ ★

$$F_B = Bvq \text{ and } F_B = \frac{mv^2}{R}$$

$$Bvq = \frac{mv^2}{R}$$

$$R = \frac{mv}{Bq} = \frac{(6.8 \times 10^{-27})(4 \times 10^4)}{(3 \times 10^{-2})(3.2 \times 10^{-19})} = 2.8 \times 10^{-2} \text{ m}$$

24. Compute the speed of this charged particle if it moves through this combination of fields undeflected.

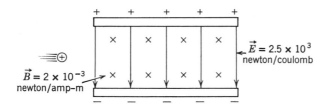

★ ★ ★ ★ ★

$$v = \frac{E}{B} = \frac{2.5 \times 10^3}{2 \times 10^{-3}} = 1.25 \times 10^6 \text{ m/sec}$$

25. Thomson's experiment measured the ratio of the _____ of an electron to the _____ of an electron.

★ ★ ★ ★ ★

charge ; mass

26. Atoms of the same element which have different masses are called _____ of that element.

★ ★ ★ ★ ★

isotopes

27. The device which uses electric and magnetic fields to measure the masses of different isotopes of the same element is the _____ _____.

★ ★ ★ ★ ★

mass spectrometer

28. The cyclotron is a particle _____ which uses a combination of electric and magnetic fields to increase the _____ energies of small _____ particles like ions or electrons.

★ ★ ★ ★ ★

accelerator ; kinetic ; charged

29. The function of the electric field in a cyclotron is to [(*a*) keep the ion moving in a semicircular path while it is in a Dee/(*b*) provide the force which increases the speed of an ion while it crosses the gap between the Dees]. The function of the magnetic field is to _____. (*Choose* (*a*) *or* (*b*) *above.*)

★ ★ ★ ★ ★

(*b*) ; (*a*)

30. A high-frequency oscillator periodically changes the _____ on the Dees. It can be set to do this at equal time intervals because the time it takes an ion to move in its semicircular path through a Dee (depends on/is independent of) the radius of its path.

★ ★ ★ ★ ★

charge ; is independent of

31. Evidence that the actual charge carriers of an electric current in a metal are (positive/negative) is provided by an experimental observation called the _____ effect.

★ ★ ★ ★ ★

negative ; Hall

32. A moving-coil ammeter is a device which uses the rotation of a coil of conducting wire in a _____ field to detect and measure electric _____ in the wire.

★ ★ ★ ★ ★

magnetic ; current

33. The moving-coil ammeter operates on the fact that the amount of rotation of a coil placed in a magnetic field is (directly proportional to/ inversely proportional to/independent of) the current in the coil.

★ ★ ★ ★ ★

directly proportional to

34. An electric motor is a device which transforms (electric/mechanical) energy into (electric/mechanical) energy.

★ ★ ★ ★ ★

electric ; mechanical

35. Splitting a bar magnet in two parts results in [(*a*) an isolated N-pole/(*b*) an isolated S-pole/(*c*) two magnets, each with its own N-pole *and* S-pole].

★ ★ ★ ★ ★

(*c*)

36. The supposed current which runs around the surface of a bar magnet and theoretically accounts for its permanent magnetic field is called an _____ current.

★ ★ ★ ★ ★

amperian

37. Certain metals like iron, cobalt, and nickel exhibit magnetic effects which are easily observable in our daily experience. These are called _____ substances. They consist of regions called _____ in which the magnetic fields of many _____ are all aligned in one direction.

★ ★ ★ ★ ★

ferromagnetic ; domains ; atoms

38. When the domains of a ferromagnetic sample are randomly directed, the sample (is/is not) magnetized.

★ ★ ★ ★ ★

is not

PROBLEMS

1. What is the magnetic force on a straight wire 1 meter in length? The current of 5 amp is at right angles to the field of 10^{-5} newton/amp-m.

2. What is the force between two parallel wires that are 0.1 meter apart when each wire is 2 meters long and has a current of 3 amp? Is the force attractive or repulsive?

3. What is the magnitude of the magnetic field in the center of a single loop of wire 0.4 in. in diameter with a current of 0.5 amp flowing through the loop?

4. If side BC in Panel 35 is 0.5 meter and a straight wire is placed parallel to it at a distance of 0.2 meter, and the current in BC is 5 amps while the current in the straight wire is 10 amp, what is the magnetic force exerted on BC by the current in the long straight wire? What is the direction of this force?

5. What is the force on an element of wire 0.02 meter long carrying 1 amp that is placed perpendicular to a magnetic field B of 10^{-3} newton/amp-m?

6. If a charge Q of 10^{-16} coulomb moves into a magnetic field B of 10^{-4} newton/amp-m, at a velocity of 10^5 meters/sec., (a) what is the magnetic force on the charge; (b) what is the direction of this force; and (c) what is the shape of the path of Q?

7. What is the radius of the path of one electron (mass 9×10^{-31} kg) moving at 5×10^5 m/sec. in a magnetic field of 10^{-3} newton/amp-m?

8. For conditions in Problem 7, at what velocity will the electron not be deflected when the electric field is 10^3 newton/coulomb?

9. What is the kinetic energy of an electron if it passes through a hole which has a potential difference of 7×10^3 volts compared to the cathode emitting the electron?

10. What is the speed of an electron under a potential difference of 4000 volts? The mass of an electron is approximately 9×10^{-31} kg, and the charge on an electron, q_e is 1.6×10^{-19} coulomb.

11. Explain how Thomson contributed to the measurement of the mass of an electron.

12. Compute the speed of an undeflected hydrogen ion moving in a combined magnetic field of 5×10^{-2} newton/amp-meter and electric field of 5×10^{-2} newton/coulomb. Assume that these fields exert forces on the ion in opposite directions as in a velocity selector.

13. Explain with the aid of a diagram how the mass of isotopes of atoms is determined with a mass spectrometer.

14. Compute the speed of a hydrogen ion (mass 1.67×10^{-27} kg) trapped in a uniform magnetic field $B = 5$ newton/amp-m if the radius of its path is 1 meter. Charge on the ion is 1.6×10^{-19} coulomb. Also compute its period of revolution.

15. Explain how the Hall effect proves that charge carriers in metals are negative.

16. Why is a commutator necessary in a d-c motor?

17. Explain how paramagnetic, diamagnetic, and ferromagnetic substances differ.

18. Compare the size of a magnetic domain with the size of an iron atom.

19. Explain why ferromagnetic substances can no longer be magnetized when they are heated up to their Curie temperatures.

Chapter Five

ELECTROMAGNETIC INDUCTION

OBJECTIVES

Upon successful completion of this chapter, the student should be able to:

1. Describe induced currents and induced EMF.
2. Describe induced EMF quantitatively.
3. Define magnetic flux and relate it to induced EMF.
4. Describe the electric generator, the induction coil, the transformer, the betatron, and the electromagnetic principles involved in their operation.
5. Solve problems involving alternating current circuits with capacitors and coils as elements; define and compute reactance and impedance.
6. Describe electromagnetic waves and the mechanism of their production.
7. Describe oscillating circuits and their use as detectors of electromagnetic waves.

INTRODUCTORY NOTE

In our study of electricity and magnetism we have encountered electric and magnetic fields and have seen that an electric current is surrounded by a magnetic field which radiates in concentric circles from the conductor carrying the current. In short, an *electric* field placed across the ends of a wire produces a magnetic field around the wire. In this chapter we consider the possibility of an inverse effect: namely, the electric current induced in a conductor when a magnetic field moves relative to the wire. This effect is called electromagnetic induction and is the source of many applications of physics to industry and commerce. Spark coils which are basic to the ignition system of automobile engines, electric generators, and transformers are all creatures of electromagnetic induction.

Section 1.   Induced Currents and Induced EMF

1. Refer to Panel 43. The letter in the upper right-hand corner is _____.
★   ★   ★   ★   ★

P

2. Panel 43. In Fig. 1, a coil of wire, consisting of many loops insulated from one another, is represented by the single loop. The ends of the coil are attached to a moving-coil ammeter A which is a device which enables us to detect and measure a _____ in the coil.

* * * * *

current ; (The device used to measure the *very small currents* produced in this experiment is called a *galvanometer*. It operates on the same principles as the moving-coil ammeter.)

3. Panel 43. The inset enables us to read the galvanometer. In Fig. 1, there (is a/is no) current in the coil.

* * * * *

is no

4. Panel 43. An arrow indicates the direction in which the bar magnet is moving. In Fig. 2, the magnet is moving (toward/away from) the coil. The galvanometer indicates that there (is a/is no) current in the coil.

* * * * *

toward ; is a

5. Panel 43. In Fig. 3, the bar magnet is (moving toward/moving away from/ held stationary inside) the coil. The galvanometer indicates that there (is a/is no) current in the coil.

* * * * *

held stationary inside ; is no

6. Panel 43. In Fig. 4, the bar magnet moves (toward/away from) the coil, and the galvanometer indicates that there (is a/is no) current in the coil.

* * * * *

away from ; is a

7. Panel 43. The existence of a current in this coil appears to depend on the _____ of the bar magnet. When the bar magnet is at rest or is not present, there (is a/is no) current in the coil.

* * * * *

motion (*or* movement, etc.) ; is no

8. Panel 43. Compare Figs. 2 and 4. When the magnet moves toward the coil the deflection of the galvanometer is to the (left/right); when it moves away from the coil, the deflection is to the (left/right). The current in Figs. 2 and 4 have (the same direction/opposite directions).

* * * * *

left ; right ; opposite directions

9. Panel 43. In Figs. 2 and 4, the N-pole of the magnet is nearer the coil. A natural experiment is to reverse the magnet and move it toward the coil

(Fig. 5) when the *S*-pole is nearer the coil. We find that the needle of the ammeter is deflected right. Suppose the magnet is then moved away from the coil. We then expect the galvanometer needle to be (deflected right/deflected left/undeflected).

★   ★   ★   ★   ★

deflected left

10. These figures show a series of experiments in which a magnet is held stationary and a coil of wire with its ends attached to galvanometer *A* is held

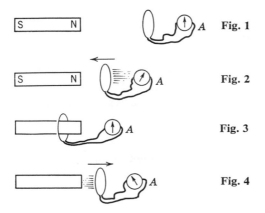

Fig. 1

Fig. 2

Fig. 3

Fig. 4

stationary (Figs. 1 and 3) or is moved toward or away from the magnet as indicated. These experiments show that when the *coil is moving* there (is a/is no) current in the coil and that when the coil and magnet are at rest relative to each other, there (is a/is no) current in the coil.

★   ★   ★   ★   ★

is a ; is no

11. The experiments shown in Panel 43 and in the figures of Frame 10 lead us to expect a current in the coil whenever the coil and the magnet are

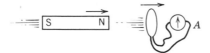

(at rest/moving) *relative to one another*. If both coil and magnet are moving in the *same* direction at the *same* speed, they (are/are not) moving relative to one another and we expect to find (a current/no current) in the coil due to their motion.

★   ★   ★   ★   ★

moving ; are not ; no current

12. Refer to Panel 44. The letter in the upper right-hand corner is _____.
★ ★ ★ ★ ★

Y

13. Panel 44. The loops in each figure represent separate coils, *a* and *b*, of conducting wire which are *at rest* relative to one another throughout the experiment. The insets show readings on a galvanometer connected to coil *b*. Coil *b* (is/is not) connected to a seat of EMF. Coil *a* (is/is not) connected to a seat of EMF.
★ ★ ★ ★ ★

is not ; is (a battery represented by)

14. Panel 44. In each figure, there (is a/is no) motion of coil *a* relative to coil *b*. In Fig. 1, the switch to coil *a* is (open/closed) and (a current/no current) flows in coil *a*. The galvanometer indicates that there (is a/is no) current in *b*.
★ ★ ★ ★ ★

is no ; open ; no current ; is no

15. Panel 44. In Fig. 2 the switch has just been closed and a _____ has started to develop in coil *a*.
★ ★ ★ ★ ★

current

16. Panel 44, Fig. 2. The current in *a* increases from zero to a steady rate very rapidly (a small fraction of a second). During this build-up of current in *a*, there is a rapid deflection of the galvanometer needle from zero to the left and back again to zero. This indicates that there is a (steady/very short-lived) current in *b* while the current in *a* is building up to a steady rate.
★ ★ ★ ★ ★

very short-lived

17. Panel 44. In Fig. 3, the switch is closed, and there is now a constant current in *a*. The galvanometer indicates that there (is a/is no) current in *b*.
★ ★ ★ ★ ★

is no

18. Panel 44, Fig. 3 shows that there is no current in coil *b* while there is (no current/a constant current) in coil *a*. Figure 1 shows that there is no current in *b* while there is (no current/a constant current) in *a*.
★ ★ ★ ★ ★

a constant current ; no current

19. Panel 44. Consider Fig. 4. In this case the switch has just been opened. In the very short time it takes the current in *a* to decrease from its constant steady value to zero, there is a deflection in the galvanometer. While the current in *a* is decreasing, there (is a/is no) current in *b*.

⋆   ⋆   ⋆   ⋆   ⋆

is a

20. Panel 44. Figure 4 shows that there is a current in *b* while the current in *a* is (constant/decreasing/increasing). Figure 2 shows that there is a current in *b* while the current in *a* is (constant/decreasing/increasing).

⋆   ⋆   ⋆   ⋆   ⋆

decreasing ; increasing

21. Panel 44. The experiments shown here lead us to conclude that when two coils at rest are set up like *a* and *b* here, a current flows through the one *not* attached to a seat of EMF only while the current in the other is (constant/changing).

⋆   ⋆   ⋆   ⋆   ⋆

changing

22. Let us see what the experiments in Panels 43 and 44 have in common. In Panel 43, we are, in effect, moving a _____ field relative to the coil.

⋆   ⋆   ⋆   ⋆   ⋆

magnetic

23. Panel 44. When the circuit of coil *a* is closed, a current rapidly builds up in *a*. At the same time a _____ field develops in the space around *a*. As this field moves out into the space around *a*, it (is/is not) moving relative to *b*. This field *moves* only while the current in *a* is (constant/increasing).

⋆   ⋆   ⋆   ⋆   ⋆

magnetic ; is ; increasing

24. Panel 44. In Fig. 3, the current in *a* is constant. The magnetic field around *a* is (moving/at rest) relative to *a* and *b*. In Fig. 4, when the circuit is opened, the current in *a* decreases rapidly, and the field around *a* (remains constant/increases/decreases).

⋆   ⋆   ⋆   ⋆   ⋆

at rest ; decreases

25. Panel 44. While the current in *a* is decreasing, the magnetic field around *a* (remains constant/increases/decreases) and is (moving/at rest) relative to *b*.

⋆   ⋆   ⋆   ⋆   ⋆

decreases ; moving

26. Panel 44. Throughout this experiment coils *a* and *b* are (moving/at rest) relative to one another. In Figs. 2 and 4, the magnetic field of *a* and coil *b* are (at rest/moving) relative to one another.

★ ★ ★ ★ ★

at rest ; moving

27. Panel 44. There is a current in *b* whenever coil *b* and the _____ _____ of coil *a* are (at rest/moving) relative to one another.

★ ★ ★ ★ ★

magnetic field ; moving

28. Panel 44. There is no current in *b* when *b* and the magnetic field of *a* are (at rest/moving) relative to one another. In principle, the situations in Panels 43 and 44 (are/are not) similar. (*Explain your answer.*)

★ ★ ★ ★ ★

at rest ; are (In panel 43 it was the relative motion of the magnet and coil which produced a current in the coil. This is in principle the same situation as we have in Panel 44.)

29. One way of describing the effects of Panels 43 and 44 is to consider what happens to the number of magnetic field lines which pass through the loop

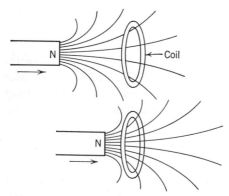

as the magnetic field moves towards or away from it. As the magnet moves closer to the coil, the number of magnetic field lines through the loop (increases/decreases/remains constant) and there (is a/is no) current in the coil.

★ ★ ★ ★ ★

increases ; is a

30. Refer to figure Frame 29. When the magnet stops moving relative to the coil, the number of magnetic field lines in the loop (increases/decreases/ remains constant) and there (is a/is no) current in the coil.

★ ★ ★ ★ ★

remains constant ; is no

31. In this figure the magnet is moving away from the coil. The number of

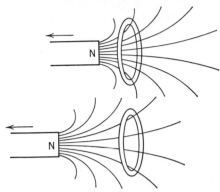

magnetic field lines in the loop (increases/decreases/remains constant) and there (is a/is no) current in the coil.

★ ★ ★ ★ ★

decreases ; is a

32. In general, a current flows in a coil while there is (a decrease only/an increase only/an increase or decrease/no change) in the number of magnetic field lines in the loop.

★ ★ ★ ★ ★

an increase or decrease

33. Reviewing Panels 43 and 44, current flows in the coil of Panel 43 and in coil *b* of Panel 44 only while there is (a change/no change) in the number of _____ _____ _____ in the loop.

★ ★ ★ ★ ★

a change ; magnetic field lines

34. As this coil moves from right to left, or from left to right, through this

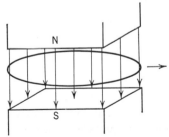

uniform magnetic field, the number of field lines in its loop (changes/remains constant) and there (is a/is no) current in the coil.

★ ★ ★ ★ ★

changes ; is a

35. As this coil moves up and down, i.e., parallel to the field, the number of

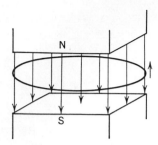

magnetic field lines passing through its loop (changes/remains constant) and there (is a/is no) current in the coil.

★   ★   ★   ★   ★

remains constant ; is no

36. The current which flows in a coil of wire while the number of magnetic lines passing through its loop changes is called an *induced current*. The current in coil *a* of Fig. 3, Panel 44, (is/is not) an induced current. The current in coil *b* of Fig. 2 (is/is not) an induced current.

★   ★   ★   ★   ★

is not ; is

37. Panel 43, Figs. 2 and 4. The currents in the coil in these figures are the result of changes in the _____ of _____ _____ _____ passing through the loop of the coil. Currents produced in this way are called _____ currents.

★   ★   ★   ★   ★

number (of) magnetic field lines ; induced

38. We saw in Chapter 3 that electric currents flow in conductors while a potential difference is maintained between points in the conductor. A device which maintains such a potential difference is called a _____ of _____.

★   ★   ★   ★   ★

seat (of) EMF

39. We assume that an induced current flows because the motion of the _____ _____ relative to the coil provides a potential difference between any two points on the coil. For this reason we say that an *induced* current results from an _____ EMF.

★   ★   ★   ★   ★

magnetic field ; induced

40. *Electromagnetic induction* is the name given to phenomena like induced currents and induced EMF. These phenomena occur when currents (remain constant/vary) and when magnetic fields (remain constant/vary). The existence of a magnetic force between two long, straight, parallel wires carrying steady currents (is/is not) associated with electromagnetic induction.
★   ★   ★   ★   ★

vary ; vary ; is not

41. Devices like the electric generator and the transformer depend on the changing magnetic fields produced by varying currents and the currents produced by changing magnetic fields. Such devices (are/are not) based on principles of electromagnetic induction.
★   ★   ★   ★   ★

are

42. Induced currents and induced EMF's occur in conductors like coils of wire when the conductor and a _____ _____ are (at rest/ moving) relative to each other. We associate such currents and EMF's with _____ induction.
★   ★   ★   ★   ★

magnetic field ; moving ; electromagnetic

Section 2.   Quantitative Treatment of Induced EMF
$\mathscr{E} = Bvl$
Lenz's Law

1. Refer to Panel 45. The letter in the upper right-hand corner is _____.
★   ★   ★   ★   ★

B

2. Panel 45 In Fig. 1, a rectangular loop of wire of width *l* is being pulled at a speed *v* to the right through a uniform magnetic field. As it moves, the number of magnetic field lines inside the rectangular loop (changes/remains constant) and there (is an/is no) induced current in the loop.
★   ★   ★   ★   ★

changes ; is an

3. Panel 45. As the loop moves to the right, the conduction electrons in the wire move with it. These electrons are charged particles moving in a _____ field. There will be a _____ force on them because of their motion (as part of the loop).

⋆ ⋆ ⋆ ⋆ ⋆

magnetic ; magnetic

4. Panel 45. Apply the right-hand rule for magnetic forces on charged particles moving in magnetic fields to the conduction electrons in the section *ab* of the rectangular loop. These electrons move from (*a* to *b*/*b* to *a*) and tend to go (clockwise/counterclockwise) around the loop.

⋆ ⋆ ⋆ ⋆ ⋆

Application of rule: Fingers into the page, thumb to the right because electrons are negatively charged. The palm of the right hand faces down. Hence, the conduction electrons move **from *a* to *b*** and around the loop in a **counterclockwise** direction.

5. Panel 45, Fig. 1. The *electric current* in the loop when $\vec{v}$ is to the right is (clockwise/counterclockwise).

⋆ ⋆ ⋆ ⋆ ⋆

clockwise

6. Panel 45, Fig. 1. The magnetic force on a conduction electron in the side *ab* of the rectangle is $F_B = $ _____ in terms of B, q, and v:

⋆ ⋆ ⋆ ⋆ ⋆

Bvq

7. Panel 45, Fig. 1. The work done on a single conduction electron by the magnetic force F_B moving it through the distance l is:

(1) $W = $ _____ in terms of F_B and l.

(2) $F_B = Bvq$

(3) Work $= $ _____ in terms of l, B, v, and q.

⋆ ⋆ ⋆ ⋆ ⋆

$F_B l$

$W = F_B l = Bvql$

8. Panel 45, Fig. 1.

(1) $W = Bvql$

(2) The induced EMF, $\mathscr{E} = \dfrac{W}{q}$

(3) $\mathscr{E} = $ _____ in terms of field, l, and speed with which l is moving through the field.

⋆ ⋆ ⋆ ⋆ ⋆

Bvl

9. Panel 45, Fig. 1. Suppose $B = 6 \times 10^{-4}$ newton/amp-m, $v = 2$ m/sec, and $l = 0.20$ m. The induced EMF is $\mathscr{E} = $ _____ volt.

⋆   ⋆   ⋆   ⋆   ⋆

$\mathscr{E} = Bvl = (6 \times 10^{-4}$ newton/amp-m$)(2$ m/sec$)(0.20$ m$)$

$= 2.4 \times 10^{-4} \dfrac{\text{newton}}{\text{amp-m}} \cdot \dfrac{\text{m}}{\text{sec}} \cdot \text{m}$

$= 2.4 \times 10^{-4} \dfrac{\text{nt}}{\text{coul/sec}} \cdot \dfrac{\text{m}}{\text{sec}} = 2.4 \times 10^{-4} \dfrac{\text{nt-m}}{\text{coulomb}} = 2.4 \times 10^{-4} \dfrac{\text{joule}}{\text{coulomb}}$

$= \mathbf{2.4 \times 10^{-4}}$ **volt**

10. Panel 45, Fig. 1. With what speed v in meters per second must the section ab of this loop be moving through $\vec{B}$ to produce an induced EMF of 5 volts if $l = 0.20$ m and $B = 3 \times 10^{-2}$ newton/amp-m?

⋆   ⋆   ⋆   ⋆   ⋆

$\mathscr{E} = Bvl$

$v = \dfrac{\mathscr{E}}{Bl} = \dfrac{5 \text{ volts}}{(3 \times 10^{-2} \text{ newton/amp-m})(0.20 \text{ m})}$

$= 8.33 \times 10^{2} \dfrac{\text{joules/coulomb}}{\text{newton/amp}}$

$= 8.33 \times 10^{2} \dfrac{(\text{newton-m/coul})}{\text{newton/coulomb/sec}}$

$= 8.33 \times 10^{2} \dfrac{\text{m}}{\text{coulomb}} \cdot \dfrac{\text{coulomb}}{\text{sec}} = \mathbf{8.33 \times 10^{2}}$ **m/sec**

11. $\mathscr{E} = Bvl$. We can save a lot of time used in deriving units for our answer when we use this formula, if we remember the units for which it is consistent. These are _____ for B, _____ for v, _____ for $\mathscr{E}$, and _____ for l.

⋆   ⋆   ⋆   ⋆   ⋆

newton/amp-m ; m/sec ; volts ; m

12. Panel 45, Fig. 1. Compute B if the induced EMF is 0.5 volt when l is 50 cm and v is 250 cm/sec.

⋆   ⋆   ⋆   ⋆   ⋆

$\mathscr{E} = Bvl$

$B = \dfrac{\mathscr{E}}{vl}$, where $\mathscr{E} = 0.5$ volt, $v = 2.5$ m/sec, and $l = 0.50$ m

$B = \dfrac{(0.5)}{(2.5)(0.50)} = 0.4$ newton/amp-m

13. Panel 45. The EMF produced in this loop drives an electric _____ around the loop in a _____-wise direction.

* * * * *

current ; clockwise

14. Panel 45, Fig. 1. While the loop is moving to the right, there is an induced current moving in the loop. In section *ab* it moves from (*a* to *b*/*b* to *a*). An induced current like any other electric current in a conductor (undergoes/ does not undergo) a magnetic force when it is placed in a magnetic field.

* * * * *

b to *a* ; undergoes

15. Panel 45, Fig. 1. Determine the direction of the magnetic force on the section *ab* due to the induced current in *ab*. It is directed (up/down/into the page/out of the page/left/right).

* * * * *

left (Fingers into page ; thumb up ; palm of right hand faces left.)

16. Panel 45, Fig. 1. Suppose $\vec{v}$ is reversed and the loop is pushed from right to left through the field. Then the induced current in *ab* moves from (*a* to *b*/*b* to *a*) and the magnetic force on *ab* due to the induced current in *ab* is directed to the right/left).

* * * * *

a to *b* ; right

17. Panel 45, Fig. 1. When the motion of the loop is to the right, the current induced in *ab* is such that the magnetic field tends to push *ab* to the (right/left). When the motion of the loop is to the left, the current induced in *ab* is such that the magnetic field tends to push *ab* to the (right/left).

* * * * *

left ; right

18. The action of the magnetic field on the induced current is one example of a principle called Lenz's law which states that _____ electric currents always (oppose/reinforce) the change that produces them.

* * * * *

induced ; oppose

19. Panel 45, Fig. 1. In this figure the "change" producing the induced current is the _____ of the loop in the magnetic field. The interaction of the induced current with the magnetic field is such that a _____ force is produced which tends to (slow down/speed up) the loop. This is one illustration of _____'s law.

* * * * *

movement *or* motion ; magnetic ; slow down ; Lenz('s)

20. Panel 45. Refer to Fig. 3. This is a cross section of a loop of wire. The current in the loop runs into the page at the bottom (× mark) and out of the page at the top ⊙, and has been induced by the motion of the magnet (toward/away from) it.

★　★　★　★　★

toward

21. Panel 45, Fig. 3. Apply the right-hand rule to determine the direction of the magnetic field at the center of the loop due to the induced current. The field moves from (left to right/right to left).

★　★　★　★　★

Wrap fingers of right hand around loop in direction of induced current, and the thumb indicates the direction of magnetic field. In this case the thumb indicates a field from *left to right*.

22. Panel 45, Fig. 3. This means that the right-hand face of the loop acts like a (N-/S-) pole and tends to (repel/attract) the magnet moving towards it.

★　★　★　★　★

N- ; repel

23. Panel 45, Fig. 3. The current induced in the loop by the motion of the magnet toward the loop is such that it tends to (oppose/reinforce) the change which produces it. Figure 3 (is/is not) an example of Lenz's law.

★　★　★　★　★

oppose ; is

24. Panel 45. Lenz's Law is especially helpful in determining the direction of induced currents. In Fig. 4, the magnet is moving away from the loop. According to Lenz's law the current induced in the loop should flow in such a way that it tends to (increase/decrease) the speed of the magnet.

★　★　★　★　★

decrease

25. Panel 45, Fig. 4. The induced current in the loop tends to slow the magnet down; the magnetic field of the loop (attracts/repels) the bar magnet. This will happen if the magnetic field produced by the induced current is directed from (right to left/left to right).

★　★　★　★　★

attracts ; right to left

26. Panel 45, Fig. 4. If the magnetic field produced by i in the figure must point from right to left, the induced current must flow (into/out of) the page at the top and (into/out of) the page at the bottom.

★　★　★　★　★

into ; out of

27.

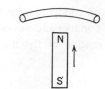

Draw an arrow over this cross section of a loop to indicate the direction of the induced current in it.

★ ★ ★ ★ ★

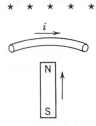

28. Draw an arrow under this cross section of a loop to indicate the direction of its induced current.

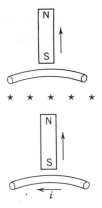

★ ★ ★ ★ ★

29. To determine the direction of an induced current in a loop of wire we use a principle known as _____ _____ which states that an induced current (opposes/reinforces) the change which produces it.

★ ★ ★ ★ ★

Lenz's law ; opposes

30. Panel 45, Figs. 1 and 2. In effect, Lenz's law states that to produce electric energy in the loop we must do _____ against the magnetic field. This electric energy must come from somewhere. Lenz's Law is an application of the law of conservation of _____ to induced currents.

★ ★ ★ ★ ★

work ; energy

Section 3. Magnetic Flux: $\phi = AB \sin \theta$

Induced EMF in Terms of Change in Magnetic Flux:

$$\mathscr{E} = \frac{\Delta\phi}{\Delta t}$$

1. We find it convenient to define a physical quantity called the *magnetic flux* through a surface of area A as the *product* of the *area* times the field

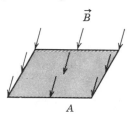

$\vec{B}$

A

times the sine of the angle θ between $\vec{B}$ and the surface. If we use ϕ (the Greek letter *phi*) to represent magnetic flux, then, in symbols; $\phi =$ _____.

★   ★   ★   ★   ★

$\phi = AB \sin \theta$

2. Refer to figure in Frame 1. $\vec{B} = 2 \times 10^{-2}$ newton/amp-m *perpendicular* to A, and $A = 3 \times 10^{-4}$ m². Since $\sin 90° = 1$, $\phi =$ _____
(*number and units*). ϕ is the product of a vector quantity times a _____
quantity. ϕ (is/is not) a vector quantity.

★   ★   ★   ★   ★

$\phi = AB \sin \theta = (3 \times 10^{-4}\text{ m}^2)(2 \times 10^{-2}\text{ newton/amp-m})(\sin 90°)$

$= 6 \times 10^{-6} \dfrac{\text{newton-m}}{\text{amp}}$

scalar ; is

3.

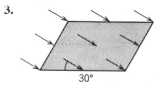

30°

Find $\sin 30°$ in your trigonometric tables and compute the magnetic flux. $\vec{\phi}$ has the same direction as $(A/\vec{B})$. $A = 5 \times 10^{-3}$ m²; $\vec{B} = 4 \times 10^{-2}$ newton/amp-m.

★   ★   ★   ★   ★

$\sin 30° = 0.5$

$\phi = AB \sin \theta = (5 \times 10^{-3}\text{ m}^2)(4 \times 10^{-2}\text{ newton/amp-m})(0.5)$

$= 10 \times 10^{-5} \dfrac{\text{newton-m}}{\text{amp}} = 1 \times 10^{-4} \dfrac{\text{newton-m}}{\text{amp}}$

$\vec{B}$

4. In this figure, $\vec{B}$ is (perpendicular/parallel) to the surface A. The angle between $\vec{B}$ and A is _____ degrees and $\phi =$ _____ newton-m/ amp.

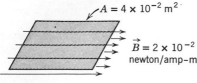

$A = 4 \times 10^{-2} \, m^2$

$\vec{B} = 2 \times 10^{-2}$
newton/amp-m

$\star \quad \star \quad \star \quad \star \quad \star$

parallel ; 0 *or* zero ; 0 *or* zero

5. Magnetic flux through a surface is defined as the _____ of the _____ field times the _____ of the surface times the _____ of the angle between them. It is a _____ quantity.
$\star \quad \star \quad \star \quad \star \quad \star$

product ; magnetic ; area ; sine ; vector

6. $\vec{\phi} = A\vec{B} \sin \theta$. As θ increases, sine θ (increases/decreases/remains constant). The maximum value of sin θ occurs when $\theta =$ _____ degrees. ϕ is a maximum when $\vec{B}$ is (perpendicular/parallel) to the surface A.
$\star \quad \star \quad \star \quad \star \quad \star$

increases ; 90 ; perpendicular

7. $\phi = A\vec{B} \sin \theta$. A change in A produces (a change/no change) in ϕ. A change in the magnitude of $\vec{B}$ produces (a change/no change) in ϕ. A change in the direction of $\vec{B}$ produces (a change/no change) in $\vec{\phi}$.
$\star \quad \star \quad \star \quad \star \quad \star$

a change ; a change ; a change

8. We will use $\Delta\phi$ to represent the *change in magnetic flux* which occurs as $\vec{B}$ or A changes. $\vec{\phi}_2$ is (greater/less) than $\vec{\phi}_1$ because _____ is

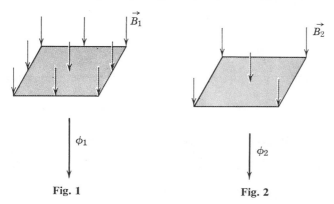

Fig. 1	Fig. 2

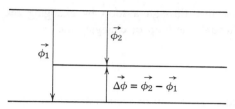

Fig. 3

greater than _____.

$\Delta \vec{\phi} =$ _____ $-$ _____.

$\star$ $\quad\star$ $\quad\star$ $\quad\star$ $\quad\star$

less ; $\vec{B}_1$, $\vec{B}_2$, $\vec{\phi}_2 - \vec{\phi}_1$

9. Refer to Fig. 3 in previous frame. Note that $\Delta \vec{\phi}$ in this case [(*a*) has the same direction as $\vec{\phi}_1$ and $\vec{\phi}_2$/(*b*) is opposite to both $\vec{\phi}_1$ and $\vec{\phi}_2$].

$\star$ $\quad\star$ $\quad\star$ $\quad\star$ $\quad\star$

(*b*)

10. We use $\Delta \vec{\phi}$ to represent the _____ in the *magnetic flux* as time goes on. If $\vec{\phi}_1$ represents the magnetic flux at time t_1 and $\vec{\phi}_2$ at some later time t_2, then $\Delta \vec{\phi} =$ _____.

$\star$ $\quad\star$ $\quad\star$ $\quad\star$ $\quad\star$

change ; $\vec{\phi}_2 - \vec{\phi}_1$

11. The magnetic flux through the loop (area A_1) in Fig. 1 here is (greater than/less than/equal to) the magnetic flux through the loop (area A_2) in Fig. 2.

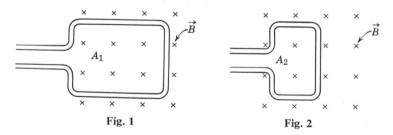

Fig. 1   **Fig. 2**

A change in the area of a loop immersed in a uniform magnetic field (changes/ does not change) ϕ.

$\star$ $\quad\star$ $\quad\star$ $\quad\star$ $\quad\star$

greater than ; changes

Magnetic Flux: $\phi = AB \sin \theta$ **245**

12. We can change the magnetic flux through a loop by changing the
_____ _____ through the loop or changing the _____
of the loop.

* * * * *

magnetic field ; area

13. Refer to Panel 45, Figs. 1 and 2. We found in Section 2 of this chapter
that the induced EMF in part *ab* of the loop as it moves with speed *v* across
the magnetic field *B* is $\mathscr{E} =$ _____.

* * * * *

Bvl

14. Panel 45. Compare Fig. 1 and 2. In the time interval Δt between Figs. 1
and 2, the section *ab* has moved a distance $x_1 - x_2$ or _____ as shown in
Fig. 2.

* * * * *

Δx

15. Panel 45, Figs. 1 and 2.

(1) $\mathscr{E} = Bvl$

(2) $v =$ _____ (in terms of Δx and Δt).

* * * * *

$$\frac{\Delta x}{\Delta t}$$

16. Panel 45, Figs. 1 and 2.

(1) $\mathscr{E} = Bvl$

(2) $v = \dfrac{\Delta x}{\Delta t}$

(3) $\mathscr{E} =$ _____ (in terms of B, l, Δt and Δx).

* * * * *

$$B\frac{\Delta x l}{\Delta t} \; or \; \frac{B \, \Delta x l}{\Delta t}$$

17. Panel 45, Figs. 1 and 2.

(1) $\mathscr{E} = Bvl$

(2) $\mathscr{E} = \dfrac{B \, \Delta x l}{\Delta t}$

(3) The product $l \, \Delta x$ is the _____ in the _____ through which $\vec{B}$
passes.

* * * * *

change ; area

18. Panel 45, Figs. 1 and 2. As the rectangular loop moves to the right, there is a change in the area through which $\vec{B}$ passes. Let ΔA represent this change. In the time interval Δt from Fig. 1 to Fig. 2, $\Delta A =$ _____ (in terms of l and Δx).

★   ★   ★   ★   ★

$l \, \Delta x$

19. Panel 44, Figs. 1 and 2.

(1) $\mathscr{E} = Bvl$

(2) $v = \dfrac{\Delta x}{\Delta t}$

(3) $\mathscr{E} = \dfrac{B \, \Delta x}{\Delta t} \, l$

(4) $\Delta A = l \, \Delta x$

(5) $\mathscr{E} =$ _____ (in terms of B, the change in the area through which $\vec{B}$ passes, and Δt).

★   ★   ★   ★   ★

$B \dfrac{\Delta A}{\Delta t}$

20. We have seen that a change in the area through which a magnetic field passes constitutes a change in magnetic _____. In symbols, we can describe what happens in Figs. 1 and 2 of Panel 45 as $\Delta \phi =$ _____.

★   ★   ★   ★   ★

flux ; $B \, \Delta A$

21. Panel 45, Figs. 1 and 2.

(1) $\mathscr{E} =$ _____ (in terms of the field, speed and length of ab).

(2) $v =$ _____ (in terms of Δx and Δt).

(3) $\mathscr{E} =$ _____ (in terms of field, Δx, Δt and length of ab).

(4) $\mathscr{E} =$ _____ (in terms of field, ΔA, Δt).

(5) $\mathscr{E} =$ _____ (in terms of change in magnetic flux and Δt).

★   ★   ★   ★   ★

(1) $\mathscr{E} = Bvl$; (2) $v = \dfrac{\Delta x}{\Delta t}$; (3) $\mathscr{E} = B \dfrac{\Delta x}{\Delta t} l$ or $\dfrac{Bl \, \Delta x}{\Delta t}$;

(4) $\mathscr{E} = \dfrac{B \, \Delta A}{\Delta t}$; (5) $\mathscr{E} = \dfrac{\Delta \phi}{\Delta t}$

22. We have shown that induced EMF can be described as the rate of _____ of _____ _____ per unit _____, at least in

the situation shown in panel 45 where the $\Delta\phi$ results from a change in the
_____ through which $\vec{B}$ passes.

★   ★   ★   ★   ★

change ; magnetic flux ; time ; area

23. $\mathcal{E} = \dfrac{\Delta\phi}{\Delta t}$. It can be shown experimentally that this equation is perfectly general and applies whether it is a change in A or a change in $\vec{B}$ which produces $\Delta\phi$. In Panel 45, Figs. 3 and 4, it is the change in $(\vec{B}/A)$ which produces $\Delta\phi$ and therefore an induced EMF.

★   ★   ★   ★   ★

$\vec{B}$ (Because the area of the loop remains constant.)

24. Refer to Panel 45, Figs. 3 and 4. Here the $\Delta\phi$ which produces an induced EMF in the coil results from a change in (the area of the coil/the magnetic field inside the coil).

★   ★   ★   ★   ★

the magnetic field inside the coil

25. Refer to Panel 46. The letter in the upper right-hand corner is _____.

★   ★   ★   ★   ★

K

26. Panel 46. Refer to Fig. 1. Here the $\dfrac{\Delta\phi}{\Delta t}$ which produces an induced EMF results from a change in $(A/\vec{B})$.

★   ★   ★   ★   ★

A

27. Panel 46. Refer to Fig. 2. In (a), the coiled conductor is stretched and attached to stops. When the stops are removed the area of the loop in the magnetic field (increases/decreases/remains constant) and an EMF (is/is not) induced in the coil.

★   ★   ★   ★   ★

decreases ; is

28. Panel 46. Figure 3 is a schematic drawing of an electromagnet. Wire in the form of solenoids is wrapped around the ends of a piece of iron. When current flows through the solenoids a magnetic field is produced across the gap. The magnitude and direction of this field depends on the _____ in the solenoids.

★   ★   ★   ★   ★

current

29. Panel 46, Fig. 3. As i increases, the magnetic field between the gap (increases/decreases). The purpose of the iron is to concentrate this field in the gap so that it passes through an area which has the same dimensions as the pole faces. All of $\vec{B}$ (is/is not) within the loop.

★   ★   ★   ★   ★

increases ; is

30. Panel 46, Fig. 3. We can change the magnetic flux in the loop by changing the _____ in the solenoid. It (is/is not) necessary to move the loop or the field to produce a change in magnetic flux.

★   ★   ★   ★   ★

current ; is not

31. Panel 46, Fig. 3. $\mathscr{E} = \dfrac{\Delta\phi}{\Delta t}$. If we change the current in the solenoids, the change in $\vec{B}$ takes place entirely *within* the loop. There (is a/is no) change in ϕ, and there (is an/is no) EMF produced in the loop.

★   ★   ★   ★   ★

is a ; is an

32. Panel 46, Fig. 3. For an EMF to be induced in a loop, it is necessary that there be a _____ in the magnetic _____ within the loop. It (is/is not) always necessary for the loop to cut across magnetic field lines.

★   ★   ★   ★   ★

change ; flux ; is not

33. In Chapter 3 we found that the existence of an electric current between two points in a conductor is evidence that (a magnetic/an electric) field exists in the conductor between those points.

★   ★   ★   ★   ★

an electric

34. Panel 46. Experiment shows that there (is a/is no) current in the loop in Fig. 3 while there is a change in the field between the magnets but no part of the field touches the conductor. This is evidence that there (is an/is no) electric field in the loop.

★   ★   ★   ★   ★

is a ; is an

35. To explain the existence of an electric field around a changing magnetic field, refer back to Panel 31, Fig. 2. There we see that an *electric* current is surrounded by (an electric/a magnetic) field which radiates from the wire in concentric circles.

★   ★   ★   ★   ★

a magnetic

36. It is not unreasonable, therefore, to suggest that a changing magnetic field might be surrounded by (an electric/a magnetic) field which radiates

from it in concentric circles, and that this accounts for the _____
field we know to exist in the loop of Fig. 3, Panel 46.
★ ★ ★ ★ ★

an electric ; electric

37. Let us pursue this analogy further. We saw that the magnetic field B a
distance d from a long, straight wire carrying current i is found by the

equation: $B = $ _____
★ ★ ★ ★ ★

$2 \times 10^{-7} \dfrac{i}{d}$

38. $B = 2 \times 10^{-7} \dfrac{i}{d}$.

The magnetic field at a point around a long, straight wire carrying a current
is (directly/inversely) proportional to the distance of the point from the wire.
★ ★ ★ ★ ★

inversely

39. Suppose a changing magnetic field represented here by the shaded area
is, in fact, surrounded by an electric field, which has the value E at a distance

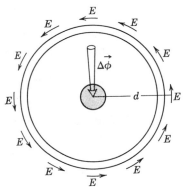

d. Let q be the charge on a conduction electron in the wire loop shown here.
The electric force on q is $F = $ _____.
★ ★ ★ ★ ★

Eq

40. Refer to figure in Frame 39.
(1) $F = Eq$.
(2) The work done in moving a conduction electron around the circumference
$(= 2\pi d)$ of the loop is $W = $ _____ (in terms of E, q, and d).
★ ★ ★ ★ ★

$W = Eq(2\pi d)$

41. Refer to figure in Frame 39.

(1) $F = Eq$.

(2) $W = Eq(2\pi d)$.

(3) The induced EMF, $\mathscr{E} =$ _____ (*In terms of $\Delta\phi$ and Δt*).

(4) $\mathscr{E} =$ _____ (*In terms of W and q*) and $\mathscr{E} =$ _____

(*In terms of E and d*).

★   ★   ★   ★   ★

$$\mathscr{E} = \frac{\Delta\phi}{\Delta t} \; ; \mathscr{E} = \frac{W}{q} \; ; \mathscr{E} = \frac{W}{q} = \frac{Eq(2\pi d)}{q} = E(2\pi d)$$

42. (1) $\mathscr{E} = \dfrac{\Delta\phi}{\Delta t}$. (2) $\mathscr{E} = E(2\pi d)$.

(3) Use (1) and (2) to solve for E in terms of $\Delta\phi$, d, and Δt: $E =$ _____.

★   ★   ★   ★   ★

$$E(2\pi d) = \frac{\Delta\phi}{\Delta t} \; ; E = \frac{1}{2\pi d} \cdot \frac{\Delta\phi}{\Delta t}$$

43. $B = 2 \times 10^{-7}\dfrac{i}{d}$. At a point a distance d from a long, straight wire carrying

a current, the _____ field varies (directly/inversely) with d.

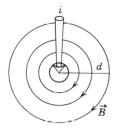

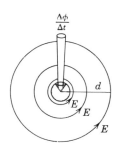

$E = \dfrac{1}{2\pi d} \cdot \dfrac{\Delta\phi}{\Delta t}$. At a point a distance d from a changing magnetic field, the

induced _____ field varies (directly/inversely) with d.

★   ★   ★   ★   ★

magnetic ; inversely ; electric ; inversely

44. $E = \dfrac{1}{2\pi d} \dfrac{\Delta \phi}{\Delta t}$ This equation for induced electric field has been verified experimentally. It is added evidence that a (changing/constant) magnetic flux is surrounded by an electric field in the same way that an electric current in a conductor is surrounded by a magnetic field.

★ ★ ★ ★ ★

changing

45. We can attribute induced currents and induced EMF's in the most general way to changing magnetic _____. This change may be due to a change in the magnitude or the direction of the _____ _____ or to a change in the _____ through which it passes.

★ ★ ★ ★ ★

flux ; magnetic field ; area

46. We can account for induced currents and EMF's by assuming that _____ fields radiate from regions in which there is a (constant/changing) magnetic _____.

★ ★ ★ ★ ★

electric ; changing ; flux

Section 4.   The Generator

1. Refer to Panel 47. The letter in the upper right-hand corner is ____ .

★ ★ ★ ★ ★

A

2. Panel 47. In Fig. 1, a hand crank attached to the axis of loop *abcd* is rotated as shown through a uniform magnetic field $\vec{B}$ so that sections *ab* and *cd* of the loop move at constant speed *v*. If *ab* = *cd* = *l*, then the induced EMF is either *ab* or *cd* is $\mathscr{E}$ = _____.

★ ★ ★ ★ ★

Bvl

3. $\mathscr{E} = Bvl$. We derived this equation for Fig. 1 of Panel 45 where $\vec{v}$ and $\vec{B}$ were (perpendicular/parallel) to each other.

★ ★ ★ ★ ★

perpendicular

4. $\mathscr{E} = Bvl \sin \theta$ is the general equation for induced EMF. θ is the angle between the direction *l* is moving and $\vec{B}$. In Fig. 1 of Panel 47, *ab* and *cd* are moving (perpendicular/parallel) to the field and θ is _____ degrees.

★ ★ ★ ★ ★

perpendicular ; 90

5. Panel 47. Refer to Fig. 2. In this figure the crank has been rotated through 90°. *ab* and *cd* are now moving (perpendicular/parallel) to the field and θ is _____ degrees. In this case, the induced EMF in *ab* or *cd* is a (maximum/minimum).

★ ★ ★ ★ ★

parallel ; 0 *or* zero ; minimum

6. Panel 47. Figs. 1 and 2. $\mathscr{E} = Bvl \sin \theta$.
The value of sin θ varies from a minimum of zero when *l* is moving (perpendicular/parallel) to $\vec{B}$ to a maximum of 1 when *l* is moving (perpendicular/parallel) to $\vec{B}$.

★ ★ ★ ★ ★

parallel ; perpendicular

7. Panel 47, Figs. 1 and 2. The induced EMF in *ab* at *any* time is given by the equation $\mathscr{E} = Bvl \sin \theta$. Of these, *B* is (constant/variable); *v* is (constant/variable); *l* is (constant/variable); sin θ is (constant/variable) as the loop rotates in $\vec{B}$.

★ ★ ★ ★ ★

constant ; constant ; constant ; variable

8. $\mathscr{E}_{ab} = Bvl \sin \theta$ becomes $\mathscr{E}_{ab} = Bvl$ when *ab* is moving perpendicular to $\vec{B}$ and sin θ = ____ (*Number*). The induced EMF in *ab* is a (maximum/minimum) when *ab* is moving perpendicular to $\vec{B}$. When *ab* is moving parallel to $\vec{B}$, the induced EMF in *ab* is a (maximum/minimum).

★ ★ ★ ★ ★

1 ; maximum ; minimum

9. Panel 47. At any given instant in its rotation through $\vec{B}$, the induced EMF in *ab* is $\mathscr{E}_{ab}$ = _____. At the same instant, the induced EMF in *cd* is $\mathscr{E}_{cd}$ = _____. Since at any given instant $\mathscr{E}_{cd}$ and $\mathscr{E}_{ab}$ tend to push electric current in the same direction, the total induced EMF is ($\mathscr{E}_{ab} + \mathscr{E}_{cd}/\mathscr{E}_{ab} - \mathscr{E}_{cd}$).

★ ★ ★ ★ ★

$Bvl \sin \theta$ and $Bvl \sin \theta$ (since *ab* = *cd* = *l*)

$\mathscr{E}_{ab} + \mathscr{E}_{cd}$

10. Panel 47, Figs. 1 and 2. The *total* induced EMF in the coil at any instant is $\mathscr{E}$ = _____ (in terms of *v*, *B*, *l*, θ).

★ ★ ★ ★ ★

$\mathscr{E} = \mathscr{E}_{ab} + \mathscr{E}_{cd} = Bvl \sin \theta + Bvl \sin \theta = 2Bvl \sin \theta$

11. Panel 47, Figs. 1 and 2. The maximum total induced EMF occurs when $\theta =$ _____ degrees and $\mathscr{E} =$ _____ (in terms of B, v, and l).

★ ★ ★ ★ ★

$90°$; $2Bvl$

12. Panel 47, Figs. 1 and 2. In Fig. 1, ab is moving (upward/downward) through the field while cd is moving (upward/downward). The current induced in the loop by this motion is from d to c to b to a around the loop. In Fig. 2, ab and cd are moving parallel to the field. At this instant there (is an/is no) induced current in the loop. As the loop continues to rotate from Fig. 2 clockwise as shown, ab is moving (upward/downward) and cd is moving (upward/downward) and the induced current (flows from d to c to b to a/flows from a to b to c to d/is zero).

★ ★ ★ ★ ★

upward ; downward ; is no ; downward ; upward ; flows from a to b to c to d.

13. Panel 47, Figs. 1 and 2. When ab and cd reverse the directions in which they move through the field, the induced current in the coil (reverses its direction/continues to flow in the same direction).

★ ★ ★ ★ ★

reverses its direction

14. Panel 47. Refer to Fig. 3. This is a graph for the induced current in the loop for a single rotation of the loop through $360°$, starting with its position in Fig. 2. We call this an *alternating* current, because it changes its _____ at _____ degrees, i.e., when it has gone through one-half a rotation.

★ ★ ★ ★ ★

direction ; 180

15. Panel 47, Figs. 2 and 3. As the loop rotates from its position in Fig. 2 through $180°$, an induced current flows around the loop in the direction $abcd$. Figure 3 shows that this current is a maximum when ab and cd are moving (perpendicular/parallel) to the field, while the loop is moving through the second half of its rotation, i.e., from $180°$ to $360°$, the current in the loop flows in the direction ($abcd$/$dcba$). For this reason, the current in the loop is called an _____ current.

★ ★ ★ ★ ★

perpendicular ; *dcba* ; alternating

16. The device drawn in Panel 47 is an elementary form of electric generator. An electric generator is a device in which mechanical energy (the turning of the crank) is transformed into _____ energy.

★ ★ ★ ★ ★

electrical

17. An alternating current changes its magnitude and direction in certain intervals of time. A *direct* current may or may not change its magnitude, but

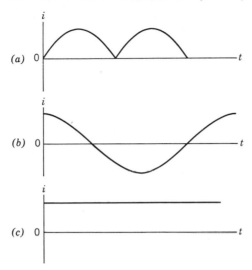

it *never* changes its direction. (*a*) is a graph of (alternating/direct) current; (*b*) is a graph of (alternating/direct) current; (*c*) is a graph of (alternating/direct) current.

★ ★ ★ ★ ★

direct (changes magnitude ; no change in direction) ; alternating ; direct.

18. Refer to figure in Frame 17. (*a*) represents a *pulsating* direct current and (*c*) a *steady* direct current. The current in the loop of an electric generator is (a pulsating direct/a steady direct/an alternating) current.

★ ★ ★ ★ ★

an alternating

19. A current which changes its magnitude but not its direction is called a _____ direct current. A current which is constant in magnitude and direction is a _____ direct current.

★ ★ ★ ★ ★

pulsating ; steady

20. Commercial electric generators have many loops rather than the single one shown in Panel 47. If there are *N* loops, then the induced EMF is multiplied by a factor *N*. A generator with *N* loops, provides an induced EMF, $\mathcal{E} = $ _____ (in terms of *B*, *v*, *l*, θ, and *N*).

★ ★ ★ ★ ★

$2NBvl \sin \theta$

21. $\mathcal{E} = 2NBvl \sin \theta$. This is not an easy equation to apply directly in practice. Another equation which uses the frequency of rotation f in revolutions per second is more convenient: $\mathcal{E} = 2\pi fNBA \sin \theta$ and A is the area enclosed by the loop. This becomes $\mathcal{E}_{max} =$ _____, when $\theta =$ _____ degrees.

★ ★ ★ ★ ★

$2\pi fNBA$; 90

22. Refer to Panel 48. The letter in the upper right-hand corner is _____.

★ ★ ★ ★ ★

T

23. Panel 48. Read Problem 1. We have the equation: $\mathcal{E}_{max} = 2\pi fNBA$. In this problem: $f = 2400$ revolution per minute = _____ revolutions per second. $A =$ _____ m^2.

★ ★ ★ ★ ★

$f = \dfrac{2400 \text{ rpm}}{60 \text{ sec/min}} = 40$ rps ; $A = (0.10 \text{ m})(0.25 \text{ m}) = 0.025 \text{ m}^2$

24. Panel 48, Problem 1. Compute the maximum induced EMF in volts.

★ ★ ★ ★ ★

$\mathcal{E}_{max} = 2\pi fNBA = 2(3.14)(40)(50)(0.025)(2 \times 10^{-2}) = 6.28$ volts

25. We will return to the other problems described in Panel 48 later. Now refer to Panel 49. The letter in the upper right-hand corner is _____.

★ ★ ★ ★ ★

H

26. Panel 49. Figure 1 is a drawing of an electric generator. _____ energy used to rotate the coil through a _____ field is transformed into _____ energy in the coil. The current in the coil is (alternating/direct) current.

★ ★ ★ ★ ★

mechanical ; magnetic ; electric ; alternating

27. Panel 49, Fig. 1. To use the electric energy produced in the coil of the generator, some mechanism must be introduced to allow current developed in the rotating coil to flow into an external circuit. This mechanism consists of a pair of *metal slip rings* attached rigidly to the same shaft which is used to rotate the coil. The slip rings touch pieces of *conducting* material called brushes which are *not* attached to the rotating shaft but are always in contact with the slip rings. The slip rings (rotate/do not rotate) with the coil. The brushes (move/do not move) with the shaft.

★ ★ ★ ★ ★

rotate ; do not move

28. Panel 49, Figs. 1 and 2. Since the slip rings and the brushes (are/are not) conductors and (are/are not) always in contact with each other, the electric current induced in the rotating coil (is/is not) always connected to the external circuit.

★ ★ ★ ★ ★

are ; are ; is

29. Panel 49. The purpose of the brushes is to connect the rotating coil to the _____ circuit. The purpose of the slip rings is to keep the rotating coil in (off and on/constant) contact with this circuit.

★ ★ ★ ★ ★

outside *or* external, etc. ; constant

30. The slip ring-brush device provides a mechanism by which [(*a*) the coil and the external circuit rotate at the same rate/(*b*) the coil can rotate and the external circuit remain stationary].

★ ★ ★ ★ ★

(*b*)

31. Panel 49. The current which flows in the external circuit (is/is not) exactly the same as the current induced in the rotating coil. The current in the external circuit is (an alternating/a steady direct/a pulsating direct) current.

★ ★ ★ ★ ★

is ; alternating

32. A generator which uses the slip rings and brushes to transmit induced current to an external circuit is often called an *alternator*. In an alternator, the current in the rotating coil (is/is not) alternating current, and the current in the external circuit (is/is not) alternating current.

★ ★ ★ ★ ★

is ; is

33. A device called a *split-ring commutator* is sometimes used instead of a pair of slip rings. A split-ring commutator provides a pulsating direct current to the external circuit while the coil develops an alternating current. A generator which uses a split-ring commutator (is/is not) an alternator.

★ ★ ★ ★ ★

is not (Because it does not provide alternating current to the external circuit.)

34. An electric generator which transmits current from the coil to the external circuit through a split-ring commutator provides the external circuit with (alternating/direct) current. An electric generator which transmits current from the coil to the external circuit through slip rings provides the external circuit with (alternating/direct) current.

★ ★ ★ ★ ★

direct ; alternating

35. An electric generator using a split-ring commutator to provide current to an external circuit is often called a d-c generator. The current in the rotating coil of a d-c generator is (alternating/direct); the current in the external circuit is (alternating/direct).

* * * * *

alternating ; direct

36. An electric generator which uses the slip ring device in Panel 49 to provide current to an external circuit is called (a d-c generator/an alternator). An electric generator which uses a split-ring commutator to provide current to an external circuit is called (a d-c generator/an alternator).

* * * * *

an alternator ; a d-c generator

37. Whether it is an alternator or a d-c generator, an electric generator transforms _____ energy into _____ energy. An electric motor transforms _____ energy into _____ energy.

* * * * *

mechanical ; electric ; electric ; mechanical

38. Which of these graphs describe the current in the rotating coil of an electric generator?

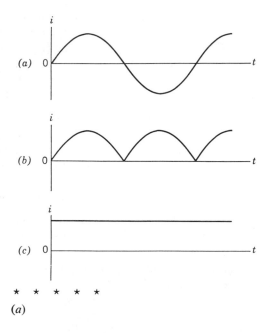

* * * * *

(*a*)

39. The coil of an electric generator is rotating at a speed of f revolutions per second in a field B. There are N turns in the coil and the loop area is A. Write an equation which relates $\mathscr{E}_{max}$, the maximum induced EMF, with f, A, N, and B.

★ ★ ★ ★ ★

$2\pi fNAB$

40. At an instant when it is moving at an angle θ to the magnetic field, the induced EMF of the coil described in Frame 39 is $\mathscr{E} =$ _____

★ ★ ★ ★ ★

$2\pi fNAB \sin \theta$

41. Panel 48. Read Problem 2.

$f =$ _____ revolutions per second

$A =$ _____ m^2

$N =$ _____ turns

★ ★ ★ ★ ★

$$f = \frac{1800 \text{ rpm}}{60 \text{ sec/m}} = 30 \text{ rps}$$

$A = \pi r^2 = \pi(0.05)^2 = 0.0025\pi \text{ m}^2$

$\mathscr{E}_{max} = 2\pi fNAB$

$$N = \frac{\mathscr{E}_{max}}{2\pi fAB} = \frac{10}{2\pi(30)(0.0025\pi)(5 \times 10^{-1})} \approx 14$$

Section 5. The Transformer, Induction Coil, Betatron

1. Refer to Panel 50. The letter in the upper right-hand corner is ____.

★ ★ ★ ★ ★

T

2. Panel 50. Refer to Fig. 1. This is a coil which is wrapped around a bar of iron that *has not* been magnetized. The ends of the coil have been attached to a switch S and a battery A. When the switch is closed, there is a _____ in the coil and a magnetic _____ in the iron.

★ ★ ★ ★ ★

current ; flux *or* field

3. Panel 50. Figure 2 is a graph of current in the coil plotted against time. When the switch is closed at time t_1, the current [(a) reaches its maximum value instantaneously/(b) reaches its maximum value gradually].

★ ★ ★ ★ ★

(b)

4. Panel 50, Figs. 1 and 2. The time interval t_1 to t_2 is a very small fraction of a second. During this time, the current in the coil (increases/decreases/remains constant) and the magnetic flux in the iron core (increases/decreases/remains constant).

★ ★ ★ ★ ★

increases ; increases

5. Panel 50, Figs. 1 and 2. From time t_2 to time t_3, the current in the coil is (increasing/decreasing/constant) and the magnetic flux in the iron core is (increasing/decreasing/constant). At time t_3 the switch is opened. During the interval between t_3 and t_4, the magnetic flux in the iron core is (increasing/decreasing/constant).

★ ★ ★ ★ ★

constant ; constant ; decreasing (Because current is decreasing.)

6. Panel 50. In Fig. 3, a loop of wire *not* connected to the coil, core, or battery is placed around the coil. There will be an EMF induced in this loop only while the magnetic flux in the core is (constant/changing).

★ ★ ★ ★ ★

changing

7. Panel 50, Figs. 2 and 3. There will be an induced EMF in the loop around the coil and iron core during the intervals (t_1 to t_2/t_2 to t_3/t_3 to t_4).

★ ★ ★ ★ ★

t_1 to t_2 ; t_3 to t_4

8. Panel 50, Figs. 2 and 3. There is an induced EMF in the loop [(a) while the switch is closed/(b) for a short time immediately after the switch is opened or closed]. There is no EMF in the loop during the time the current in the coil is (constant/varying).

★ ★ ★ ★ ★

(b) ; constant

9. Panel 50, Fig. 3. We can maintain an induced EMF in the loop if we have a device which will periodically open and close the switch. Such a device is called an *interrupter* (sometimes a vibrator). When the current in the coil has reached its maximum value at t_2, the interrupter will (close/open) the circuit.

★ ★ ★ ★ ★

open

10. To maintain an induced EMF in the loop of Fig. 3, Panel 50, an interrupter must open the circuit (i.e. open the switch) at times _____

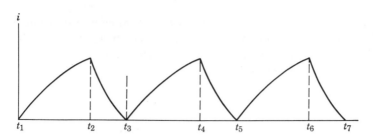

(Use symbols from the figure in this frame.) and close the circuit at times

_____.

★ ★ ★ ★ ★

t_2, t_4, t_6 ; t_1, t_3, t_5, t_7

11. Panel 50. In Fig. 4, two separate coils are wrapped around an iron core. Only the (primary/secondary) coil is attached to the battery and switch.
★ ★ ★ ★ ★

primary

12. Panel 50, Fig. 4. The purpose of the interrupter is to maintain a (constant/varying) current in the primary coil. As a result, there is a (constant/varying) magnetic flux in the iron core which produces an *induced* EMF in the loops of the _____ coil.
★ ★ ★ ★ ★

varying ; varying ; secondary

13. Panel 50, Fig. 4. The change of magnetic flux in the core depends on how rapidly the current in the _____ coil increases or decreases as the circuit is closed or opened. As this happens, an EMF (call it $\mathscr{E}$) is induced in each loop of the _____ coil, so that if there are N loops the potential difference across the gap $T_1 T_2$ is _____ (use N and $\mathscr{E}$).
★ ★ ★ ★ ★

primary ; secondary ; $N\mathscr{E}$

14. Panel 50, Fig. 4. There is a simple mathematical relationship which enables us to find the potential difference V_s induced across the ends of the secondary coil. The ratio of this potential difference to the potential difference V_p across the ends of the primary coil is the same as the ratio of the number, N_s, of turns of wire in the secondary coil to the number of turns, N_p, in the primary. In symbols, $\dfrac{V_s}{V_p} =$ _____.

★ ★ ★ ★ ★

$\dfrac{N_s}{N_p}$

15. Panel 50, Fig. 4. The potential difference across the ends of the primary coil is the terminal voltage of the _____ supplying its current. The potential difference across the ends of the secondary coil is the _____ of the EMF's induced in its individual loops.

★   ★   ★   ★   ★

battery ; sum

16. Panel 50, Fig. 4. Generally N_p is much smaller than N_s; this means that a low potential difference (about 6 to 12 volts) in the primary produces a (higher/lower) potential difference in the secondary coil.

★   ★   ★   ★   ★

higher

17. Panel 50, Fig. 4. Let $N_p = 10$ turns and $N_s = 1000$ turns. If the battery supplies the primary with 6 volts, the potential difference between T_1 and T_2

is _____ volts.

★   ★   ★   ★   ★

$$\frac{V_s}{V_p} = \frac{N_s}{N_p}$$

$$V_s = V_p \frac{N_s}{N_p} = (6 \text{ volts})\left(\frac{1000}{10}\right) = 600 \text{ volts.}$$

18. Panel 50, Fig. 4. This device is called an *induction coil*. It is a device in which electromagnetic _____ is used to provide a (low/high) potential difference in the secondary when a low potential difference is supplied to the primary. To do this the number of turns in the secondary must be (greater than/less than/equal to) the number of turns in the primary.

★   ★   ★   ★   ★

induction ; high ; greater than

19. Panel 50, Fig. 4. When the induced potential across T_1 and T_2 is sufficiently great, the air in the gap becomes a conductor and a *spark* crosses the gap. For this reason an _____ _____ is sometimes called a spark coil.

★   ★   ★   ★   ★

induction coil

20. Panel 50, Fig. 4. The potential difference required to produce a spark across $T_1 T_2$ depends on a variety of factors, among them the humidity, the distance between T_1 and T_2, etc. Suppose a spark occurs when the potential difference across T_1 T_2 is 5000 volts. If V_p is 12 volts and N_p is 100 turns,

$N_s =$ _____ turns.

★   ★   ★   ★   ★

$$\frac{V_s}{V_p} = \frac{N_s}{N_p}$$

$$N_s = \frac{V_s}{V_p} N_p = \frac{5000}{12}(100) \approx 41,667$$

21. The sparks provided by induction coils are especially useful in automobile ignition systems (see Fig. 5 of Panel 50). The spark occurs when the _____ _____ induced across the gap in the secondary is sufficiently (low/high) to make the air in the gap a _____ of electricity.

★   ★   ★   ★   ★

potential difference *or* electric potential ; high ; conductor

22. Refer to Panel 51. The letter in the upper right-hand corner is ____.

★   ★   ★   ★   ★

J

23. Panel 51. Refer to Fig. 1. This is a device called a _____. It differs from the induction coil inasmuch as the battery and interrupter connected in the primary have been replaced by a seat of EMF called an _____, which is an electric _____ which supplies (direct/alternating) current to an external circuit.

★   ★   ★   ★   ★

transformer ; alternator ; generator ; alternating

24. Panel 51, Fig. 1. The purpose of the battery and interrupter combination in an induction coil was to provide a (constant/changing) magnetic flux in the iron core. An alternating current is one which (changes/does not change) in magnitude and direction.

★   ★   ★   ★   ★

changing ; changes.

25. Panel 51, Fig. 1. The alternator supplying a _____ performs the same function as the battery-interrupter combination in an induction coil.

★   ★   ★   ★   ★

transformer

26. Panel 51, Fig. 1. The alternator supplying a transformer accounts for the changing _____ _____ in the iron core, which in turn produces an induced EMF in the (primary/secondary) coil.

★   ★   ★   ★   ★

magnetic flux ; secondary

27. Panel 51, Fig. 1. In a transformer, the secondary coil is connected to some external circuit to which it provides a current. The secondary coil (is/is not) connected to the terminals of the alternator; its EMF is that produced by the changing magnetic flux in the _____ _____.

★   ★   ★   ★ ˙★

is not ; iron core

28. Panel 51, Fig. 1. The current in the primary of a transformer is (direct/ alternating) current. The current induced in the secondary coil is (direct/ alternating). Explain.

★   ★   ★   ★   ★

alternating ; alternating (Because it is induced by a magnetic flux which changes in the same way the current in the primary changes.)

29. Panel 51, Fig. 1. The relationship between N_s, V_s, N_p, and V_p for a transformer is identical to their relationship for an induction coil. If the alternator supplies 100 volts to a primary with 50 turns of wire, compute the potential difference in a secondary coil of 1000 turns.

★   ★   ★   ★   ★

$$\frac{V_s}{V_p} = \frac{N_s}{N_p}$$

$$V_s = V_p \frac{N_s}{N_p} = (100)\left(\frac{1000}{50}\right) = 2000 \text{ volts}$$

30. The (primary/secondary) coil in either an induction coil or a transformer is the coil connected to a seat of EMF like a battery or a generator. The (primary/secondary) coil is the coil in which an EMF is _____ by the changing _____ _____ in the _____ _____.

★   ★   ★   ★   ★

primary ; secondary ; induced ; magnetic flux ; iron core

31. The purpose of an *induction coil* is to produce a higher potential in the secondary than there is in the primary coil. The number of turns in the primary of an induction coil is (always/sometimes/never) greater than the number of turns in the secondary.

★   ★   ★   ★   ★

never

32. A transformer is sometimes used to produce a larger potential in the secondary than is provided to the primary coil. This is known as a *step-up* transformer. In a step-up transformer N_p is (greater than/less than/equal to) N_s.

★   ★   ★   ★   ★

less than

33. Other transformers are constructed to provide a potential in the secondary which is less than that provided to the primary coil. This is a *step-down* transformer. The transformer in Fig. 1 of Panel 51 is a (step-up/step-down) transformer. Explain.

★ ★ ★ ★ ★

step-up (Because there are more turns in the secondary than there are in the primary.)

34. The primary of a transformer is supplied with 500 volts and has 2000 turns. Its secondary has 100 turns and supplies a potential of _____ volts. This is a (step-down/step-up) transformer.

★ ★ ★ ★ ★

$$\frac{V_s}{V_p} = \frac{N_s}{N_p}$$

$$V_s = V_p \frac{N_s}{N_p} = (500)\left(\frac{100}{2000}\right) = 25 \text{ volts}$$

step-down

35. When a transformer provides a V_s which is greater than V_p, it is called a _____ transformer. When a transformer supplies a V_s which is less than V_p, it is a _____ transformer.

★ ★ ★ ★ ★

step-up ; step-down

36. In Section 5 of Chapter 3 we learned that the power supplied in an electric circuit element with a potential difference V and a current i is $P =$ _____.

★ ★ ★ ★ ★

iV

37. When this power is used for a time t, the energy used is $W =$ _____ (*In terms of i, V, and t*).

★ ★ ★ ★ ★

$$P = \frac{W}{t} \; ; \; W = Pt \; ; \; W = iVt$$

38. Let the current in the primary of a transformer be i_p. The potential difference in the primary is V_p. In a time t, the energy supplied by the alternator to the primary is $W_p =$ _____.

★ ★ ★ ★ ★

$i_p V_p t$

39. (1) $W_p = i_p V_p t$. (2) Let V_s and i_s represent corresponding quantities in the secondary coil. The energy supplied to the secondary in a time t is

$W_s =$ _____. (3) According to the law of conservation of energy, $W_p = W_s$ or $i_p V_p =$ _____.

$\star \quad \star \quad \star \quad \star \quad \star$

$i_s V_s t;$

$i_p V_p \not{t} = i_s V_s \not{t}$

$i_p V_p = i_s V_s$

40. In a transformer, (1) $i_p V_p = i_s V_s$ or $\dfrac{i_p}{i_s} =$ _____ (*In terms of V_p and V_s*). (2) Since $\dfrac{V_s}{V_p} = \dfrac{N_s}{N_p}, \dfrac{i_p}{i_s} =$ _____ (*In terms of N_p and N_s*).

$\star \quad \star \quad \star \quad \star \quad \star$

$\dfrac{V_s}{V_p}; \dfrac{N_s}{N_p}$

41. For a transformer:

(1) $\dfrac{V_s}{V_p} = \dfrac{N_s}{N_p}$ (2) $\dfrac{V_s}{V_p} = \dfrac{i_p}{i_s}$ (3) $\dfrac{i_p}{i_s} = \dfrac{N_s}{N_p}$

(1) Shows that the potential difference in the secondary varies (directly/inversely) with the number of turns in the secondary. (2) Shows that the current and the potential in the secondary are (directly/inversely) proportional. (3) Shows that the current and the number of turns in the secondary are (directly/inversely) proportional to each other.

$\star \quad \star \quad \star \quad \star \quad \star$

directly ; inversely ; inversely

42. In a step-up transformer,

$N_s(>/=/<)N_p, \qquad V_s(>/=/<)V_p, \qquad i_s(>/=/<)i_p$

and the energy supplied to the secondary in any given time interval (is greater/is never greater) than the energy supplied to the primary during the same interval.

$\star \quad \star \quad \star \quad \star \quad \star$

> ; > ; < ; is never greater

43. Panel 48. Read Problem 3. This is a (step-up/step-down) transformer. For part (a), $N_p =$ _____ turns; $V_p =$ _____ volts; $V_s =$ ____ volts; $N_s =$ _____ turns.

$\star \quad \star \quad \star \quad \star \quad \star$

step-down ; 600 ; 120 ; 5

$\dfrac{N_s}{N_p} = \dfrac{V_s}{V_p}$

$N_s = N_p \dfrac{V_s}{V_p} = 600\left(\dfrac{5}{120}\right) = 25$

44. Panel 48. Problem 3. For part (b), $V_s =$ _____ volts, $V_p =$ _____ volts, $i_s =$ _____ amp, and $i_p =$ _____ amp.
★　★　★　★　★

5 ; 120 ; 2.8 ;

$$\frac{V_s}{V_p} = \frac{i_p}{i_s} \; ; \; i_p = i_s \frac{V_s}{V_p} = (2.8) \left(\frac{5}{120}\right) \approx \textbf{0.12 amp}$$

45. Panel 51. Refer to Fig. 2. This is a transformer in which the _____ coil consists of a single closed loop of wire. As the current in the primary increases from zero to its maximum in one direction, conduction electrons move around the loop, their speeds (increasing/decreasing/remaining constant) as the current in the primary increases.
★　★　★　★　★

secondary ; increasing

46. Panel 51, Fig. 2. If the primary has many turns, and the secondary is a thick piece of copper wire so that its electrical resistance is (high/low), the electric current in the secondary will be many times (less/greater) than the current in the primary because the current in the secondary is (directly/inversely) proportional to the number of turns.
★　★　★　★　★

low ; greater ; inversely

47. Panel 51, Fig. 2. The energy supplied to the secondary loop here is observable in a form of energy we call _____ which results from collisions between _____ _____ and the lattice of the solid conductor.
★　★　★　★　★

heat ; conduction electrons

48. Panel 51, Fig. 2. We could use all of the energy supplied by the transformer to the secondary to increase the _____ energy of conduction electrons if there was no _____ for them to interact with.
★　★　★　★　★

kinetic ; lattice

49. Panel 51. Figure 3 is a schematic drawing of a betatron, which consists of a hollow glass doughnut-shaped tube from which the air has been evacuated. When electrons are introduced into the tube it becomes a _____ of electric charge. Since there is no lattice inside the tube, these electrons encounter (greater/less) electrical resistance than they do in the copper loop of Fig. 2.
★　★　★　★　★

conductor ; less

50. Panel 51, Fig. 3. When an alternating current is applied to the coils wrapped around the large iron core, there is a change in the _____ _____ in the gap in the core and this produces an induced EMF in the doughnut which causes the _____ in it to move.

* * * * *

magnetic flux ; electrons

51. Panel 51, Fig. 3. The motion of electrons in the doughnut constitutes an induced electric _____, so that we can think of the betatron as a kind of (step-up/step-down) transformer.

* * * * *

current ; step-down

52. Panel 51, Fig. 3. The energy supplied to the electrons in the doughnut by the betatron increases their _____ and consequently their _____ energies.

* * * * *

speeds ; kinetic

53. Panel 51, Fig. 3. The ring of magnets around the doughnut serves to keep the _____ in a circular path. They (increase/do not increase) the kinetic energies of the electrons in the doughnut. The purpose of the central iron core is to provide a changing _____ _____ which (increases/does not increase) the kinetic energy of the electrons.

* * * * *

electrons ; do not increase ; magnetic flux ; increases

54. A _____ is a transformer in which the coil wrapped around the iron core and connected to an outside source of alternating current is the (primary/secondary) and the electrons in the doughnut constitute the (primary/secondary). Its purpose is to increase the _____ _____ of the electrons in the doughnut. It can do this because the doughnut has been evacuated and little energy is lost to _____ since there is no lattice for the electrons to interact with such as exists in a metal conductor.

* * * * *

betatron ; primary ; secondary ; kinetic energy ; heat

55. Panel 48. Read Problem 4. The induced EMF in the doughnut is the _____ done by electric forces on an electron in one trip around the doughnut.

* * * * *

work

56. Panel 48, Problem 4. Let W represent the work done by electric forces on an electron whose charge we represent by q. The induced EMF $\mathscr{E} =$ _____ (*In terms of W and q*).

★ ★ ★ ★ ★

$$\mathscr{E} = \frac{W}{q}$$

57. Panel 48, Problem 4.

(1) $\mathscr{E} = \dfrac{W}{q}$ or $W =$ _____.

(2) If the electron makes N trips around the doughnut in $\frac{1}{250}$ sec, the total energy transformed to it in that time is $W_t =$ _____ (*In terms of E, q, and N*).

★ ★ ★ ★ ★

$\mathscr{E}q$; $N\mathscr{E}q$

58. Panel 48, Problem 4. The electron is moving at a speed of 2.8×10^8 m/sec for $\frac{1}{250}$ sec. How far does it travel in that time?

★ ★ ★ ★ ★

distance = speed × time

distance = 2.8×10^8 m/sec × $\frac{1}{250}$ sec = 1.12×10^6 m

59. Panel 48, Problem 4. Each time the electron makes one trip around the doughnut it travels a distance of _____ m.

★ ★ ★ ★ ★

circumference = 2π (radius) = $2(3.14)(0.5) = 3.14$ m

60. Panel 48, Problem 4. In $\frac{1}{250}$ sec the electron travels 1.12×10^6 m. Each trip around the doughnut is 3.14 m. The number of times the electron travels around the doughnut in $\frac{1}{250}$ sec is $N =$ _____ (*Number*).

★ ★ ★ ★ ★

$$N = \frac{1.12 \times 10^6}{3.14} = 3.56 \times 10^5$$

61. Panel 48, Problem 4. We have seen that the induced EMF resulting from a change in magneitc flux $\Delta\phi$ in a time Δt is $\mathscr{E} =$ _____ (*in terms of Δt and $\Delta\phi$*). In this problem, $\mathscr{E} =$ _____ volts.

★ ★ ★ ★ ★

$\dfrac{\Delta\phi}{\Delta t}$; $\mathscr{E} = \dfrac{25 \text{ nt-m/amp}}{1 \text{ sec}} = 25$ volts

62. Panel 48, Problem 4.

(1) $W_t = N\mathscr{E}q$

(2) $N =$ _____ (*Number*) trips around the doughnut

    $\mathscr{E} =$ _____ volts

    $q =$ _____ coulomb

(3) $W_t =$ _____ joules

★   ★   ★   ★   ★

$N = 3.56 \times 10^5$; $\mathscr{E} = 25$ volts ; $q = 1.6 \times 10^{-19}$ coul ; $W_t = N\mathscr{E}q =$
$(3.56 \times 10^5)(25)(1.6 \times 10^{-19}) = 1.42 \times 10^{-12}$ joule

Section 6.   *A-C Circuits with Coils and Capacitors*
                    Inductive and Capacitive Reactance
                    Impedance and Ohm's Law for A-C Circuits

1. In Chapter 3 we studied electric current and electric resistance in cases
where the current-time graphs are similar to the one in this figure. We were
dealing there with (alternating/steady direct/pulsating direct) currents

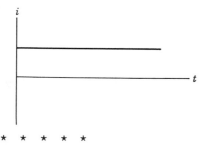

★   ★   ★   ★   ★

steady direct

2. In our study of steady direct currents we considered only those circuit
elements in which electric energy was transformed into heat. Such elements
are called _____ and are represented by (*a/b/c/d*).

    (*a*)

    (*b*)

    (*c*)

    (*d*)

★   ★   ★   ★   ★

resistors ; *d*

3. We will let the symbol 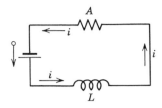 represent a coil of wire. While a steady direct current flows in this circuit, a kind of energy called _____ is

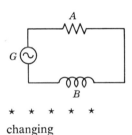

developed in circuit element *A*. There is (no magnetic field/a changing magnetic field/a constant magnetic field) in and around *L*.

★ ★ ★ ★ ★

heat ; a constant magnetic field

4. *G* represents a seat of EMF which provides alternating current to the circuit. In this case the magnetic field developed in and around *B* is (constant/ changing).

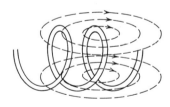

★ ★ ★ ★ ★

changing

5. A coil of wire in an *alternating current circuit* provides an interesting application of Lenz's law. The changing magnetic field around any single loop

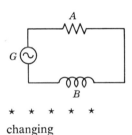

of the coil produces an induced current of its own in adjacent loops. According to Lenz's law this *self-induced* current (opposes/reinforces) the alternating current which produces it.

★ ★ ★ ★ ★

opposes

6. Let I be the current provided by the alternator G to this circuit and let i be the *self-induced* current in L. The current actually measured by ammeter A is $(I + i/I - i)$.

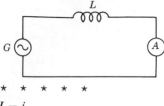

★ ★ ★ ★ ★

$I - i$

7. The opposing current induced in a coil through which an alternating current is flowing is an example of electromagnetic induction called _____ induction and can be predicted from (Ohm's/Lenz's/Coulomb's) law.
★ ★ ★ ★ ★
self ; Lenz's

8. We will use a-c and d-c to abbreviate "alternating current" and "direct current." Self-induction occurs when there is a _____ in (an a-c/a steady d-c) circuit.
★ ★ ★ ★ ★
coil ; a-c

9. In an a-c circuit containing a coil, all other things being equal, the current is (greater than/less than/equal to) the current in another a-c circuit in which there is no coil.
★ ★ ★ ★ ★
less than

10. In a steady d-c circuit containing a coil, all other things being equal, the current is (greater than/less than/equal to) the current in another d-c circuit in which there is no coil because in a steady d-c circuit there (is/is no) self-induction in a coil.
★ ★ ★ ★ ★
equal to ; is no

11. In its external effects, a coil in an a-c circuit reduces current and acts like (an increase/a decrease) in circuit resistance.
★ ★ ★ ★ ★
an increase

12. A coil in an a-c circuit has the external effect of increasing the resistance of the circuit inasmuch as it tends to (increase/decrease) the current in the circuit. Observation shows that it does *not* increase the heat developed in the circuit, and in this respect it (resembles/does not resemble) an ordinary resistor.

★　★　★　★　★

decrease ; does not resemble

13. For this reason, we call the added electrical resistance attributable to a coil in an a-c circuit *reactance* rather than resistance. Specifically, the reactance due to a *coil* in an a-c circuit is called *inductive reactance*. Electric energy used to overcome inductive reactance (is/is not) observed as heat.

★　★　★　★　★

is not

14. The electric energy used to overcome inductive reactance must go into some form of energy other than heat. (*Think*! What is it we associate with a coil in an a-c circuit which we do not associate with an ordinary resistor?) It is a changing _____ _____.

★　★　★　★　★

magnetic field

15. The electric energy used to overcome inductive reactance is stored as _____ energy in the magnetic field around the coil.

★　★　★　★　★

potential

16. We measure inductive reactance in ohms because it exhibits the external effect of electrical _____ inasmuch as it leads to a lessening of the electric _____ in the circuit.

★　★　★　★　★

resistance ; current

17. Since inductive reactance, which we will denote by X_L, is the result of a somewhat different physical mechanism than ordinary resistance (R), we

cannot combine X_L and R directly by simple addition. We add them as if they were vector quantities acting perpendicular to each other. The sum of X_L and R, therefore, is $Z =$ _____.

★　★　★　★　★

Use the Pythagorean theorem on the triangle,

$Z^2 = X_L^2 + R^2$

$Z = \sqrt{X_L^2 + R^2}$

18. This Pythagorean sum of X_L, representing _____ _____, and R in an a-c circuit containing a coil is called the *impedance* of the circuit and is usually represented by Z. In this circuit, $Z =$ _____ ohms.

$R = 12$ ohms

$X_L = 5$ ohms

★ ★ ★ ★ ★

inductive reactance ;

$$Z = \sqrt{R^2 + X_L^2} = \sqrt{12^2 + 5^2} = \sqrt{144 + 25} = \sqrt{169} = 13 \text{ ohms}$$

19. The Pythagorean sum of the reactance and the resistance in an a-c circuit is called the _____ of the circuit.

★ ★ ★ ★ ★

impedance

20. The _____ of this circuit is 3 ohms. The _____ of this circuit is 5 ohms. The _____ of this circuit is 4 ohms.

$R = 4$ ohm

$X_L = 3$ ohms

★ ★ ★ ★ ★

(inductive) reactance ; impedance ; resistance

21. A *capacitor* is an electric device consisting of two conductors separated by an insulator. Two metal plates separated by a piece of glass (constitute/do not constitute) a capacitor. Two pieces of glass separated by a copper plate (constitute/do not constitute) a capacitor.

★ ★ ★ ★ ★

constitute ; do not constitute

22. We use the symbol ⊣⊢ to represent a capacitor as a circuit element. The vertical lines represent the two _____ while the gap between them represents the _____ which separates them.

★ ★ ★ ★ ★

conductors ; insulator

23. Refer to Panel 52. The letter in the upper right-hand corner is _____.
★   ★   ★   ★   ★

Q

24. Panel 52. Figure 1 shows a capacitor connected to a d-c circuit in which a steady direct current can be provided by a battery. In Fig. 2, the switch S has just been closed, current flows in the direction indicated for a small fraction of a second. During this time plate P_1 of the capacitor becomes (negatively/positively) charged while P_2 becomes (negatively/positively) charged.
★   ★   ★   ★   ★

positively ; negatively

25. Panel 52, Fig. 3. The charges on P_1 and P_2 are such that the capacitor has an electric potential equal to that provided by the battery and opposite to it. This means that current (continues/ceases) to flow in the circuit.
★   ★   ★   ★   ★

ceases

26. When a capacitor is placed in a d-c circuit, current flows in the circuit while the *plates* of the capacitor are being charged. This is (an indefinitely long time/a very short time). For all *practical* purposes, then, a capacitor in a d-c circuit (prevents/does not prevent) a flow of current.
★   ★   ★   ★   ★

a very short time ; prevents

27. A capacitor in a d-c circuit has the practical effect of (a conductor/an insulator) in the circuit.
★   ★   ★   ★   ★

an insulator

28. Panel 52. Figure 4 shows a capacitor connected to the terminals of an alternator. It is characteristic of such a circuit that the direction of the _____ is reversed periodically, perhaps every $\frac{1}{120}$ sec.
★   ★   ★   ★   ★

current

29. Panel 52. Recall that the direction of electron flow is opposite that of electric current flow. In Fig. 4, electrons are flowing (toward/away from) P_1 and (toward/away from) P_2.
★   ★   ★   ★   ★

away from ; toward

30. Panel 52. Figure 5 shows what is happening $\frac{1}{120}$ sec later when the current supplied by the alternator has been reversed. Now electrons flow (toward/away from) P_1 and (toward/away from) P_2.
★   ★   ★   ★   ★

toward ; away from

31. Panel 52. In Fig. 6 $\frac{1}{120}$ sec later, the electrons have reversed their direction of flow again. As long as electrons continue to move back and forth, there (is a/is no) current in the circuit. A capacitor in (an a-c/a steady d-c) circuit prevents a continuous flow of current; a capacitor in (an a-c/a steady d-c) circuit does not prevent a continuous flow of current.
★   ★   ★   ★   ★

is a ; a steady d-c ; an a-c

32. Current will flow in [(a)/(b)] indefinitely although it will reverse its direction periodically. Current will flow in [(a)/(b)] for only a very small fraction of a second while the plates of C are charging.

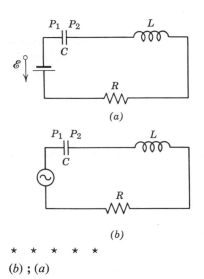

(a)

(b)

★   ★   ★   ★   ★

(b) ; (a)

33. A capacitor in an a-c circuit does not prevent the flow of current but its presence is not without complications for the circuit. With an ordinary resistor, all of the electric energy supplied by the circuit goes into _____ energy. Part of the energy supplied to a circuit containing a capacitor goes into charging its plates. This means that in an a-c circuit a certain amount of energy is always going into the creation of (a magnetic/an electric) field between the plates. This leads to a lessening of the current in the circuit and

an apparent (increase/decrease) in the total electric resistance of the circuit.
★ ★ ★ ★ ★

heat ; an electric ; increase

34. Like the "resistance" introduced into an a-c circuit by a coil, this "resistance" introduced by the insertion of a capacitor in an a-c circuit is (similar/dissimilar) to ordinary electric resistance inasmuch as its external effect is the continual production of electric fields and not heat.
★ ★ ★ ★ ★

dissimilar

35. We call this effect of a capacitor on the current in an a-c circuit its *capacitive reactance.* Like the _____ reactance of a coil in an a-c circuit it is measured in units called _____ and is added to ordinary resistance of the circuit with the aid of the _____ theorem.
★ ★ ★ ★ ★

inductive ; ohms ; Pythagorean

36. We will use X_c to represent the _____ reactance of a _____ in the same way we used X_L to represent the _____ reactance of a _____ when these devices are circuit elements in an a-c circuit.
★ ★ ★ ★ ★

capacitive ; capacitor ; inductive ; coil

37. The energy used to overcome the capacitive reactance of a capacitor goes into the continual creation of _____ fields across the plates of the capacitor. The energy used to inductive reactance of a coil goes into the continual creation of _____ fields in and round the coil.
★ ★ ★ ★ ★

electric ; magnetic

38. The impedance of this circuit is $Z =$ _____ (*In terms of R and X_c*).
$Z =$ _____ ohms.

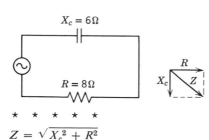

★ ★ ★ ★ ★

$Z = \sqrt{X_c^2 + R^2}$

$Z = \sqrt{36 + 64} = \sqrt{100} = 10$ ohms.

39. The capacitive and inductive reactances of a circuit are combined as if they acted in opposite directions. The combined effect of X_c and X_L is their arithmetic (sum/difference/quotient/product).

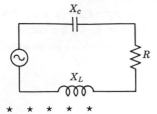

★ ★ ★ ★ ★

difference

40. The combined reactance for this circuit is _____ ohms. We compute the impedance Z of this circuit with the equation: $Z = \sqrt{(X_L - X_c)^2 + R^2}$. $Z =$ _____ ohms.

$$X_c = 3\,\Omega$$

$$R = 24\,\Omega$$

$$X_L = 10\,\Omega$$

★ ★ ★ ★ ★

$X_L - X_c = 10 - 3 = 7$ ohms

$Z = \sqrt{(X_L - X_c)^2 + R^2} = \sqrt{7^2 + 24^2} = \sqrt{49 + 576} = \sqrt{625} = 25$ ohms

41. Since a-c circuits which contain capacitors and coils exhibit reactance as well as ordinary resistance, we replace R in Ohm's law with Z. Compute the maximum current in the circuit given in Frame 40 if the maximum potential provided at the terminals of the generator is 50 volts.

★ ★ ★ ★ ★

$$i = \frac{V}{Z} = \frac{50 \text{ volts}}{25 \text{ ohms}} = 2 \text{ amp}$$

42. The alternator provides a maximum terminal potential difference of 120 volts. Compute the maximum current in this circuit.

$$X_c = 0.2\,\Omega \quad X_L = 1.7\,\Omega$$

$$R = 2.0\,\Omega$$

$$i = \frac{V}{Z} = \frac{V}{\sqrt{(X_L - X_c)^2 + R^2}} = \frac{120}{\sqrt{(1.7 - 0.2)^2 + (2.0)^2}}$$

$$= \frac{120}{\sqrt{1.5^2 + 2.0^2}} = \frac{120}{2.5} = 48 \text{ amp}$$

Section 7. Electromagnetic Waves

1. In Section 3 of this chapter we accounted for the existence of induced currents in coils (see Panel 46) as the result of _____s in magnetic flux.

★ ★ ★ ★ ★

changes

2. We saw that the electric current induced in a wire loop which was near a changing magnetic field could be accounted for by _____ fields radiating out from the changing magnetic flux in the same way that _____ fields radiated out from conductors carrying an electric current.

★ ★ ★ ★ ★

electric ; magnetic

3. We can put these conclusions as follows: Moving magnetic fields generate _____ fields in the regions through which they are moving, and moving electric fields generate _____ fields in the regions through which they are moving.

★ ★ ★ ★ ★

electric ; magnetic

4. Refer to Panel 53. The letter in the upper right-hand corner is _____.

★ ★ ★ ★ ★

A

5. Panel 53. In Fig. 1, a package of magnetic field represented by the dashed lines is moving through a volume of space with cross-sectional area K to the right. This moving package of magnetic field constitutes a changing magnetic _____ through any region of space it passes.

★ ★ ★ ★ ★

flux

6. Panel 53. In Fig. 1, the m_____ of the magnetic field $\vec{B}$ generates an

electric field $\vec{E}$ which is (parallel/perpendicular) to $\vec{B}$ and (parallel/perpendicular) to the direction in which both fields move as a single package.
$\star$ $\star$ $\star$ $\star$ $\star$
motion ; perpendicular ; perpendicular

7. Panel 53. In Fig. 2, the same package of field continues to move in the same direction. Here we show the electric field $\vec{E}$ generated in Fig. 1 as dashed lines. The motion of this electric field through any region of space through which the package moves constitutes a (constant/changing) electric field which in its turn generates a new (electric/magnetic) field.
$\star$ $\star$ $\star$ $\star$ $\star$
changing ; magnetic

8. Panel 53. As this package moves into each new region of space in its path the changing magnetic field generates (an electric/a magnetic) field in that region. The moving electric field regenerates the moving _____ field. These fields are always (parallel/perpendicular) to each other and both are always (parallel/perpendicular) to the motion of the package.
$\star$ $\star$ $\star$ $\star$ $\star$
an electric ; magnetic ; perpendicular ; perpendicular

9. The mutual generation of magnetic and electric fields in a package occurs only when the package is (at rest/moving).
$\star$ $\star$ $\star$ $\star$ $\star$
moving

10. Experiment shows that the magnitude of the electric field generated by a changing magnetic flux depends on how fast the change occurs. This means that the magnitude of the electric field generated in Fig. 1 of Panel 53 (depends on/is independent of) the speed with which the package is moving.
$\star$ $\star$ $\star$ $\star$ $\star$
depends on

11. Panel 53. The magnitude of the magnetic field generated by the electric field in Fig. 2 depends on the magnitude of the electric field generated in Fig. 1 and on the speed of the package. If $\vec{E}$ and $\vec{v}$ are *not* sufficiently large, the magnitude of the magnetic field generated in Fig. 2 (is/is not) the same as that which initially existed in Fig. 1.
$\star$ $\star$ $\star$ $\star$ $\star$
is not

12. Theory predicts that the speed at which the moving package of electric and magnetic fields is able to sustain itself is about 3×10^8 m/sec. This is, in fact, the speed of light in free space (a vacuum). Thus, if a package of electric and magnetic field moves in free space at a speed of 2×10^8 m/sec, it (is/is not) able to maintain itself indefinitely as it moves into new regions.

★　★　★　★　★

is not

13. Panel 53. A package of electric and magnetic fields such as that shown in Figs. 1 and 2 of Panel 53, which is able to sustain itself by mutual generation of electric and magnetic field as it moves through space, is called an *electromagnetic wave pulse*. An electromagnetic wave pulse moves through free space at the speed of _____ or _____ m/sec.

★　★　★　★　★

light ; 3×10^8

14. Electromagnetic wave pulses generated periodically, i.e., at constant time intervals, constitute an *electromagnetic wave*. The crossed arrows in Fig. 3 of Panel 53 represent packages of electric and magnetic field perpendicular to each other and moving as indicated at 3×10^8 m/sec. This group constitutes an electromagnetic (pulse/wave).

★　★　★　★　★

wave

15. It is no coincidence that the packages of field shown in Panel 53 have to travel at the speed of light in free space. In fact, this is very good evidence that light is one form of _____ wave.

★　★　★　★　★

electromagnetic

16. Electromagnetic waves are emitted *whenever a charged particle is accelerated*. Such a change in the motion of a charged particle provides the (stationary/moving) electric and magnetic fields which constitute an electromagnetic wave pulse. *All* electromagnetic pulses, no matter how they are produced, travel at the speed of _____ in free space.

★　★　★　★　★

moving ; light

17. We produce what are commonly called radio waves by moving charges up and down a long conductor (called an antenna) in simple harmonic motion. Such motion (is/is not) accelerated. We know, then, that radio waves must travel at a speed of _____ m/sec in free space. Radio waves (are/are not) electromagnetic waves.

★　★　★　★　★

is ; 3×10^8 ; are

18. The acceleration of *charged* particles (electrons) within molecules and atoms produce light waves and infrared waves. Infrared waves and light waves (are/are not) electromagnetic; light waves and infrared waves move at (the same speed/different speeds) in free space.

★ ★ ★ ★ ★

are ; the same speed

19. Specific kinds of electromagnetic waves are characterized by the number (measured in cycles per sec) of pulses which are emitted in a unit of time. This property of electromagnetic waves is called their *frequency*. Radio waves are emitted at a rate of about 10^6 per sec. Infrared waves are emitted at a rate of 10^{13} per sec. Radio waves and infrared waves move through space at (the same speed/different speeds). They have (the same frequency/different frequencies).

★ ★ ★ ★ ★

the same speed ; different frequencies

20. Panel 53. Figure 4 is a chart of the *electromagnetic spectrum* which shows the frequencies of several different kinds of electromagnetic waves. All waves in the electromagnetic spectrum have the same (speed/frequency).

★ ★ ★ ★ ★

speed

21. Panel 53, Fig. 4. Radio waves, infrared waves, visible and ultraviolet light, and X rays are all part of the e_____ s_____. Pulses of visible light are emitted at a (faster/slower) rate than radio waves. This means that light waves have a (higher/lower) frequency.

★ ★ ★ ★ ★

electromagnetic spectrum ; faster ; higher

22. Panel 53, Fig. 4. The electromagnetic wave pulses which constitute an X ray travel at _____ m/sec and are emitted at about _____ cycles/sec. This means that the packages of _____ and _____ fields which make up an X ray are emitted at a (faster/slower) rate than light although they travel through free space at (a faster/a slower/an equal) speed.

★ ★ ★ ★ ★

3×10^8 ; 10^{18} ; *in either order:* electric, magnetic ; faster ; an equal

Section 8. Oscillating Circuits

1. A circuit which contains only a resistance and a capacitor is called an *RC* circuit. Such a circuit has an impedance which consists of resistance and capacitive r_____. [(a)/(b)/(c)] here is an *RC* circuit.

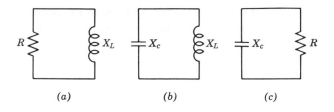

(a)   (b)   (c)

★   ★   ★   ★   ★
reactance ; (c)

2. Refer to figure in Frame 1. A circuit which consists of ordinary resistance and a coil is called an *RL* circuit. (*a*) (is/is not) an *RL* circuit; (*b*) (is/is not) an *RL* circuit.
★   ★   ★   ★   ★
is ; is not

3. Figure (*b*) in Frame 1 represents an *LC* circuit. Its total impedance is the combination of its _____ reactance and its _____ reactance. In an *LC* circuit we assume that the resistance of the connecting wires (is/is not) negligible.
★   ★   ★   ★   ★
in either order: capacitive, inductive ; is

4. Refer to Panel 54. The letter in the upper right-hand corner is _____.
★   ★   ★   ★   ★
T

5. Panel 54. The circuit in Fig. 1 consists of a coil and a capacitor. This makes it an (*RC/LC/RL*) circuit. The capacitor plates have been given equal and opposite charges. While the switch is open, there (is a/is no) current in the circuit, and all the energy of the circuit is stored in the (electric/magnetic) field of the (capacitor/coil).
★   ★   ★   ★   ★
LC ; is no ; electric ; capacitor

6. Panel 54. In Fig. 2, the switch has been closed and a current flows _____ -wise around the circuit. The result is (an increase/a decrease/ no change) in the electric field in the capacitor and (an increase/a decrease/no change) in the magnetic field of the coil.
★   ★   ★   ★   ★
counterclock(wise) ; decrease ; increase

7. Panel 54. Some time later (in Fig. 3) there is (a charge/no charge) on the plates of the capacitor. At this point all of the energy in the circuit is stored in the _____ field of the _____. Since this is an *LC* circuit, its electrical resistance (is/is not) negligible, and there (is/is no) loss of energy in the form of heat.

★ ★ ★ ★ ★

no charge ; magnetic ; coil ; is ; is no

8. Panel 54. In Fig. 4, the magnetic field in the coil (continues to increase/remains constant/begins to decrease). This induces an electric current which flows in a _____-wise direction and produces (an electric/a magnetic) field in the capacitor which (has the same direction as/is opposite to the direction) it had originally

★ ★ ★ ★ ★

begins to decrease ; counterclock(wise) ; an electric ; is opposite to the direction

9. Panel 54. In Fig. 5, all the energy of the circuit is again stored in the _____ field of the _____. In Fig. 6, current flows in a _____-wise direction, and (all/some) of the circuit energy is stored in the magnetic field of the coil. There (are/are no) losses of energy in the form of heat.

★ ★ ★ ★ ★

electric ; capacitor ; clockwise ; some ; are no

10. Panel 54. In Fig. 7, (all/some) of the energy of the circuit is stored in the *coil*. As the magnetic field collapses in Fig. 8, it produces an induced current which transfers energy from the _____ field of the _____ to the _____ field of the _____.

★ ★ ★ ★ ★

all ; magnetic ; coil ; electric ; capacitor

11. We call a system in which energy is transformed back and forth from one form to another with *negligible* loss due to heat an *oscillating* system. A mass moving up and down on a spring constitutes a system in which the energy of the system passes back and forth between the gravitational field and the electric potential energy of the spring. Such a spring-mass system (is/is not) an oscillating system.

★ ★ ★ ★ ★

is

12. As energy leaves the electric field of this capacitor in the form of current, most of it is transformed into heat in the resistor *R*. All of the energy initially stored in the electric field (is/is not) conserved in the magnetic field of *L*. Hence this (is/is not) an oscillating system.

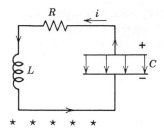

$\star$ $\star$ $\star$ $\star$ $\star$

is not ; is not

13. Panel 54. The heat developed in an LC circuit is (appreciable/neglible); an LC circuit (is/is not) an oscillating system.

$\star$ $\star$ $\star$ $\star$ $\star$

negligible ; is

14. Panel 54. The transfer of energy back and forth from the electric to the magnetic field in an LC circuit is accompanied by the flow of (a d-c/an a-c) current in the circuit.

$\star$ $\star$ $\star$ $\star$ $\star$

an a-c

15. The frequency f with which the energy in an LC circuit oscillates from one field to the other and back again depends critically on the inductive and capacitive reactances of the coil and capacitor. Inductive reactance is related to f by the equation: $X_L = 2\pi fL$, where L is a property of a coil called its inductance. The capacitive reactance of a capacitor is related to the frequency of oscillation by the equation $X_c = 1/2\pi fC$, where C is a property of the capacitor called its capacitance. The impedance of an LC circuit is *zero* when X_L and X_c are equal. Setting $2\pi fL = 1/2\pi fC$, we can solve for f to get

an equation for the *frequency* of *oscillation*: $f =$ _____ .

$\star$ $\star$ $\star$ $\star$ $\star$

$$2\pi fL = \frac{1}{2\pi fC} \; ; f^2 = \frac{1}{4\pi^2 LC} \; ; f = \frac{1}{2\pi\sqrt{LC}}$$

16. $f = 1/2\pi\sqrt{LC}$ is an equation for the _____ of _____ in an LC circuit. L and C are properties of the _____ and the _____ in the circuit.

$\star$ $\star$ $\star$ $\star$ $\star$

frequency (of) oscillation ; coil ; capacitor

17. We saw in Section 7 that an electromagnetic wave was characterized by a _____ measured in cycles per sec.

$\star$ $\star$ $\star$ $\star$ $\star$

frequency

18. When an electromagnetic wave of frequency f_w passes through a region where there is an LC circuit, it induces an electric current in the wires of the circuit. This is (a d-c/an a-c) current which oscillates with a frequency (equal to/unequal to) f_w.

★ ★ ★ ★ ★

an a-c ; equal

19. $f = 1/(2\pi\sqrt{LC})$ is the *natural* or *resonant* frequency of an LC circuit. If $f_w \neq f$, then the oscillation produced by the electromagnetic wave as it passes through the region of the circuit is likely to be short-lived, because in that case X_L and X_c are (equal/unequal) and the impedance of the circuit is (equal/unequal) to zero.

★ ★ ★ ★ ★

unequal ; unequal

20. However, if $f_w = f = 1/(2\pi\sqrt{LC})$, then the frequency of the electromagnetic wave is the _____ frequency of the circuit. In this case, the impedance of the circuit is either equal to or very close to _____ (*Number*), and it is (likely/unlikely) that the oscillation produced by the electromagnetic wave will be sustained for an appreciable length of time.

★ ★ ★ ★ ★

natural *or* resonant ; zero ; likely

21. If an electromagnetic wave moves through the region in which there is an LC circuit, and its frequency is the same as the natural frequency of the circuit, it will induce a (strong/negligible) a-c current in the circuit.

★ ★ ★ ★ ★

strong

22. Space is full of electromagnetic waves of many different frequencies. An LC circuit will *detect* (i.e., begin to oscillate with) only those that have (the same frequency as/a frequency different from) the natural frequency of the circuit.

★ ★ ★ ★ ★

the same frequency as

23. The arrow indicates that the capacitor in this circuit is a *variable* capacitor, i.e., one in which the capacitance can be varied over a range of

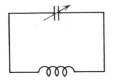

values. This means that the capacitive reactance of the circuit (can/cannot) change, and that the natural frequency of the circuit is (fixed/variable).

* * * * *

can ; variable (since $f = 1/(2\pi\sqrt{LC})$ and C is variable)

24. A variable capacitor enables us to "tune" an LC circuit over a range of electromagnetic wave frequencies. When you tune your radio to a specific station you are varying the capacitance of its _____ circuit so that its _____ frequency is the same as the frequency of the _____ waves emitted by the antenna of that station.

* * * * *

LC ; natural *or* resonant ; electromagnetic

Section 9.   *Review and Problems*

1. When a coil of wire and a magnet (are at rest/are moving) relative to one another, there is an _____ EMF in the coil.

* * * * *

are moving ; induced

2. According to Lenz's law, an induced current tends to (reinforce/oppose) the change which is producing it. While the N-pole of a magnet is being moved toward a loop of wire, it produces an induced current in the loop which makes the face of the loop nearer the magnet a (N-/S-) pole.

* * * * *

oppose ; N-

3. A current is induced in a loop whenever the total number of magnetic field lines in the loop is (constant/changing).

* * * * *

changing

4. The currents and EMF's produced in a conductor when it is moving relative to a magnetic field are called, generally, _____

_____.

* * * * *

electromagnetic induction

5. A length of wire l is moving at right angles to a uniform magnetic field $\vec{B}$ at a speed v. Write an equation for the EMF induced in the wire in terms of its length, speed and the magnitude of the field.

* * * * *

$\mathscr{E} = Bvl$

6. A 2-meter length of wire is moving at right angles to a magnetic field $\vec{B} = 3 \times 10^{-2}$ newton/amp-m at a speed of 5 m/sec. Compute the induced EMF

★ ★ ★ ★ ★

$\mathcal{E} = Bvl = (3 \times 10^{-2}$ newton/amp-m$)(5$ m/sec$)(2$m$) = 0.30$ volt

7. Lenz's law can be interpreted as requiring that _____ must be done by a coil-magnetic field system to create an _____ EMF. In effect, this is one more example of the law of conservation of _____.

★ ★ ★ ★ ★

work ; induced ; energy

8. A uniform magnetic field $\vec{B} = 3 \times 10^{-2}$ newton/amp-m passes at right angles through an area of 3m². The magnetic flux through this surface is _____ newton-m/amp.

★ ★ ★ ★ ★

$\phi = AB \sin \theta = (3$ m²$)(3 \times 10^{-2}$ newton/amp-m$) \sin 90°$

$= (3$ m²$)(3 \times 10^{-2}$ newton/amp-m$)(1) = 9 \times 10^{-2}$ newton-m/amp

9. The change in the magnetic flux inside a loop of wire is 5×10^{-1} newton-m/amp in 0.25 sec. The EMF induced in the loop is _____ volt.

★ ★ ★ ★ ★

$\mathcal{E} = \dfrac{\Delta\phi}{\Delta t} = \dfrac{5 \times 10^{-1} \text{ newton-m/amp}}{0.25 \text{ sec}} = 2$ newton-m/amp-sec $= \mathbf{2 \text{ volts}}$

10. We can describe electromagnetic induction most generally by describing it as the result of _____ in magnetic _____.

★ ★ ★ ★ ★

changes ; flux

11. For EMF to be induced in a loop it (is/is not) necessary for the loop to cross magnetic field lines.

★ ★ ★ ★ ★

is not (It is only necessary for the total magnetic flux within it to be changing.)

12. (An electric/A magnetic) field radiates from a conductor which carries an electric current. We can explain electromagnetic induction by assuming that (an electric/a magnetic) field radiates from a region in which there is a changing _____ _____.

★ ★ ★ ★ ★

A magnetic ; an electric ; magnetic flux

13. An electric generator is a device which transforms _____

energy to _____ energy. An electric motor transforms _____
energy to _____ energy.

★ ★ ★ ★ ★

mechanical ; electric ; electric ; mechanical

14. (Alternating/Pulsating direct/Steady direct) current changes its magnitude and direction periodically. (Alternating/Pulsating direct/Steady direct) current does not change its magnitude nor its direction.

★ ★ ★ ★ ★

Alternating ; Steady direct

15. [(a)/(b)/(c)] is a graph of alternating current. [(a)/(b)/(c)] is a graph of steady direct current. [(a)/(b)/(c)] is a graph of pulsating direct current.

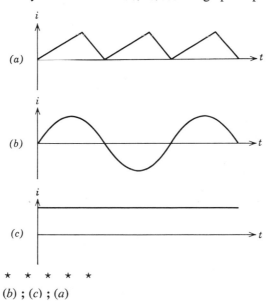

★ ★ ★ ★ ★

(b) ; (c) ; (a)

16. Compute the maximum EMF provided in a generator coil which has an area of 0.02 m², 1500 turns of wire, and rotates at 1200 revolutions per minute in a uniform magnetic field $B = 3 \times 10^{-2}$ newton/amp-m. (Review Section 4 for appropriate formula.)

★ ★ ★ ★ ★

$$\mathscr{E}_{max} = 2\pi fNBA = 2(3.14)\left(\frac{1200}{60}\right)(1500)(3 \times 10^{-2})(0.02) = 113 \text{ volts}$$

17. The current developed in the coils of an electric generator is (always/sometimes/never) an alternating current.

★ ★ ★ ★ ★

always

18. An electric generator which provides alternating current to an outside circuit is called an _____.

★ ★ ★ ★ ★

alternator

19. A 6-volt battery is used in the primary of an induction coil. Compute the potential induced in the secondary if it has 10,000 turns and the primary has 200 turns.

★ ★ ★ ★ ★

$$\frac{V_s}{V_p} = \frac{N_s}{N_p}$$

$$V_s = (6)\left(\frac{10000}{200}\right) = 300 \text{ volts}$$

20. The potential difference in the primary coil of a transformer is 200 volts; the potential difference provided to the secondary is 25 volts. This is a (step-up/step-down) transformer. If the current drawn from the secondary is 15 amp, the current in the primary is _____ amp. The power used in the secondary is _____ watts.

★ ★ ★ ★ ★

step-down ; $\dfrac{V_s}{V_p} = \dfrac{i_p}{i_s}$; $\dfrac{25}{200} = \dfrac{i_p}{15}$; $i_p = 1.9$ amp

Power $= i_s V_s = (15)(25) = 375$ watts

21. In principle the betatron is a (step-up/step-down) transformer in which the (primary/secondary) coil is replaced by the hollow doughnut-shaped tube. Energy is transferred to _____ in the tube as the _____ _____ through the hole of the doughnut changes rapidly.

★ ★ ★ ★ ★

step-down ; secondary ; electrons ; magnetic flux

22. The current in the primary of an induction coil is (direct/alternating) current. The current in the primary of a betatron is (direct/alternating) current.

★ ★ ★ ★ ★

direct ; alternating

23. In a betatron the energy supplied by the changing magnetic flux in the primary is changed to (heat/kinetic energy of electrons) in the doughnut-shaped tube.

★ ★ ★ ★ ★

kinetic energy of electrons

24. An alternating current in a coil of wire induces another electric current in the coil because it produces a (constant/varying) magnetic field in the region in and around the coil. This self-induced current (reinforces/opposes) the current which produces it.

★ ★ ★ ★ ★

varying ; opposes

25. Reactance in an a-c circuit (is/is not) effective in producing heat; it (is/is not) effective in reducing the current in the circuit.

★ ★ ★ ★ ★

is not ; is

26. The reactance due to the presence of a coil in an a-c circuit is called ———— reactance. The electric energy used to overcome this kind of reactance is stored in the —————————— ———————— of the coil.

★ ★ ★ ★ ★

inductive ; magnetic field

27. The capacitive reactance of an a-c circuit is 5 ohms ; the inductive reactance is 8 ohms. Compute the impedance of the circuit if the ordinary resistance of the circuit is 4 ohms.

★ ★ ★ ★ ★

$$Z = \sqrt{(X_L - X_c)^2 + R^2} = \sqrt{(8 - 5)^2 + (4)^2} = 5 \text{ ohms}$$

28. The energy used to overcome capacitive reactance is stored in the ———————— ———————— of the capacitor.

★ ★ ★ ★ ★

electric field

29. The combined capacitive and inductive reactance of an a-c circuit is 5 ohms. The ordinary resistance of the circuit amounts to 12 ohms. The maximum potential across the ends of the circuit is 52 volts. Compute the maximum current in the circuit.

★ ★ ★ ★ ★

$$i = \frac{V}{Z} = \frac{V}{\sqrt{(X_L - X_c)^2 + 12^2}} = \frac{52}{\sqrt{5^2 + 12^2}} = \frac{52}{13} = 4 \text{ amp}$$

30. Electromagnetic waves consist of packages of ———————————— and ———————————— ———————————— which are moving through space at the speed of ——————.

★ ★ ★ ★ ★

in either order: electric, magnetic ; fields ; light

31. Moving magnetic and electric fields continue to regenerate each other only when moving at a speed of ———————— m/sec in free space.

★ ★ ★ ★ ★

3×10^8

32. Radio waves and light travel at (the same speed/different speeds) in free space. They have (the same frequency/different frequencies).

$\star$ $\star$ $\star$ $\star$ $\star$

the same speed ; different frequencies

33. Electromagnetic waves are often produced when (charged/uncharged/either charged or uncharged) particles are moving (at constant velocity/with accelerated velocity).

$\star$ $\star$ $\star$ $\star$ $\star$

charged ; with accelerated velocity

PROBLEMS

1. Draw positions of the coil in the magnetic field in Panel 47 for each 90° of the graph.

2. What is the magnetic force on a conduction electron in a wire cutting at right angles to a magnetic field B with a value of 10^{-6} newton/amp-m, at a velocity of 10 m/sec? (Charge q on an electron is 1.6×10^{-19} coulomb.)

3. In a generator where B is 5×10^{-5} newton/amp-m and the velocity is 4 m/sec, and the length of one element of wire cutting through the field is 0.1 meter, what is the induced EMF?

4. In the section of ab of Panel 45, an EMF of 1 volt is induced. The length of ab is 0.05 meter and the magnetic field B is 10^{-3} newton/amp-m. At what velocity must the electron move to induce this voltage?

5. What is the length of a single length of wire cutting through a B field of 5.2×10^{-2} newton/amp-m at a velocity of 1 m/sec, inducing a voltage of 0.5 millivolt (0.0005 volt)?

6. What is the value for magnetic flux ϕ if the field B is 2×10^{-5} newton/amp-m, and the area of the field cut is 2×10^{-5} m² when the coil is cutting perpendicular to the lines of flux?

7. If in Problem 6 the coil is cutting the lines of force at 60°, what is the flux?

8. If the flux is 5×10^{-5} newton-m/amp and the area of the flux being cut at 90° is 2×10^{-4} m², what is the value for the field B?

9. What is the EMF if $\Delta\phi$ is 10^{-5} newton-m/amp and the Δt is 0.2 sec?

10. What is the work done in moving a conduction electron around the circle of wire which is 2 m in diameter? The voltage (EMF) is 2 volts, and $q = 1.6 \times 10^{-19}$ coulomb for an electron.

11. What is the maximum induced EMF in volts in a generator with a coil that has 100 turns and rotates at 100 rpm? The area of the magnetic field that is cut is 10^{-4} m and the magnetic field is 10^{-3} newton/amp-m.

12. For the conditions in Problem 11, plot a graph of the induced current for one complete revolution starting with the angle between flux and coil at $0°$ versus time.

13. What is the EMF if its coil is $30°$ to the magnetic field in Problem 11?

14. If a transformer has a primary of 240 turns operating on 120 volts a-c, and the secondary has 24 turns, what is the secondary voltage? If the primary current is 5 amperes, what is the maximum current in the secondary?

15. If a dental X-ray tube (high-voltage) transformer has a primary of 120 turns and 240 volts are supplied, what is the number of turns for the secondary in order for it to deliver 100,000 volts for the X-ray tube?

16. What is the work done in moving an electron in the doughnut of a betatron if the induced EMF is 50 volts and the number of trips per second is 10^5?

17. What is the impedance of an a-c circuit with an inductive reactance of 10 ohms and a capacitive reactance of 6 ohms?

18. What is the impedance when the capacitive reactance of a circuit is 10 ohms, the inductive reactance is 5 ohms, and the ordinary resistance is 3 ohms?

Panel 1

5. Another glass rod (which has *not* been rubbed with silk) is brought near the rubbed end of the suspended rod. The suspended rod is attracted to it (Fig. 3).

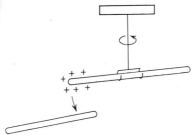

Fig. 3

6. A rubber rod is then brought near the end of the suspended glass rod. They also attract each other (Fig. 4).

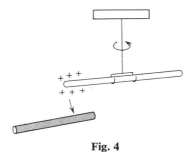

Fig. 4

7. A glass rod is then rubbed with a silk cloth. When it is brought near the rubbed end of the suspended glass rod, the suspended rod is *repelled* (Fig. 5).

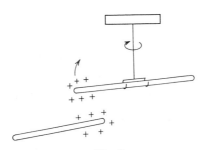

Fig. 5

Panel **1**

1. A glass rod is hung from a support by a silk thread (Fig. 1).

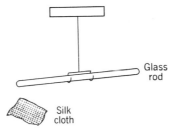

Fig. 1

2. A silk cloth is brought near one end of the rod. *Nothing happens.*

3. One end of the rod is rubbed vigorously with the silk cloth. The rod and the cloth are then separated.

4. Now when the cloth is brought near the *rubbed* end of the suspended rod, the rod is attracted to it (Fig. 2).

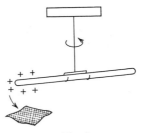

Fig. 2

3. Another rubber rod (which has not been in contact with the animal fur) is then brought near the suspended rod. The suspended rod is attracted to it (Fig. 2).

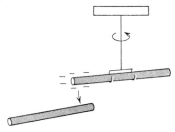

Fig. 2

4. A glass rod which is uncharged (i.e., not recently rubbed with silk) is next brought near the charged rubber rod. The rods attract each other.

5. The second rubber rod (the one used in Step 3 above) is rubbed with a piece of animal fur and brought near the suspended rubber rod. Now the rubber rods *repel* each other (Fig. 3).

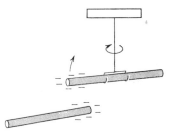

Fig. 3

6. The experimenter then brings a glass rod rubbed with silk cloth near the suspended rubber rod. He observes that it attracts the rubber rod (Fig. 4).

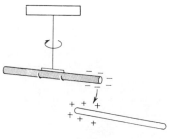

Fig. 4

Panel **2**

In this experiment we use a *rubber* rod and a cloth of wool or other animal fur, and observe the effects.

1. A rubber rod is suspended from a support by a silk thread, and a piece of animal fur (wool, etc.) is brought near it. Nothing happens.

2. One end of the rubber rod is then rubbed vigorously with the animal fur. It is then observed that when the animal fur is brought near the rubbed end of the rod, the rod is attracted to it (Fig. 1).

Fig. 1

Panel 3

3. The charged end of the second rod is then brought near the other end (the unrubbed end) of the suspended rod. Note the attraction in Fig. 2.

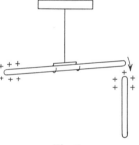

Fig. 2

4. A *negatively* charged rod is then brought near the same end of the suspended rod. Note the attraction in Fig. 3.

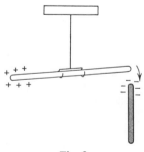

Fig. 3

1. One end of a glass rod is rubbed with silk and the rod is suspended by a thread from a support. The charged end is indicated in the accompanying figures by the (+) signs.

2. Another glass rod is held in the hand; the end of this rod is rubbed with silk and is brought near the end of the suspended rod which has been rubbed in Step 1. (See Fig. 1.)

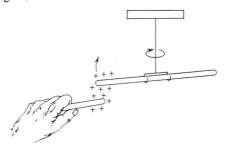

Fig. 1

1. Several light plastic balls are coated with aluminum paint. One of them is then suspended from a support by a silk thread.

2. A positively charged glass rod is brought near (but not allowed to touch) the ball, and the ball is attracted to it.

3. A negatively charged rubber rod is then brought near the suspended ball (but not allowed to touch it). The ball is attracted toward it in the same way it was observed to be attracted to the glass rod in Step 2.

4. The charged glass rod is again brought near and this time allowed to touch the ball (Fig. 1). As soon as the ball touches the rod, it snaps back away from the rod and thereafter is repelled by the positively charged glass rod (Fig. 2).

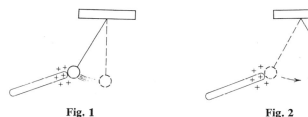

Fig. 1   **Fig. 2**

5. The experimenter touches the ball with his hand, and finds that it is again attracted to the charged glass rod when the latter is brought near but not allowed to touch it.

6. The ball is then touched with a charged rubber rod; the experimenter observes that it is again repelled as soon as it makes contact with the rod.

7. Two other balls are then hung side by side as in Fig. 3 and allowed to touch. One of the charged rods is touched to the ball on the left. The result is shown in Fig. 4.

Fig. 3   Fig. 4

Panel **4**

Panel 5

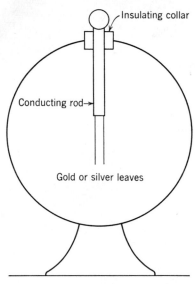

Insulating collar

Conducting rod→

Gold or silver leaves

Fig. 1

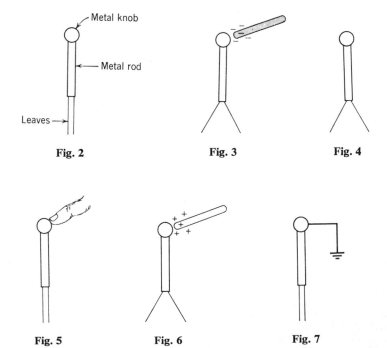

Metal knob

Metal rod

Leaves →

Fig. 2

Fig. 3

Fig. 4

Fig. 5

Fig. 6

Fig. 7

Panel 5

Figure 1 is a cross-section of a device called an *electroscope* which is used to detect electric charges. It consists of a metal ball fitted on top of a metal rod which is inserted in a collar made of an insulating material such as rubber, plastic, etc., to insulate it from the frame of the instrument. At the bottom of the rod are pasted two very light-weight leaves of gold or silver. The frame container and base are used only to house the ball, rod, and leaves and to protect the leaves from air currents, etc. A simplified drawing of an uncharged electroscope without the frame and housing is shown in Fig. 2.

Panel 6

2. A negatively charged rod is brought near (but not touching) the positively charged electroscope. The result is shown in Fig. 2.

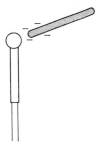

Fig. 2

3. In Fig. 3, the negatively charged rod has been removed.

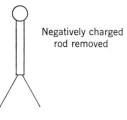

Negatively charged
rod removed

Fig. 3

4. The electroscope is discharged by grounding and then is given a negative charge by contact. The procedure followed in Steps 2 and 3 above is repeated with a *positively* charged test rod. (See Figs. 4 to 6.)

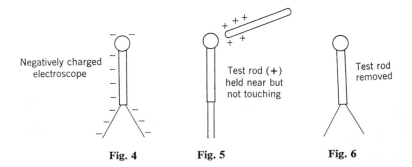

Negatively charged
electroscope

Test rod (+)
held near but
not touching

Test rod
removed

Fig. 4   **Fig. 5**   **Fig. 6**

Panel 6

13

1. A positively charged rod is used to charge an electroscope by contact. The rod is removed and the electroscope is left as shown in Fig. 1.

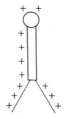

Fig. 1

Panel 7

1. A negatively charged rod is brought near an *uncharged* electroscope. The leaves diverge (Fig. 1).

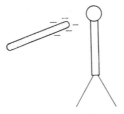

Fig. 1

2. While the rod is still held close to the knob, the electroscope is grounded (e.g., by touching the knob with the finger) (Fig. 2).

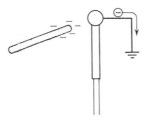

Fig. 2

3. The ground connection (finger) is removed from the knob while the rod is held close to the knob (Fig. 3). The rod is removed and the leaves are observed to diverge (Fig. 4).

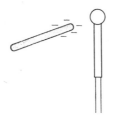

Fig. 3   **Fig. 4**

Panel 7

Panel 8

Fig. 1

Fig. 2

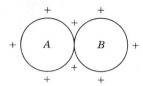

Fig. 3

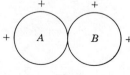

Fig. 4

Fig. 5

Panel 8

17

Panel 9

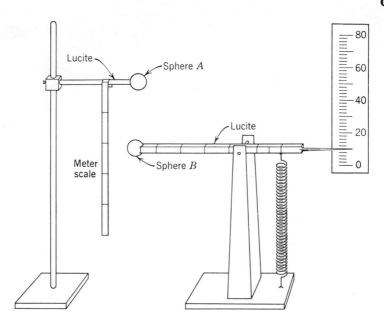

This is a device used to measure quantitatively the electric forces exerted by different amounts of charge placed at varying distances from each other. Hollow metallic spheres (hollow so that they are light) are placed at the ends of insulating (lucite) rods. The upper sphere can be adjusted so that it is always a specified distance from the lower sphere.

The lower sphere is balanced by a pointer attached to a sensitive coil spring. Since the extension of the spring is directly proportional to the force stretching it, the displacement of the pointer along the scale on the right is a good measurement of the electric force which pushes the lower sphere down and stretches the spring upwards. If the force between the charged spheres is an attracting force, then the pointer will be displaced downward.

Panel 9

The following is an experiment in which the apparatus described in Panel 9 is used to establish quantitative relations between electric force, charge, and distance.

1. A positive charge is placed on sphere A by touching it with a positively charged object.

2. Sphere A is then touched to sphere B and then adjusted a fixed distance from B. The fixed distance between A and B in this experiment is 25 cm. When A and B are set at this distance, the pointer moves from 10 to 45.

3. The changes in pointer readings are then recorded for the following: (*a*) after A has been touched with C (uncharged); (*b*) after C has been grounded to remove its charge and then touched to A again; (*c*) after Step (*b*) has been repeated; (*d*) after C is again discharged by grounding and touched to B.

4. The observations resulting from Steps 2 and 3 above are summarized in the following chart:

	I	II	III	IV	V
Experiment Step	Distance Between A and B	Charge on B	Charge on A	Product of Charges on A and B	Change in pointer reading
2	25 cm	1	1	1	35
3(*a*)	25 cm	1	$\frac{1}{2}$	$\frac{1}{2}$	$17\frac{1}{2}$
3(*b*)	25 cm	1	$\frac{1}{4}$	$\frac{1}{4}$	$8\frac{3}{4}$
3(*c*)	25 cm	1	$\frac{1}{8}$	$\frac{1}{8}$	$4\frac{3}{4}$
3(*d*)	25 cm	$\frac{1}{2}$	$\frac{1}{8}$	$\frac{1}{16}$	$2\frac{3}{16}$

5. Both A and B are discharged by grounding and the pointer returns to its original position at 10 on the scale.

6. Sphere A is again charged by contact. It is then touched to sphere B. Sphere A is then placed so that the distance between its center and the center of B is 30 cm. The pointer is observed to move from 10 to 30 on the scale.

7. Pointer readings are then taken for various distances between A and B. The results are recorded in the table below. During this part of the experiment, the charges on A and B remain constant.

Distance Between Centers	Charge on A	Charge on B	Displacement of Pointer
30 cm	1	1	20
15 cm	1	1	80
45 cm	1	1	$8\frac{8}{9}$
60 cm	1	1	5
75 cm	1	1	$3\frac{1}{5}$

Panel **10**

2. The electric force of repulsion between two equally charged objects at a distance of 10 meters between their centers is determined to be 9.2×10^{-4} newton. Compute the charge on each object in units of elementary charge.

3.

q_1 has a charge of 2.0×10^{-6} coulomb. q_2 has a charge of -2.0×10^{-6} coulomb. q_3 has a charge of 4.0×10^{-6} coulomb. (a) Compute the magnitude and the direction of the electric force of q_1 on q_2. (b) Compute the magnitude and direction of the electric force of q_3 on q_2. (c) Compute the magnitude and direction of the vector sum of the electric forces of q_1 and q_3 on q_2. (d) Compute the magnitude and the direction of the vector sum of the electric forces of q_1 and q_2 on q_3.

4. The angle between AB and BC is 90 degrees. Compute the magnitude of the vector sum of the electric forces on q_2 by q_1 and q_3 if q_1, q_2, and q_3 each represents a charge of 1.0×10^{-6} coulomb.

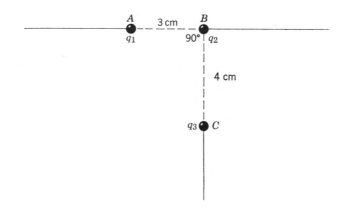

5. According to the Rutherford-Bohr model of the atom, a hydrogen atom consists of a central proton with an electron moving around it in a circular orbit of radius equal to 0.53×10^{-10} meter. Assuming that the centripetal force producing this acceleration is due solely to the electric force between the proton and the electron, compute the speed of the electron. (Use the mass of the electron given in Problem 1 of this panel.)

Panel **11**

1. The mass of an electron has been determined experimentally to be about 9.0×10^{-31} kg. (*a*) Compute the gravitational force of attraction between two electrons when they are 1 meter apart. (Use $G = 6.67 \times 10^{-11}$ newton-m^2/kg^2.) (*b*) Compute the electric force of repulsion between two electrons at the same distance. (Use $k = 2.3 \times 10^{-28}$ newton-m^2/(elem. chge.)^2.) (*c*) What is the ratio of the electric force between two electrons to the gravitational force between them at the same distance?

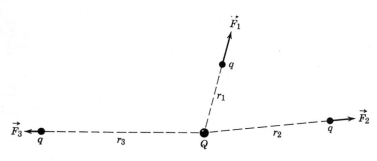

Fig. 1

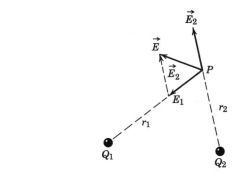

Fig. 2

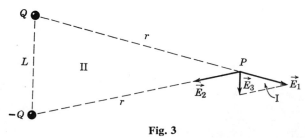

Fig. 3

Panel **12**

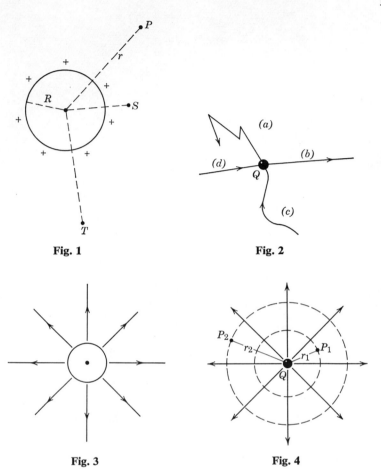

Fig. 1

Fig. 2

Fig. 3

Fig. 4

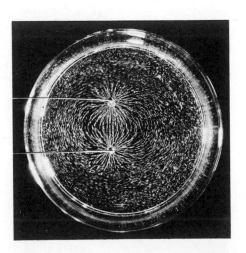

Fig. 1 Photograph of electric field pattern formed when two rods with equal and opposite charges are placed in grass seeds floating in an insulating liquid.

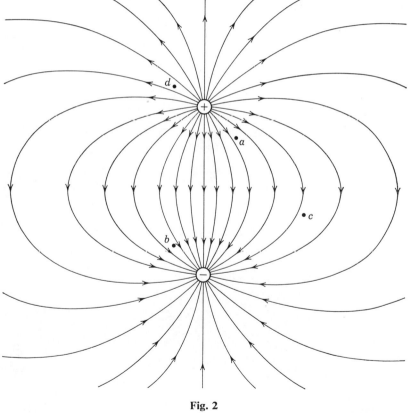

Fig. 2

Panel **14**

Panel 14

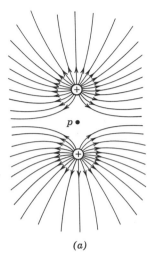

(a)

Fig. 1a

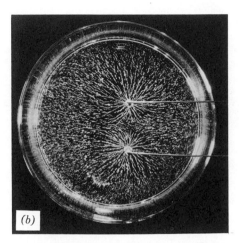

Fig. 1b Pattern formed when two rods with the same charge are placed in grass seed floating in an insulating liquid. (Courtesy Educational Services, Inc.)

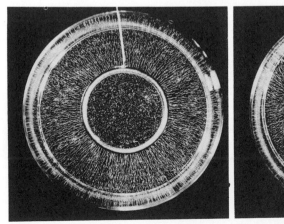

Fig. 2 Field around a charged cylinder.   **Fig. 3** A charged conductor of irregular shape.

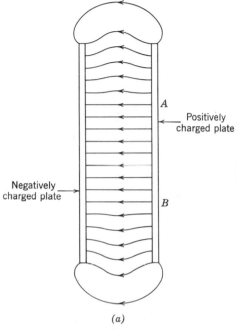

Positively
charged plate

Negatively
charged plate

A

B

(a)

Fig. 4*a*

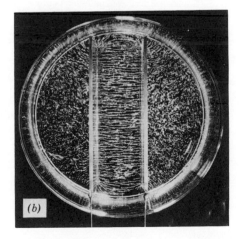

(b)

Fig. 4*b* Parallel conducting plates with equal
and opposite charges.

Panel **15**

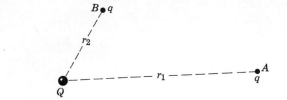

Fig. 1

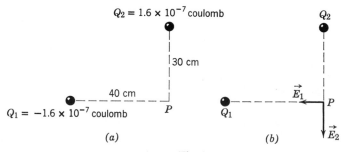

Fig. 2

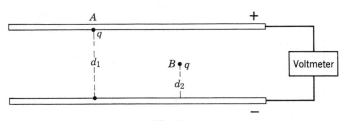

Fig. 3

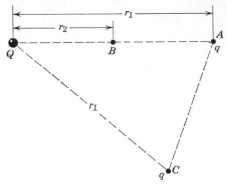

Fig. 1

Fig. 2

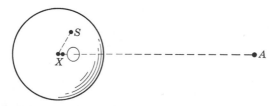

Fig. 3

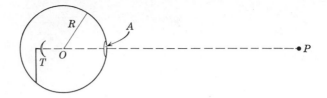

Fig. 1. A hollow metal sphere with center at O and radius $R = 0.50$ meter has a charge of $Q = -6.25 \times 10^{12}$ elem. chge. Target T is placed inside the sphere. Protons start from rest at P, accelerate toward the opening at A, pass into the sphere, and hit the target. P is 5 meters from the center of the sphere.

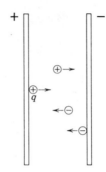

Fig. 2. A side view of two parallel plates with equal but opposite charges. The space between the plates is a vacuum.

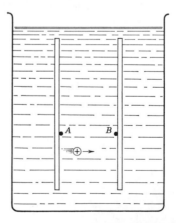

Fig. 3. The parallel plates described in Fig. 2, but immersed in a conducting liquid.

Panel **18**

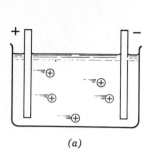 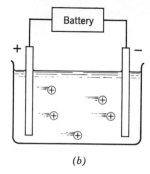

(a) (b)

Fig. 1

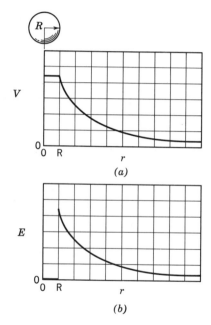

(a)

(b)

Fig. 2

Panel 20

1. Suppose that the positive charge in an atom is distributed over the surface of a sphere which has a radius of about 10^{-10} meter. Suppose that the atom appears neutral as seen from the outside because just enough electrons are deposited in its surface to cancel its positive charge.

Assuming that this model is correct and neglecting the effect of the electrons, calculate (a) the magnitude of the electric field at the surface of a gold atom if you know that the positive charge of a gold atom is determined by the fact that it has 79 protons; (b) the magnitude of the electric potential at the surface of a gold atom.

2. *The Rutherford*, or *nuclear*, model of the atom assumes that the positive charge in an atom is not spread out but is in fact concentrated in a very small region (called the *nucleus*) at the center of the atom. The radius of this nucleus in the gold atom is estimated to be about 10^{-14} meter. Neglecting the effect of electrons, calculate (a) the electric field at the surface of the gold nucleus; (b) the electric potential at the surface of the gold nucleus.

3. An electric potential difference of 90 volts is placed across two parallel plates which are 3×10^{-3} meter apart.

(a) Compute the electric field between these plates.

(b) Compute the electric force acting on a 5×10^{-5} coulomb charge half-way between the plates.

(c) Compute the electric potential at a point 1.5×10^{-3} meter from the negative plate.

(d) Calculate the electric field between these plates if the potential difference across them is increased to 180 volts and the distance between them is increased to 6×10^{-3} meter.

(e) An alpha particle (mass 6.7×10^{-27} kg and charge 2 elem. chge.) moves from rest at the positive plate through a small hole in the negative plate. Assume a vacuum between the plates, and calculate the kinetic energy of the alpha particle after it has passed through the hole if the electric potential across the plates is 2×10^3 volts and the distance between them is 3×10^{-3} meter.

(f) Compute the speed of the alpha particle after it emerges from the hole in the negative plate.

Panel 20

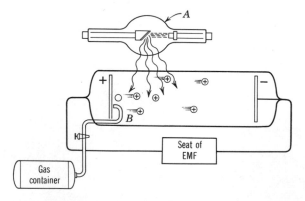

Fig. 1. X-rays from tube A knock electrons off atoms of a gas which is introduced into the space between the plates at **B.**

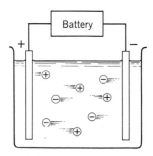

Fig. 2. A battery is attached to two plates immersed in a solution in which positive ions of hydrogen (H⁺) and negative ions of chlorine (Cl⁻) are free to move.

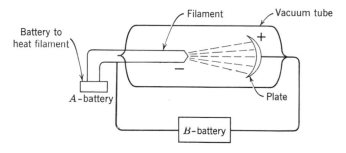

Fig. 3. The A-battery heats the filament. The B-battery provides the electric field between the filament and plate.

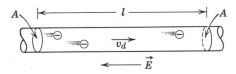

Fig. 4. Conduction electrons drifting at an average velocity $\vec{v}_d$ under the influence of the electric field $\vec{E}$.

Panel **21**

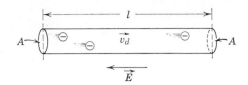

We can calculate the electron drift velocity in a wire conductor as follows. Let i be the electric current in the wire. Q is the charge carried by all the conduction electrons in a length l of wire with a uniform cross-sectional area A, if n represents the number of conduction electrons in a unit of volume (e.g., cm³) of the specific material (e.g., aluminum, copper, etc.) from which the wire is made.

If Q is measured in coulombs, it is equal to the product $(1.6 \times 10^{-19}) \times n \times$ (volume of wire of length l). Since the volume of this length of wire is lA,

$$Q = 1.6 \times 10^{-19} nlA \text{ coulomb}$$

If it takes a time t for the charge to pass any point in the conductor, then:

(1) $i = \dfrac{Q}{t} = \dfrac{1.6 \times 10^{-19} nlA}{t}$

But the average drift velocity, $v_d = \dfrac{l}{t}$ or $t = \dfrac{l}{v_d}$. Substituting for t in (1) we get:

(2) $\qquad\qquad i = (1.6 \times 10^{-19} nAv_d)$ coulomb/sec.

Solving (2) for the electron drift velocity,

(3) $v_d = \dfrac{i}{1.6 \times 10^{-19} nA}$

where v_d is in cm/sec if n is the number of conduction electrons per cm³.

The current and cross-sectional area are easily measured and n can be computed from the atomic weight and the density of the material of the wire. For copper wire with a diameter of about 0.16 cm carrying a current of 10 amp, $v_d \approx 10^{-2}$ cm/sec. Compare this with the measured *random* speed of the free electrons, which is $\approx 10^8$ cm/sec.

Panel 22

Table 1. An experiment is performed to compare the electric resistances of *equal* lengths of aluminum, copper, and steel. Each sample has the same cross-sectional area. All parts of the experiment are controlled in such a way that the temperature of the wire is at 20°C at all times. The results are summarized as follows:

Material	Length (m)	Cross Section (m²)	Temp. (°C)	Resistance (ohms)
Aluminum	1	2×10^{-6}	20	1.4×10^{-2}
Copper	1	2×10^{-6}	20	0.9×10^{-2}
Steel	1	2×10^{-6}	20	9×10^{-2}

Table 2. Resistivities of common conductors in ohm-meter at 20°C.

Aluminum	2.8×10^{-8}
Copper	1.7×10^{-8}
Carbon	3.5×10^{-5}
Iron	1.0×10^{-7}
Nickel	7.8×10^{-8}
Silver	1.6×10^{-8}
Steel	1.8×10^{-7}
Tungsten	5.6×10^{-8}

Panel **23**

1. Calculate the electrical resistance in ohms of 30 meters of copper wire which has a cross-sectional area of 5×10^{-6} m². Assume room temperature is 20°C.

2. The cross-sectional area of a sample of steel wire is 2×10^{-6} m². Its resistance is measured at 20°C and is found to be 50 ohms. How long is the wire?

3. One hundred meters of aluminum wire are used to carry a current of 2×10^{-3} amp between two points with an electric potential difference of 1500 volts. Assume room temperature. What is the cross-sectional area of the wire?

4. Calculate the electrical resistance of 10 cm of silver wire which has a cross-sectional area of 0.5 mm². Assume a temperature of about 20°C.

5. The resistance of a sample of wire 25 feet long is 500 ohms. What is the resistance of a sample of the same wire 75 feet long if the cross-sectional area is the same and there is no change in temperature?

6. A sample of wire 300 feet long with a resistance of 50 ohms has a cross-sectional area of 4×10^{-6} m². Compute the resistance of another sample which has the same length and a cross-sectional area of 2×10^{-6} m². Both resistances are measured at 0°C.

7. A sample of wire 2 meters long with a cross-sectional area of 2×10^{-6} m² has a resistance of 5 ohms. What is the resistance of a sample of wire made of the same material 100 meters long with a cross-sectional area of 5×10^{-6} m² at the same temperature?

8. The ends of a copper wire 10 meters long and 2×10^{-6} m² in cross-sectional area are connected to the terminals of a battery. The potential difference maintained by the battery is 6 volts. Compute the power used.

Panel **24**

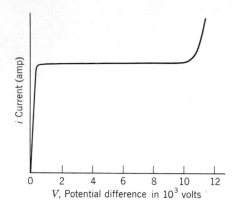

Fig. 1. A graph showing how current varies with potential difference placed across plates in a tube containing a gas like argon. (See Fig. 1 of Panel 21.)

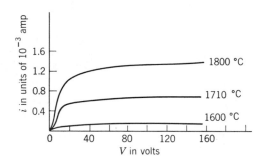

Fig. 2. This graph shows how current varies with potential difference placed across the space between a *plate* and a heated *filament*. (See Fig. 3 of Panel 21.) Each curve represents the *i-V* curve at a different filament temperature.

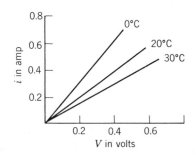

Fig. 3. A graph showing how current in a wire conductor varies with potential difference across its ends. (See Fig. 4 of Panel 21.) Each line represents the *i-V* relationship at a different temperature.

Panel **25**

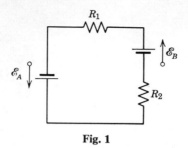

Fig. 1

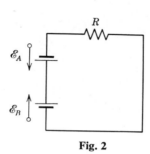

Fig. 2

Fig. 3

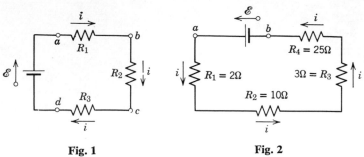

Fig. 1　　　　　　　　　　**Fig. 2**

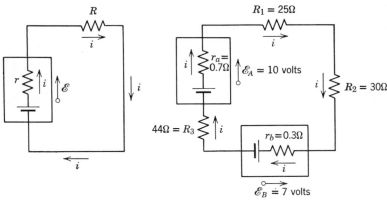

Fig. 3　　　　　　　　　　**Fig. 4**

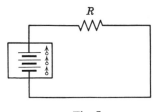

Fig. 5

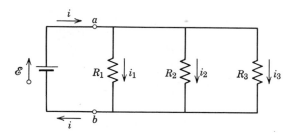

Water   Thick   Very
oil   thin oil

Fig. 1

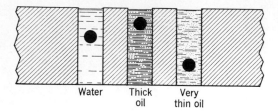

Fig. 2

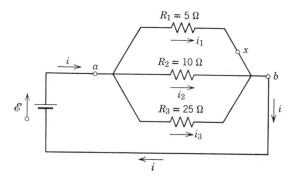

Fig. 3

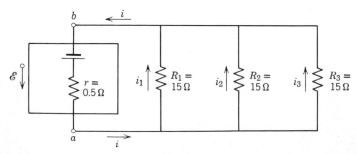

Fig. 4

1. Three resistors, 2 ohms, 4 ohms, and 8 ohms, are arranged in series. The total potential difference across them is 70 volts. (*a*) Compute the combined resistance. (*b*) Compute the current in the 8-ohm resistor. (*c*) Compute the potential difference across the 4-ohm resistor. (*d*) A 14-ohm resistor is added to the circuit in series with the original three resistors. How does it affect the answers to (*a*), (*b*), and (*c*) above?

2. The three resistors originally used for the circuit in Problem 1 above are put into a parallel arrangement across which there is then placed a potential difference of 70 volts. (*a*) What is the combined resistance? (*b*) What is the current in the 8-ohm resistor? (*c*) What is the potential difference across the 4-ohm resistor? (*d*) A 14-ohm resistor is added to this circuit parallel to the original resistors. How does it affect your answers to (*a*), (*b*), and (*c*) above?

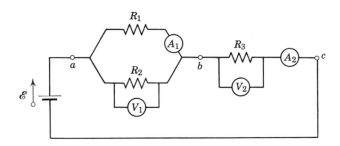

3.

Given: $\mathscr{E} = 45$ volts

$R_1 = 6\ \Omega$

$R_2 = 3\ \Omega$

$R_3 = 5\ \Omega$

$V_{ab} = 12$ volts

Find: (*a*) The reading in volts in $-\!(V_1)\!-$

(*b*) The reading in amps in $-\!(A_1)\!-$

(*c*) The reading in volts in $-\!(V_2)\!-$

(*d*) The reading in amp in $-\!(A_2)\!-$

(*e*) The terminal voltage of the battery.

(*f*) The potential difference across the internal resistance of the battery.

Panel 29

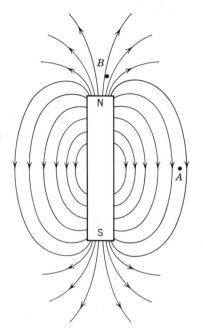

Fig. 2

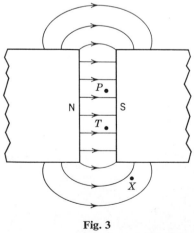

Fig. 3

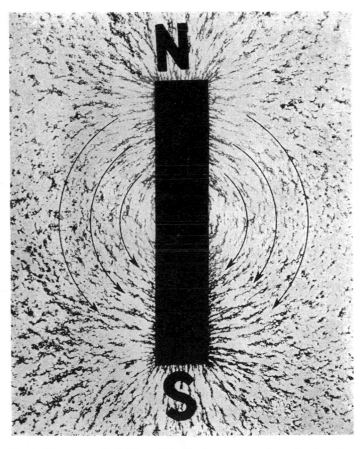

Fig. 1. The magnetic field pattern of a bar magnet formed when the magnet is covered with a piece of plate glass and small iron filings are then sprinkled over the top of the glass

Fig. 2(*a*). Photograph of pattern formed by iron filings as a current passes through long, straight wire.

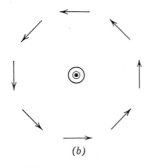

(*b*)

Fig. 2(*b*). Compass needles in the space around a long, straight wire carrying a current out of page.

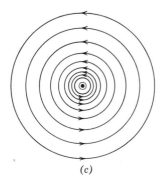

(*c*)

Fig. 2(*c*). Magnetic field lines around a long, straight wire carrying current out of page.

Panel 31

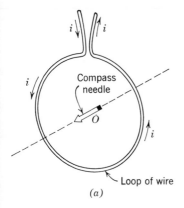

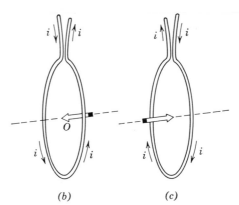

Fig. 1

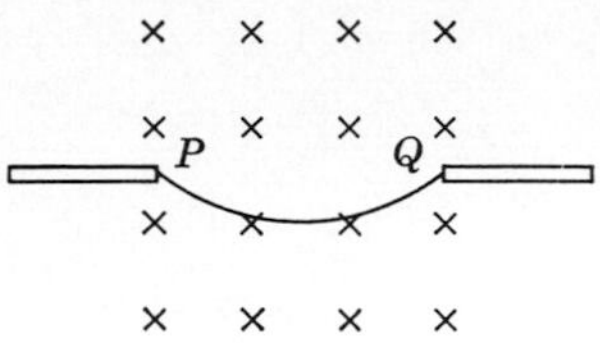

Fig. 1

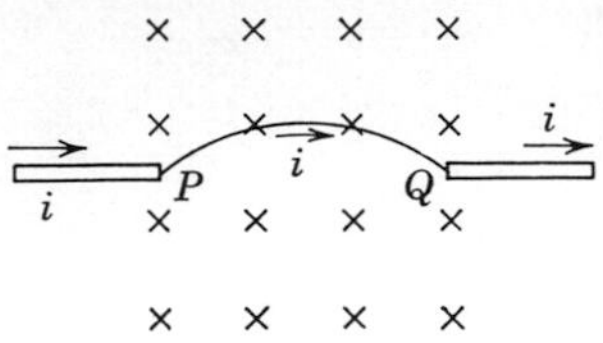

Fig. 2

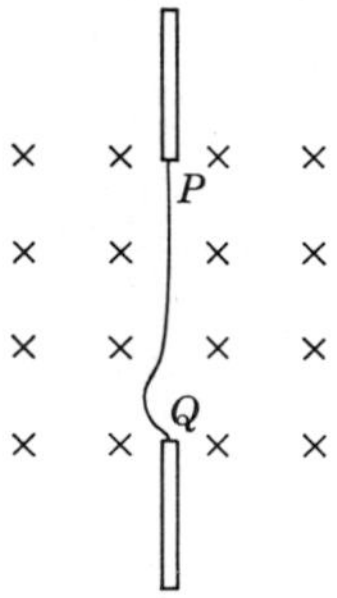

Fig. 3

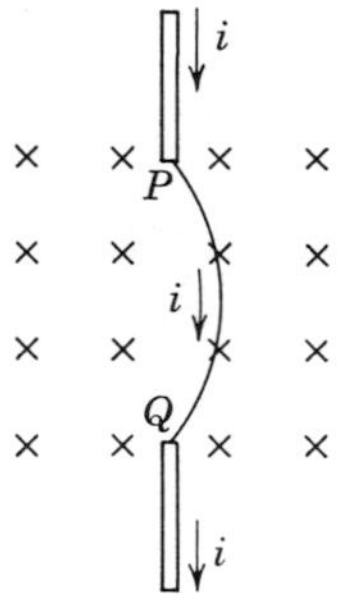

Fig. 4

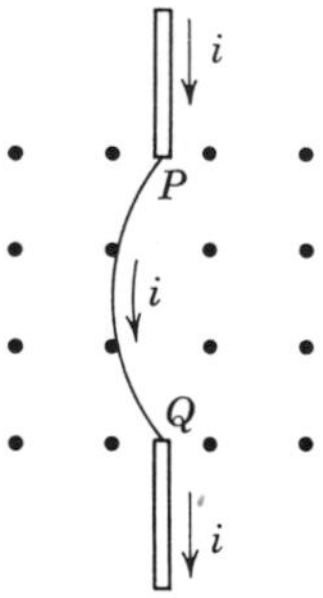

Fig. 5

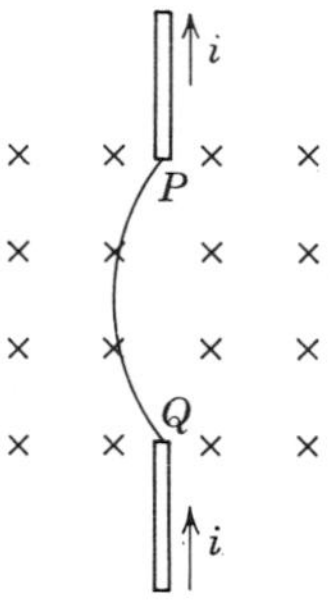

Fig. 6

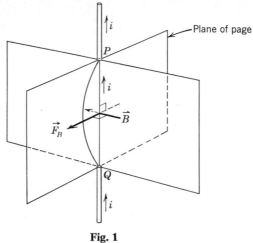

Fig. 1

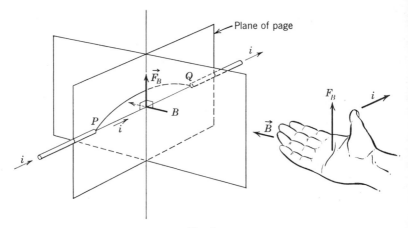

Fig. 2

Right-hand-rule for direction of $\vec{F}_B$ applied to Fig. 2 above. Right hand is extended so that the fingers point in the direction of $\vec{B}$ and the thumb in the direction of i. $\vec{F}_B$ is then interpreted as being directed at right angles to and *away* from the palm of the hand.

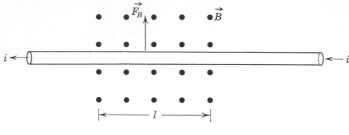

Fig. 1

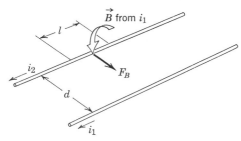

Fig. 2

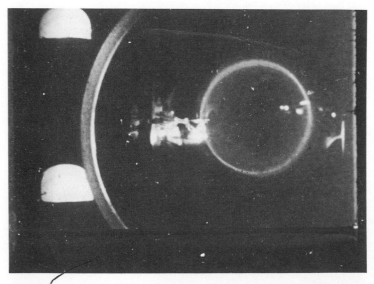

Fig. 3. The effect of a uniform magnetic field on the path followed by a beam of electrons. The electrons start at the left and move clockwise in the field.

3. An electron enters a uniform magnetic field in Fig. 3. Its speed is 4×10^7 m/sec. The magnitude of the field B is 1×10^{-2} newton/amp-m. Compute the magnitude of the magnetic force on this electron. Describe how it will move under the influence of this field. (Use mass of electron $= 9 \times 10^{-31}$ kg.)

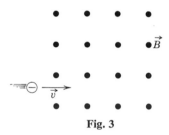

Fig. 3

4. In Fig. 4, a positively charged particle Q enters the space between two large parallel plates with equal but opposite charges. At right angles to the field produced between the plates there is a magnetic field (represented by cross marks) into the page. Compute the velocity v for which Q will be *undeflected* as it moves between the plates. You are given that $E = 1.5 \times 10^3$ newton/coulomb and $B = 2.0 \times 10^{-2}$ newton/amp-m.

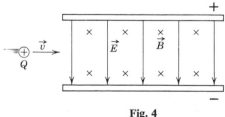

Fig. 4

Panel 35

1. In Fig. 1, loops 2 and 3 are in the same plane which is at right angles to the plane of loop 1. Loop 1 is in the plane of the page. $R_1 = R_2 = 25$ cm. $R_3 = 10$ cm. (*a*) Compute the resultant field at the center, O, if i_3 is 10 amp and i_2 is 10 amp and there is no current in loop 1. (*b*) Compute the magnitude of the resultant field at O, if i_2 and i_3 are each 10 amp and i_1 is also 10 amp.

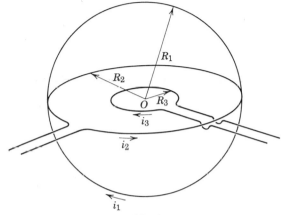

Fig. 1

2. Compute the magnitude and direction of the resultant magnetic force on this rectangular conducting loop (Fig. 2).

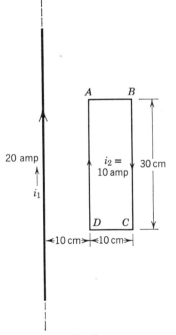

Fig. 2

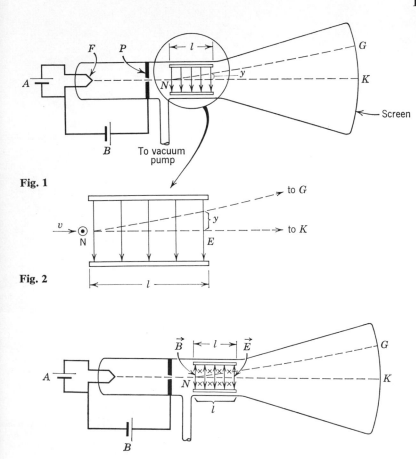

Fig. 1

Fig. 2

Fig. 3. Thomson's experiment. When E and B are both zero, the undeflected beam strikes the screen at K. When B is zero and a field E exists in the space between the plates, the electron beam is deflected to G. A magnetic field B is then applied and adjusted until the beam again strikes K.

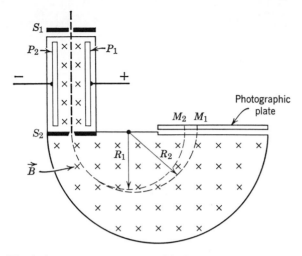

Fig. 1. A mass spectrometer. Positively charged ions enter S_1 from a chamber above (not shown here) where atoms of an element are changed into positive ions.

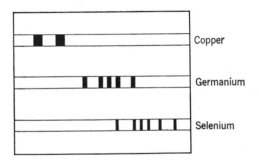

Fig. 2. Mass spectra photographs for isotopes of copper, germanium, and selenium.

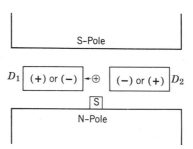

Fig. 2. Side view of cyclotron shown in Fig. 1. *S* is a source of ions for the cyclotron.

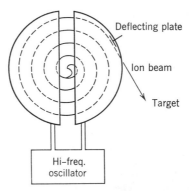

Fig. 3. Top view of the Dees through the *S*-pole of the cyclotron magnet, showing the deflecting plate which is used to remove ions from the cyclotron.

Panel **38**

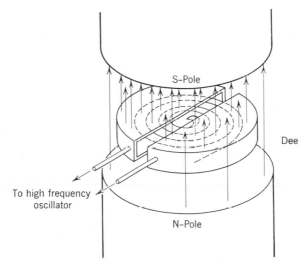

Fig. 1. A cyclotron. Hollow half-cylinders (Dees) made of a metal (like aluminum or copper), through which a uniform magnetic field can pass without distortion, are connected to a source of EMF (not shown) called a high-frequency oscillator. The function of the oscillator is to alternate the electric charges on the Dees periodically. The dashed spiral in the figure represents the path of an ion in the cyclotron.

In each of these figures a flat strip of copper carries a current in the direction shown. The cross marks represent a uniform magnetic field in which the strip is immersed. In Fig. 1, a positively charged particle is shown moving downward, which is the direction positive charge carriers would move if they were in fact responsible for the electric current i. In Fig. 2, a negatively charged particle is shown moving upward.

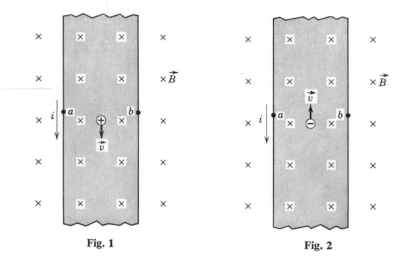

Fig. 1   Fig. 2

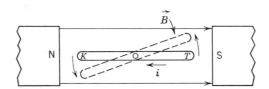

Fig. 3

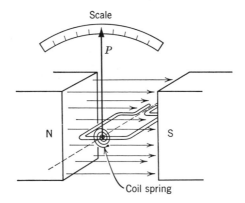

Fig. 4

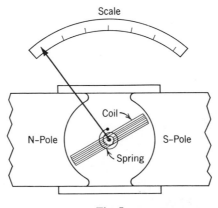

Fig. 5

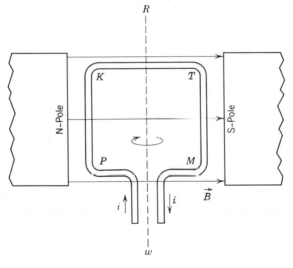

Fig. 1

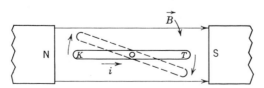

Fig. 2. A view of Fig. 1 looking down from R.

This is a schematic drawing of an elementary electric motor. $\vec{B}$ represents a uniform magnetic field through which the loop rotates. Two half-rings (called a split-ring commutator) are attached to the ends of the loop and rotate with it. Contacts called *brushes* rest on the rings and supply current to the loop from a battery. The brushes do not rotate but remain in fixed positions while the commutator rotates under them.

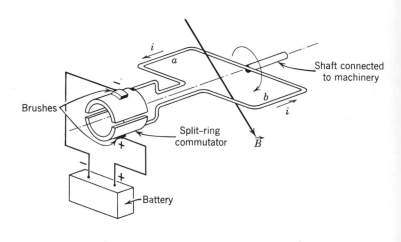

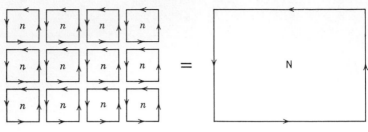

Fig. 3

Fig. 4. Magnetic domains in an *unmagnetized* sample of ferromagnetic material. The dimensions of each domain are about 10^{-5} meter.

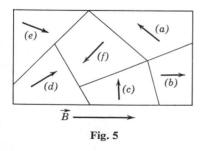

Fig. 5

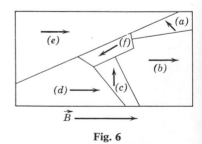

Fig. 6

Panel **42**

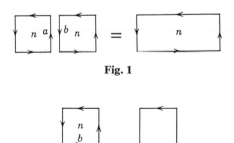

Fig. 1

Fig. 2

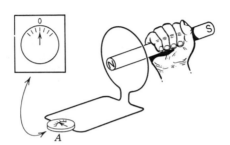

Fig. 3

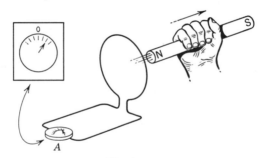

Fig. 4

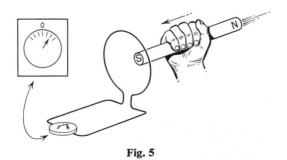

Fig. 5

Panel **43**

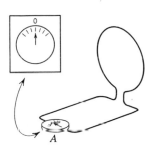

Fig. 1

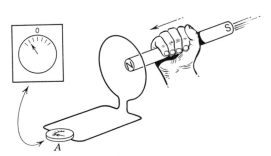

Fig. 2

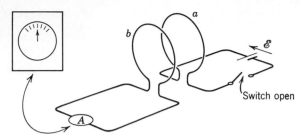

Fig. 1

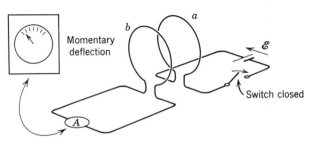

Momentary deflection

Fig. 2

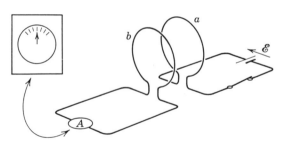

Fig. 3

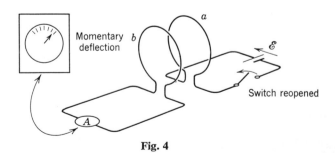

Momentary deflection

Fig. 4

Panel **44**

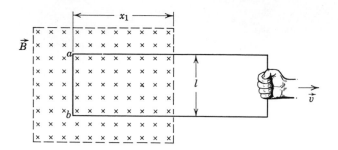

Fig. 1

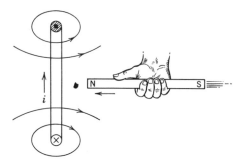

Fig. 2

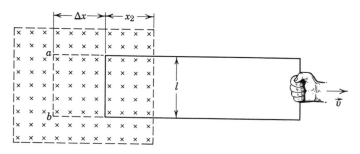

Fig. 3

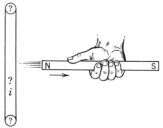

Fig. 4

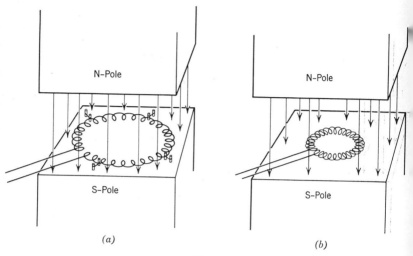

(a)   *(b)*

Fig. 2

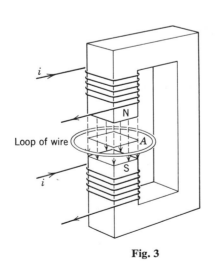

Fig. 3

***Panel* 46**

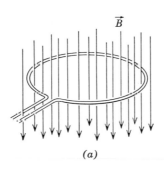

(a)

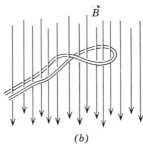

(b)

Fig. 1

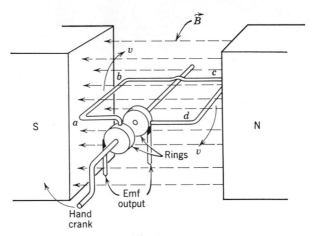

Fig. 1

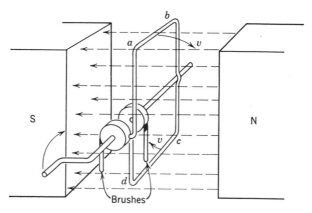

Fig. 2

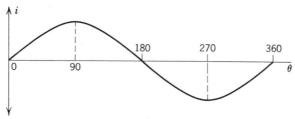

Fig. 3

(Use $\pi = 3.14$ where necessary.)

1. A flat rectangular coil 0.1 m wide and 0.25 m long is composed of 50 turns or wire and is rotating at a speed of 2400 revolutions per minute in a magnetic field of 2×10^{-2} newton/amp-m. Compute the maximum induced EMF.

2. A circular coil with a radius of 0.05 m rotates at a speed of 1800 revolutions per minute in a magnetic field of 5×10^{-1} newton/amp-m. How many turns of wire are required in the loop if its maximum induced EMF is to be 10 volts?

3. The primary of a transformer has 600 turns and is connected to the terminals of a 120-volt alternating current line. If the secondary coil has to supply a potential difference of 5 volts at its terminals and a current of 2.8 amperes, find (*a*) the number of turns in the secondary; (*b*) the current in the primary.

4. An electron in the doughnut of a betratron is traveling at a speed of 2.8 × 10^8 m/sec. This is close to the speed of light and is therefore relatively constant. The radius of the doughnut is 0.50 meter and the rate of increase of magnetic flux through the hole in the doughnut is 25 newton-m/ampere per sec. The current in the primary increase for $\frac{1}{250}$ sec. Compute the total energy transferred to a single electron in this time by the betatron.

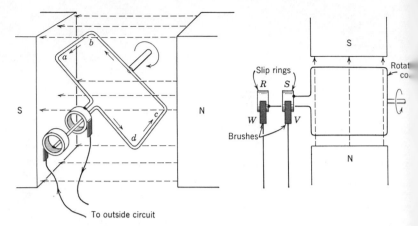

Fig. 1. A schematic drawing of an *electric generator*, showing slip-rings and brushes.

Fig. 2. A top view of Fig. 1.

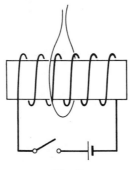

Fig. 3

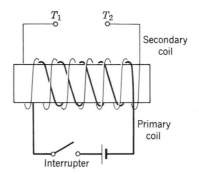

Fig. 4. A simple induction coil.

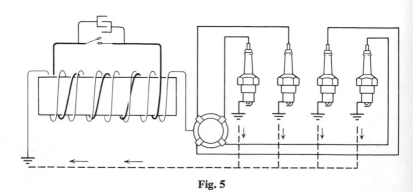

Fig. 5

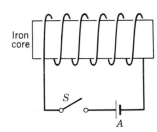

Fig. 1

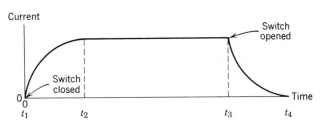

Fig. 2

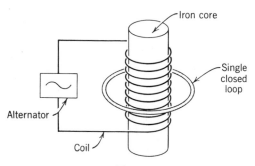

Fig. 2

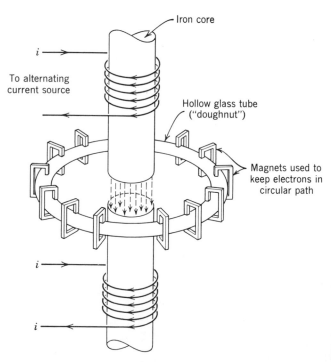

Fig. 3. A betatron.

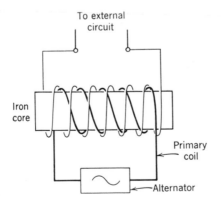

Fig. 1. A transformer.

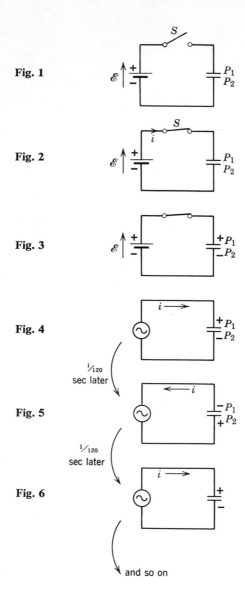

Fig. 1

Fig. 2

Fig. 3

Fig. 4

$^1/_{120}$ sec later

Fig. 5

$^1/_{120}$ sec later

Fig. 6

and so on

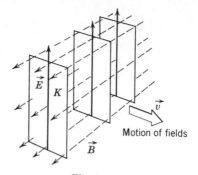

Fig. 1

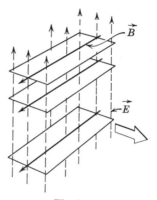

Fig. 2

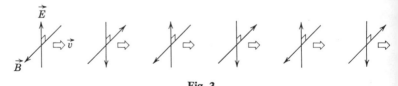

Fig. 3

Frequency in cycles per sec

10^4 10^5 10^6 10^7 10^8 10^9 10^{10} 10^{11} 10^{12} 10^{13} 10^{14} 10^{15} 10^{16} 10^{17} 10^{18} 10^{19}

Radio waves | Infrared | Ultraviolet | X–rays

Visible light

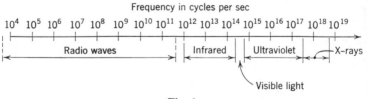

Fig. 4

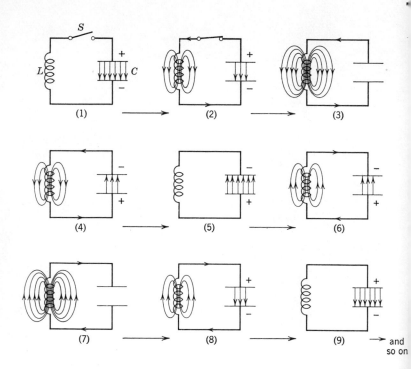

(1)   →   (2)   →   (3)

(4)   →   (5)   →   (6)

(7)   →   (8)   →   (9) → and
so on